SYMMETRIES IN ELEMENTARY PARTICLE PHYSICS

CONTRIBUTORS:

J. Ashkin

S. M. Berman

G. Bernardini

L. C. Biedenharn

M. M. Block

N. Cabibbo

R. P. Feynman

R. Gatto

P. Kabir

P. Tarjanne

G. Zweig

SYMMETRIES IN ELEMENTARY PARTICLE PHYSICS

1964 International School of Physics "Ettore Majorana,"
a CERN-MPI-NATO Advanced Study Institute

Editor: A. ZICHICHI

Discussions led by R. P. FEYNMAN

1965

ACADEMIC PRESS New York and London

ACADEMIC PRESS INC.
111 Fifth Avenue, New York, New York 10003

United Kingdom Edition published by
ACADEMIC PRESS INC. (LONDON) LTD.
Berkeley Square House, London W.1

Library of Congress Catalog Card Number: ***65-25353***

PRINTED IN THE UNITED STATES OF AMERICA.

FOREWORD

During two weeks in August-September 1964, 120 physicists from twenty-eight countries met in ERICE to attend the second course of the International School of Physics "Ettore Majorana", the proceedings of which are contained in this book.

The countries represented at the school were: Australia, Austria, Belgium, Canada, China, Czechoslovakia, Democratic Republic of Germany, Denmark, Federal Republic of Germany, France, Greece, Hungary, India, Ireland, Israel, Italy, Netherlands, Norway, Pakistan, Poland, Rumania, South Africa, Sweden, Switzerland, Turkey, United Kingdom, United States and Yugoslavia.

The School was sponsored by the European Organization for Nuclear Research (CERN), the Italian Ministry of Public Education (MPI) and the North Atlantic Treaty Organization (NATO). Many organizations gave their moral and financial support; we would like to acknowledge in a particular way the National Science Foundation of the United States of America and the Federazione degli Industriali Siciliani. The personal scientific sponsorship of Professors Gilberto BERNARDINI, Richard P. FEYNMAN and Victor F. WEISSKOPF was of vital importance for the realization and the great success of the school. Our gratitude to them is very deep and sincere. The school had the great fortune of having among its enthusiastic supporters the Italian Minister of State Dr. Bernardo MATTARELLA, to whom we wish to express our most sincere and grateful appreciation.

The programme of the school was greatly influenced by two remarkable discoveries: the Ω^- and the $K_2^0 \to \pi^+\pi^-$. Both results encouraged a tremendous development in both theoretical and experimental work. At present, one may believe that we understand how isospin and hypercharge are inter-related, and we have great hopes that we are on the right track to understanding the link between these internal degrees of freedom of a particle and its intrinsic angular momentum. In other words, the isospin and the hypercharge do not seem to be more mysterious than the spin.

Thanks to very recent experiments, we already know that a fifth force of the kind so far considered cannot be responsible for the two-pion-decay-mode of the K_2^0-meson, and we still have to wait for further experimentation to know whether the fundamental reason for the presence of this decay mode is really T-violation. These aspects of one of the most fundamental branches of Science and their possible implications, together with all necessary background, were taught and discussed in ERICE. I hope that the reader will enjoy the book as much as the students enjoyed attending the lectures and the discussions. This is, in fact, the first year that the discussions have been reproduced as faithfully as possible. It was felt that they could not be omitted without seriously injuring the spirit of the School.

At various stages of my work, I enjoyed the collaboration of many friends whose contributions have been extremely important for the School and are highly appreciated. I would like to thank them most warmly: Dr. T. Massam, who acted as deputy director, Drs. L.C. Biedenharn, M.J. Levine, J.D. Reichert and W.S. Wagner who acted as scientific secretaries; Misses Y. Dawson, S. Greenstreet, I. Speer and Mrs. L. Brusa, who were responsible for the typing and duplication of all lectures and discussions in Erice; Miss M. Hoeksema who acted as secretary of the course; and Misses Y. Dawson, C. Mason and Mrs. K. Wakley who were responsible for the final typing of all the proceedings in Geneva. A final word of acknowledgement to all those who, in Erice and in Geneva, helped me on so many occasions and to whom I feel very much indebted.

A. ZICHICHI

Geneva - 1964

TABLE OF CONTENTS

OPENING SPEECH

LECTURES

SEMINARS

DISCUSSIONS

CLOSING LECTURE

* * *

OPENING CEREMONY

Alla cerimonia inaugurale di apertura del corso, che ha avuto luogo nel salone dell'albergo Jolly in Erice, Mercoledì 26 Agosto, hanno partecipato: S.E. il Ministro On.le Avv.to Bernardo MATTARELLA, l'On.le Avv.to Enzo Occhipinti Presidente di Commissione Legislativa dell'Assemblea Regionale Siciliana, S.E. il Prefetto di Trapani Dr. A. Malarbi, il Presidente della Commissione Provinciale di Controllo Avv.to S. Grillo, il Presidente della Sicindustria Avv.to G. Messina, il Vicepresidente dell'Amministratione Provinciale di Trapani Avv.to L. Canino, il Provveditore agli Studi Dr. G. Purpi, il Sindaco di Erice Avv.to G. Spitaleri, il Questore di Trapani Dr. Impuglisi ed altre Autorità Civili e Militari tra cui il Dr. A. Accardi, Segretario Generale della Provincia, il Presidente dell'Ordine dei Medici Dr. G. Garaffa ed il Comandante dei Carabinieri.

Il Presidente della Società Italiana di Fisica, Chiarissimo Professore Gilberto BERNARDINI dell'Università di Roma, ha tenuto il discorso inaugurale parlando sul tema: "La Fisica ed il Progresso del Pensiero Scientifico attraverso i Secoli."

* * *

Discorso inaugurale del Chiarissimo Professore G. Bernardini

"La fisica ed il progresso del pensiero scientifico attraverso i secoli"

Eccellenze, Signore e Signori,

il titolo di questo mio discorso può essere sufficiente a far pensare a molti di loro, così gentilmente venuti a sentirmi, di dover trascorrere un'ora ascoltando un fisico che dice, per un verso o per un altro, quanto importante sia la fisica. Sapendo questo io non posso che apprezzare ancora di più la loro cortesia e mettermi nei loro panni, consapevole del fatto che nell'ultimo ventennio i fisici, ed in generale gli scienziati, hanno sfruttato a fondo il ruolo dominante da essi assunto in una società umana ormai sostanzialmente condizionata da uno sviluppo scientifico senza precedenti.

Sono molte le cause di questo sviluppo che ha origini lontane ed una storia complessa. Una storia che in media sembra essere quella dell'accrescimento e del propagarsi del benessere su masse sempre più vaste di uomini, anche se si tratta di una storia profondamente travagliata e, come sempre succede per le grandi e rapide transizioni della società umana, costruita a prezzo di tragedie collettive dove intere popolazioni patirono in una misura che sconvolgerebbe per compassione qualsiasi uomo sano di mente e di cuore anche quando esposte a simili sofferenze non fossero state diecine di milioni di uomini, ma una sola creatura umana. Di questa storia e precisamente del rapporto determinante fra progresso scientifico e progresso umano vorrei parlare oggi, pur sapendo di non poter dire loro niente che non sia già stato detto o scritto precedentemente. Questo mio discorso ha però un'aspirazione: vorrei convincere loro che il chiamare il nostro tempo enfaticamente l'Era della Scienza è connesso ad un'ingenua, spesso rozza, indiscriminata esaltazione della mente umana, che è bene combattere ed eliminare, specialmente attraverso la larga diffusione di un'autentica cultura scientifica. Vorrei dimostrare che è assurdo il ritenere più o meno inconsciamente che si sia costituita e si stia sviluppando una nuova classe di maghi ogni giorno in azione per produrre un nuovo tipo di miracoli. Nè nella Scienza, nè in quelli che la coltivano come attività e professione, c'è niente che sia o debba apparire magico. Il pensare diversamente è solo frutto di una nuova forma di ignoranza, pericolosa come il feticismo e da distruggere come il feticismo. E' questo in sostanza ciò che io vorrei sapere dire a loro fino a raggiungere il loro convincimento.

Potrei cominciare col dire che l'influenza essenziale della Scienza sulla società umana sembra ovvia non solo nella storia, ma anche nella preistoria. Che gli uomini vissuti cinque o diecimila anni fa abbiano considerato quelli o quello fra loro, capace di accendere il primo fuoco, un essere degno di competere con la potenza divina non sorprende nessuno. Sembra anche del tutto naturale che gli uomini vissuti alcune migliaia di anni fa abbiano considerato come esseri superiori, facendone gli arbitri della vita delle tribù, quelli, fra loro, più intelligenti ed attivi capaci di differenziare attraverso la ripetuta osservazione di fenomeni biologici, le "male erbe", dalle piante medicinali e dai cereali, iniziando di questi ultimi la coltivazione sistematica. Ma la Scienza solo negli ultimi quattro secoli ha perduto il suo carattere sporadico ed episodico. Archimede ed Aristotele furono gli unici grandi maestri di Galileo Galilei e dei suoi contemporanei; ed invece a un secolo di distanza dalla morte di Galileo Galilei la fisica e la biologia erano già delle solide costruzioni di conoscenza e di cultura che ogni generazione ereditava dalla precedente, con chiare e sempre più vaste prospettive.

Potrebbe forse sembrare che oggi la situazione non sia molto diversa e sotto alcuni aspetti credo sia giusto il pensarlo. Tuttavia sono incline a credere che un'analisi più profonda della sequenza dei rapporti fra Scienza e Tecnica, fra quest'ultima e il progresso sociale, fra progresso sociale ed evoluzione intellettuale e morale, porterebbe a constatare che differenze profonde esistono per esempio sul ruolo esercitato dalla Scienza prima e dopo l'avvento della rivoluzione industriale, prima e dopo l'ultima grande guerra. Tracciando una breve sintesi vorrei cominciare con l'inquadrare le scoperte astronomiche di Keplero e di Galileo nell'influenza che esse ebbero sullo sviluppo spirituale degli uomini del loro tempo. Prima di queste scoperte la libertà intellettuale era limitata alle espressioni artistiche. Pittori e scultori, poeti ed architetti, erano i soli capaci di parlare agli uomini un linguaggio che potesse risvegliare in essi gli aspetti più alti della dignità umana. Come esempi, che io ricordo per la chiarezza estrema raggiunta nell'esprimere una grande visione, vorrei ricordare loro il bacio di Giuda nella Cappella degli Scrovegni e l'Adamo benedetto dal Creatore, nella cappella Sistina. Ma appena un secolo e mezzo dopo l'apparire del "Siderium Nunci" e la pubblicazione in Olanda del "Dialogo intorno a due Scienze nuove", la descrizione corretta e raffinata di tutti i fenomeni meccanici e di alcuni fenomeni fondamentali di ottica, frutto delle opere di Huyghens, Newton, Laplace, Eulero ed altri fino a Lagrange, la legge della gravitazione universale e le conseguenti grandi scoperte astronomiche, erano una luce che si distendeva lontano sul futuro di tutti gli uomini. Furono molti allora quelli capaci di leggere la grande Enciclopedia, la "Summa della Storia Moderna"; e da questi uomini colti, divenuti liberi dai pregiudizi che avevano cristallizato la società umana per oltre cinque secoli, scaturì il più grande movimento sociale della Storia: la rivoluzione francese. Il secolo successivo è invece il secolo della rivoluzione industriale, ed è in questo secolo che si comincia a delineare un rapporto fra Scienza e Società Umana, antichissimo come processo, ma essenzialmente nuovo rispetto alla scala dei tempi. Durante il diciannovesimo secolo l'intervallo di tempo che intercorre fra una serie di scoperte scientifiche e le "invenzioni" che utilizzano queste scoperte ai fini del benessere e dello sviluppo della civiltà comincia a contrarsi. La contrazione aumenterà rapidissimamente con l'estendersi ed il concatenarsi fra loro delle scienze e delle loro applicazioni, in tutte le attività umane. Fra la sintesi dei fenomeni elettromagnetici e luminosi fatta da Maxwell (esempio quasi unico nella storia del pensiero umano) e la telegrafia senza fili di Marconi, c'è un intervallo di circa cinquanta anni; fra la scoperta delle proprietà singolari dei semiconduttori e l'uso universale delle radio tascabili, delle teletrasmissioni attraverso satelliti artificiali ecc. passano meno di dieci anni.

Con la rivoluzione industriale, ha inizio questa reazione a catena sempre più rapida fra scienza ed invenzione, fra invenzione e industria. La rivoluzione industriale ebbe inizio con la macchina a vapore inventata dall'orologiaio Watt, col processo per produrre la soda caustica di Leblanc, con l'invenzione dell'illuminazione a gas di Murdoch e la costruzione del primo telaio continuo da parte del barbiere Arkwright. Lo sviluppo economico corrispondente dei paesi più progrediti fu enorme. Insieme (poichè con le macchine a vapore e con la luce artificiale che prolungava il giorno, gli uomini, anche fisicamente poco prestanti, potevano produrre quello che nel passato avrebbe richiesto ingente e qualificata mano d'opera) adolescenti e ragazzi vennero sottoposti ad una lenta sistematica decimazione perpetrata con salari di fame e quattordici ore di lavoro giornaliere.

La rivoluzione industriale con le sue glorie e le sue incredibili miserie cambiò radicalmente la società delle nazioni più civili. Al tempo stesso ebbe inizio fra la cultura scientifica e tutte le altre forme di cultura atte a migliorare il livello intellettuale e morale dei popoli civili quel divorzio di cui oggi ogni giorno, risentiamo le conseguenze. Scienza divenne sinonimo d'invenzione e quest'ultima fu un bene o un male a seconda dell'uso che ne fecero gli uomini cui le vicende storiche, di volta in volta, affidarono il destino dei popoli.

Ovviamente oggi la struttura delle società più progredite è diversa per esempio da quella che regolava la vita dell'Europa un secolo fa, ma sarebbe pericolosa e spregievole illusione addurre il merito di questa evoluzione agli uomini che direttamente coltivarono nel secolo scorso, le Scienze. Nel secolo scorso Fisica, Chimica e Biologia progredirono rapidissimamente sfruttando a fondo tutti i vantaggi dello sviluppo tecnico, ma il "Progresso" e le sue spesso imprevedibili tragiche conseguenze, furono oggetto di studio e di pensiero da parte di una nuova categoria di scienziati e filosofi: i sociologi. Al tempo stesso la Scienza come cultura diffusa e largamente educatrice perde giorno per giorno il grande prestigio e la grande influenza di cui aveva goduto nel secolo precedente.

E' mia opinione, condivisa da molti, che anche oggi, dopo tante penose esperienze, molte persone (fra le più colte, ma non direttamente impegnate in attività di ricerca scientifica) abbiano una considerazione del valore della scienza che ben poco ha in comune con il peso che si attribuisce alla cultura come elemento essenziale di civiltà.

Cultura è un bene individuale e insopprimibile; è costruita dalle migliori esperienze personali consentiteci dal nostro intelletto e dalla nostra sensabilità, e può o dovrebbe essere guida determinante per il nostro modo di vivere.

Però oggi ciò sembra raramente vero per la cultura scientifica. La connessione fra una pura scoperta scientifica e lo sviluppo industriale ed economico che ne possono derivare è cosi rapida che il senso del progresso scientifico penetra nella maggioranza degli uomini innocentemente, ma brutalmente, attraverso la constatazione giornaliera che col denaro è possibile avere una vita più facile e gradevole e naturalmente, almeno per quanto riguarda lo spirito, più superficiale.

La cultura scientifica quindi viene ignorata perchè della Scienza interessa con grossolano materialismo, solo ciò che serve. Al suo posto si sostituiscono, invadenti, altre forme di cultura più facili a essere superficialmente acquisite, meno impegnative quindi, intellettualmente e moralmente. Questo modo di procedere è secondo me (e non credo che sia una distorsione professionale) un "errore" ed è particolarmente grave errore nel nostro Paese. Per provarlo devo solo ripetere ciò che ho detto in altre occasioni. La cultura scientifica rispetto alle altre forme di cultura ha delle caratteristiche uniche e tutte positive. Si diffonde facendo appello alla ragione e non a particolari sensibilità selettive, in realtà privilegio di pochi; insegna a impostare correttamente i problemi distinguendo ciò che è essenziale da ciò che può essere, almeno temporaneamente, trascurato; non indulge ad illusioni spirituali più o meno patetiche: ci si può illudere di apprezzare musica e pittura, ma scientificamente fra capire e non capire c'è una netta barriera che si avverte con precisione anche se non si riesce a superarla.

Moralmente la cultura scientifica e specialmente quella connessa allo studio dei fenomeni fisici ha, o meglio potrebbe avere, un peso determinante. Infatti che cosa è la prima caratteristica di un alto livello morale? Non quella di non commettere errori, né quella di avere, in ogni occasione, la forza di non lasciarsi travolgere dalle passioni. Poche sono le persone capaci di tanto e in quanto così diverse da tutti gli altri, gli insegnamenti morali non sono per loro, che sono in fondo degli ammirevoli anormali. E' invece di quasi tutti commettere errori e vivere momenti di passione e di violenza. Assumere senza incertezze la responsabilità di questi errori e le conseguenze dolorose di queste passioni; impegnarsi a fondo nel mitigarne il male che ne può derivare; compensare tanto male fatto con una, almeno equivalente, misura di bene: questo è morale e questo si può chiedere a tutti.

Ma tutto ciò implica consapevolezza e coerenza; e nessuna cultura più della scientifica insegnano ad esercitare l'una e l'altra. La cultura scientifica implica infatti, verso se stessi, quell'esame umile e coraggioso, obbiettivo e senza indulgenze, che una mente educata scientificamente è consueta applicare nel cercare di capire l'andamento dei fenomeni materiali. Qualsiasi persona educata scientificamente sa che solo questa è la strada per cui procedere anche se alla fine non vi saranno compensi. Qualsiasi persona in possesso di quella mentalità che la cultura scientifica è capace di dare, può, nella condotta della propria esistenza, deviare da questa strada mentendo a sé ed agli altri, ma sapendo di rinnegare se stesso; e ciò è sempre, e per chiunque, molto penoso.

La seconda caratteristica di un alto livello morale è la libertà da ogni forma di pregiudizio. Qui non devo dilungarmi molto. I fatti parlano. Non c'è classe di uomini credo, paragonabile a quella dei culturi delle scienze, dove siano meno sentite quelle degenerazioni morali collettive, più o meno palesi, derivanti dal nazionalismo, dal razzismo e da tutte le ideologie capaci di ledere in un modo o in un altro la dignità umana. Pochi sanno meglio di loro che non esiste nessuna giustificazione a usare di un uomo, magari fino al sacrificio della vita, come uno strumento, per fini che ignora, abolendo in lui, con la violenza o con la frode morale, il diritto al libero arbitrio.

Ma ciò non può sorprendere: gli uomini educati scientificamente sono costretti ogni giorno, nel loro lavoro, a conoscere i propri limiti e la necessità di consentire agli altri, per un comune interesse, il massimo sviluppo della personalità. Menti educate scientificamente sanno ogni giorno, quanto possa essere funesto per il loro lavoro, il perseguire e cercare d'imporre schemi mentali che dimostrino di non corrispondere a ciò che la ragione e l'inesorabilità dei fenomeni naturali rendono evidente; e nazionalismi, razzismi, ideologie pseudo-sociali e fanatismi religiosi mostrano sistematicamente a menti così educate, le loro ingenue, spesso torbide, origini. A tutto ciò una sola grave obiezione può essere fatta. La rapida evoluzione della Scienza o meglio - come vorrei chiamarla ora, con un classico nome - della "Filosofia Naturale", può consentire ancora una diffusione della cultura scientifica paragonabile all'Illuminismo?

Vorrei tanto poter rispondere affermativamente e credo che potrei tentare di convincere loro e me della validità di una simile risposta. Ma il discorso sarebbe lungo e non chiaro poichè io stesso non avrei a questo proposito idee ferme come quelle prima esposte. Però posso osservare che ben poco di serio si è fatto, specialmente nel nostro Paese, in questa direzione.

Per esempio forse tutti sono consapevoli dell'uso e abuso che si è fatto in relazione all'opera di Einstein della parola relatività. Ebbene io credo che sarebbe possibile insegnare correttamente i fondamenti di questa nuova grande visione dell'universo anche negli ultimi anni di liceo.

Insegnando in un liceo comincerei dal dire dei concetti classici di spazio e tempo da Newton a Kant, da Kant a Mach. Direi della relatività Galileiana e dell'invarianza dei fenomeni in due laboratori in moto l'uno rispetto all'altro; insegnerei, seguendo uno splendido libro scritto in gioventù da Max Born, le leggi fondamentali delle onde luminose e cosa si era pensato per giustificarne le sorprendenti proprieta rispetto al comportamento, tanto dissimile, delle onde sonore. Infine parlerei di spazio e di tempo e del modo di misurarli ossia di renderli veramente oggetto di pensiero scientifico in modo razionale e coerente. Arriverei così alla relatività di Einstein e insieme avrei indotto i miei giovani allievi a seguire, quasi come narcisi, la bellezza del loro rettilineo modo di capire e pensare. Per questa stessa fiducia nella validità e possibilità di un insegnamento scientifico, fino dal suo sorgere, ossia dall'anno scorso, ho visto in questa Scuola (così tenacemente e brillantemente realizzata dagli esponenti della cultura e della politica di Trapani e dal Professore Zichichi con il sostegno del Ministro della Pubblica Istruzione, del Direttore Generale del CERN e della Società Italiana di Fisica) un elemento volto verso una diffusione della cultura fisica nell'ambito internazionale e in quello nazionale. Mi resta solo da aggiungere che a questa scuola io mi sento vincolato anche personalmente, per la breve amicizia che mi legò a Ettore Majorana, fisico fra i più grandi della mia generazione; di lui ricordo, con un'ammirazione che è cresciuta con l'andare degli anni, la mente lucidissima e l'ingegno eccezionale.

Ricordo anche il suo inquieto soffrire per una società umana - quella di allora, retta dai regimi totalitari degli anni trenta - così lontana da quella vita ideale libera e civile da lui considerata indispensabile per sopravvivere.

* * *

SYMMETRY PRINCIPLES IN PARTICLE PHYSICS

P. Kabir
Theory Division, CERN

I. INVARIANCE IN QUANTUM THEORY

Our purpose in these lectures will be to provide a general introduction to the role played by considerations of invariance, and to discuss the extent to which they may determine the laws of physics.

In classical mechanics, the Hamiltonian equations of motion,

$$f = \left[f, H \right]_c \,, \tag{1}$$

tell us that any dynamical variable f, which has a vanishing Poisson bracket with the Hamiltonian, is a constant of motion. In particular, if q_r and p_r are canonically conjugate variables,

$$p_r = \left[p_r, H \right]_c = \frac{\partial H}{\partial q_r} \,, \tag{2}$$

so that if the Hamiltonian is independent of any particular co-ordinate, the corresponding canonical "momentum" is constant in time. Moreover, one may show that p_r is the generator of infinitesimal canonical transformations which induce transformations of q_r alone. Thus a problem in classical mechanics, which is completely solved when one has found all the constants of motion, reduces to the problem of finding the generating functions of all infinitesimal transformations which leave the Hamiltonian invariant.

Since quantum mechanics may be represented, for systems for which a classical limit exists, by the same canonical formalism with the sole (but far-reaching) difference that all Poisson brackets $[f, g]_c$ are replaced by the corresponding commutators $(fg - gf)/(i\hbar)$, similar considerations naturally apply in quantum theory. However, whereas in classical mechanics the relation of an invariance property of the Hamiltonian to a conservation law expressing the constancy in time of a corresponding dynamical variable is rather remote, we are able to see this much more directly in quantum mechanics. In fact, the study of the generators of infinitesimal transformations which leave the Hamiltonian invariant has proved to be a most fruitful one, and we shall make frequent use of this concept.

But first, let us clearly state what we mean by invariance in quantum theory. All states are represented by vectors in a Hilbert space. Then we can define an operation by which from each such state $|\Psi\rangle$ we may generate a new vector $|\Psi\rangle_T$. Then we shall say that the operation which induces the transformation $|\Psi\rangle \to |\Psi\rangle_T$ is a symmetry operation if the description of physical laws in terms of the new states $|\Psi\rangle_T$ is the same as that in terms of the $|\Psi\rangle$.

The first requirement will, of course, be that the general principles of quantum theory be preserved in the new description. Specifically, for every physically realizable state $|\Psi\rangle$ (the precise meaning of this qualification to be explained below), we require that under the identity transformation

$$|\Psi\rangle_I = |\Psi\rangle \tag{3}$$

and

$$(|\Psi\rangle_{T_1})_{T_2} = |\Psi\rangle_{(T_2T_1)} , \tag{4}$$

where Eq. (3) is introduced just to fix the phase convention, and Eq. (4) states that the state obtained by successive transformations T_1 and T_2 should be the same as that obtained as the result of the transformation which represents the combined transformation. Equations (3) and (4), and the implied existence of the inverse transformation T^{-1} which brings $|\Psi\rangle_T$ back to the original state $|\Psi\rangle$, tell us that the transformations form a group. In addition, we require for any pair of realizable states $|\Psi\rangle$, $|\Phi\rangle$ that

$$(|\Psi\rangle + |\Phi\rangle)_T = |\Psi\rangle_T + |\Phi\rangle_T , \tag{5}$$

to preserve the superposition principle, and if we write $|\Psi>_T = |\Psi_T>$,

$$|<\Phi_T|\Psi_T>|^2 = |<\Phi|\Psi>|^2 . \qquad (6)$$

Equations (5) and (6) imply that the transformation may be represented by a linear operator:

$$|\Psi_T> = T|\Psi> ,$$

which must be unitary

$$<\Phi_T|\Psi_T> = <\Phi|\Psi> , \qquad (7)$$

or antiunitary

$$<\Phi_T|\Psi_T> = <\Phi|\Psi>^* . \qquad (8)$$

1. Superselection rules *)

Since there are certain conservation laws, such as that for electric charge, which are absolutely valid as far as we are aware, the total Hilbert space is separable into orthogonal subspaces A,B,C..., such that no physically measurable operator has any non-vanishing matrix element connecting any two of these subspaces. These subspaces can be labelled by the "charges" which distinguish them and it is then clear that for an arbitrary vector $|\Psi>$, the relative phases of the components $|\Psi_A>$, $|\Psi_B>$, $|\Psi_C>$.... are intrinsically unmeasurable. It is then said that a superselection rule exists between the different subspaces. A physically realizable state will then be defined to be one whose state vector lies entirely within one of the subspaces A, characterized by definite values of all the "charges" which are absolutely conserved.

Superselection rules are known to operate between states of different

i) electric charge;

ii) baryonic charge or nucleon number;

*) G.C. Wick, A.S. Wightman and E.P. Wigner, Phys.Rev. 88, 101 (1952).

iii) leptonic charge or lepton number;

iv) muonic charge or muon number; (?)

v) statistics, by which we mean the distinction between states of integral and half-integral angular momentum.

Therefore, all transformations of interest will have to satisfy the requirement that a physically realizable state be transformed into another physically realizable state, i.e. that the corresponding operators T have no matrix elements connecting different subspaces A,B,C... Furthermore, since the relative phases of vectors $|\Psi_A\rangle$, $|\Psi_B\rangle$, $|\Psi_C\rangle$ have no physical significance, the submatrices T_A, T_B, T_C in these subspaces may be multiplied by arbitrary phase factors.

2. Generators of continuous transformations

Transformations which may be derived continuously from the identity are of special interest, since they may be described most simply in terms of their generators.

To illustrate the approach, we first consider a particularly simple example. If we have a state described by the state vector $|\Psi\rangle$ in one co-ordinate system, it will, in general, be described in a co-ordinate system displaced from the first*) by an amount $-\xi$ along the x axis by

$$|\Psi_\xi\rangle = U_x(\xi)|\Psi\rangle \,. \tag{9}$$

---

*) In discussing transformations, it is always possible to adopt either of two alternative points of view. In the first, or active interpretation, the state itself is considered to be altered as a result of the transformation, and one describes the change undergone by the state as a result of the transformation. In the second, or passive interpretation, although the state is considered to be unchangeable, the manner in which it is described changes as a result of the change in the viewpoint from which it is regarded. The choice of interpretation is largely a matter of taste or psychology, and the results are equivalent. For example, in the case of the displacement considered here, a translation of the co-ordinate axes by $-\xi$ has clearly the same relative effect as a displacement of the physical system by $+\xi$.

If ξ is taken to be infinitesimal, we expect $|\Psi_\xi\rangle$ to be only infinitesimally different from $|\Psi\rangle$, i.e. we may write, for every $|\Psi\rangle$,

$$|\Psi_\xi\rangle = (1 + id_x\xi)|\Psi\rangle \quad \text{or} \quad U_x(\xi) = 1 + id_x\xi \ , \tag{10}$$

where we have arbitrarily inserted a factor i for reasons to become apparent immediately. We see that for two such states $|\Phi\rangle$, $|\Psi\rangle$,

$$\langle \Phi_\xi|\Psi_\xi\rangle = \langle \Phi|\Psi\rangle + i\xi \langle \Phi|(d_x - d_x^+)|\Psi\rangle \ , \tag{11}$$

to lowest order in ξ, so that if the scalar product $\langle \Phi|\Psi\rangle$ is to be preserved, the linear operator d_x should be chosen to be Hermitian. In mathematical language, unitarity of U_x requires hermiticity of d_x. We now establish the commutation rule satisfied by d_x. In the displaced co-ordinate system, all operators $\underline{f}$ must be correspondingly transformed according to

$$f_\xi = U_x(\xi) \ fU_x^{-1}(\xi) \ , \tag{12}$$

if they are to retain the same matrix elements between corresponding states, i.e. to represent the same operator as before. Now clearly,

$$x_\xi = x + \xi \ . \tag{13}$$

Hence

$$\begin{aligned} x + \xi &= (1 + id_x\xi) \ x \ (1 - id_x\xi) \\ &= x + i\xi(d_x x - x d_x) + o(\xi^2) \ , \end{aligned}$$

or

$$d_x x - x d_x = -i \ . \tag{14}$$

Comparing this with the canonical commutation relation

$$x p_x - p_x x = i\hbar \ , \tag{15}$$

we see that we can identify $d_x = p_x/\hbar$. The Hermitian operator p_x is thus identified (up to a factor of $\hbar$) with the generator of infinitesimal translations along the x axis. Any finite displacement can be represented by a succession of infinitesimal translations, thus a finite displacement of a along the x axis would be represented by

$$U_x(a) = \operatorname*{Lt}_{n\to\infty} \left(1 + \frac{i}{\hbar} p_x \frac{a}{n}\right)^n = e^{\frac{i}{\hbar} p_x a} . \tag{16}$$

Since there was nothing special about our choice of the x axis, we can immediately make similar statements about translations along the y and z directions, and identify p_y and p_z as the generators of infinitesimal displacements for these axes*). If we now consider successive displacements along different axes, we see that the final configuration does not depend on the order in which we make the displacements, therefore p_x, p_y, and p_z commute with each other, as we expect from the canonical commutation relations.

We could try to find the generator of time translations in the same way, but this meets with the difficulty that the time co-ordinate is different from the space co-ordinates in the sense that it is not a measurable operator. It is therefore simpler to define the generator H of infinitesimal time translations:

$$U_t(\tau) = 1 - \frac{i}{\hbar} H\tau , \tag{17}$$

as the Hamiltonian or energy operator. Equation (17) corresponds to the differential equation

$$i\hbar \frac{\partial|\Psi>}{\partial t} = H|\Psi> , \tag{18}$$

which is nothing other than the Schrödinger equation. If H does not depend explicitly on the time, it is naturally a constant of motion. Furthermore, the transformation function for an arbitrary space-time translation may now be written, using equation (16) and analogous expressions for y and z displacements, and equation (17), as

---

*) A continuous group which depends on a finite number of parameters is a Lie group.

$$U(\vec{r},t) = e^{\frac{i}{\hbar}(\vec{p}\cdot\vec{r} - Ht)} ,$$

which has exactly the form to be expected if time translations are treated on the same footing as spatial displacements.

We are now in a position to draw an important conclusion. Suppose we have a situation where the Hamiltonian of a system depends on internal co-ordinates only, i.e. the Hamiltonian is invariant under space translations:

$$U_x H U_x^{-1} = H \quad \text{or} \quad [U_x, H] = 0 . \tag{19}$$

If we consider infinitesimal translations,

$$[p_x, H] = 0 . \tag{20}$$

But since -H is the generator of infinitesimal time displacements, it follows that

$$[p_x, U_t] = 0 \quad \text{or} \quad U_t p_x U_t^{-1} = p_x . \tag{21}$$

It follows that the generator of any other transformation which leaves the Hamiltonian invariant, is also invariant under time translation.

Now, for a state $|\Psi>$ which is an eigenstate of p_x, the unitary transformations (16) reduce to phase transformations on $|\Psi>$, which do not depend on x:

$$|\Psi_a> = e^{\frac{i}{\hbar} p_x a}|\Psi> = e^{ik_x a}|\Psi> ,$$

i.e. they do not change the state at all since we can always multiply any state vector by an arbitrary phase factor without changing the result of any measurement on that state. Thus states which are invariant under any particular transformation are eigenvectors of the corresponding generators*). Furthermore, the "quantum number" k_x, which determines how the phase changes under the displacements, retains the same value at all times. In the same way, we can find the eigenvectors of other operators which commute with the Hamiltonian, and it will be our object to find those states which are simultaneously eigenstates of a maximal number of such operators, since the transformation property of these states is particularly simple. We cannot, of course, expect as in the analogous classical problem, to find simultaneous eigenstates for <u>all</u> operators which commute with the Hamiltonian but it is sufficient to find the states which are simultaneously eigenvectors of a maximal set of mutually commuting operators (which all commute with the Hamiltonian), since these by themselves form a complete set of states, in terms of which all other states may be expressed. Moreover, in these cases where the Hilbert space can be divided into subspaces which are transformed into themselves under the action of the generators, it suffices to consider each subspace separately**).

---

*) We note that in a general sense, the dimension of the representation for the translation operators is infinite. Physically this is obvious, since there is not limit to the momentum which can be associated with a state, so the number of eigenstates of momentum must be unlimited also. More formally, if p_x and x are represented by finite matrices, the commutation rule (15) cannot be satisfied: the trace of the left-hand side vanishes while the right-hand side gives ni, where n is the dimension of the representation. Nonetheless, we are able to give a simple description of all space and time translations because their generators all commute with each other, and hence we can find simultaneous eigenstates for all of them; the representations of the <u>generators</u> is one-dimensional. We shall presently study examples where various generators do not commute, but finite-dimensional representations do occur, and these will be of greatest interest.

**) According to the Peter-Weyl theorem [Math.Annalen <u>97</u>, 737 (1927)], for finite-dimensional representations of semi-simple Lie groups, the existence of one subspace which is reducible, i.e. which transforms into itself under the action of all the generators, implies that all other subspaces are also reducible, i.e. the representation is fully reducible, or decomposable.

We now pass on to another familiar group of transformations which will illustrate a complementary aspect of group representations. The real rotations in three dimensions are generated by infinitesimal rotations in the three co-ordinate planes. Let us represent the infinitesimal transformation corresponding to an infinitesimal rotation around the z axis by an angle α by

$$U_{R3}(\alpha) = 1 + \frac{i}{\hbar} J_{12}\alpha \ . \tag{22a}$$

We can similarly define infinitesimal rotations around the other axes

$$\begin{aligned} U_{R1}(\alpha') &= 1 + \frac{i}{\hbar} J_{23}\alpha' \\ U_{R2}(\alpha'') &= 1 + \frac{i}{\hbar} J_{31}\alpha'' \ , \end{aligned} \tag{22a}$$

and we recognize that the generators J_{12}, J_{23}, and J_{31} must be Hermitian operators. Proceeding exactly as in the case of the translation operators, we would find commutation rules

$$[\varphi, J_{12}] = i\hbar \ ,$$

where φ is the azimuthal angle around the z axis, and similar relations for the other rotations.

The generators J_{12}, J_{23}, and J_{31} do <u>not</u> commute, since the result of two rotations depends, in general, on the order in which we perform them. We can find the commutators of the J_{ij} by using explicit representations found by considering their effects on an explicit function of the co-ordinates. For example, an infinitesimal rotation by φ around the z axis transforms a function $\chi(x,y,z)$ into:

$$\begin{aligned} \chi_\varphi &= \chi(x - \varphi y,\ y + \varphi x, z) \\ &= [1 + i\varphi \cdot i(y \frac{\partial}{\partial x} - x \frac{\partial}{\partial y})]\chi \end{aligned} \tag{22b}$$

$$\therefore\ J_{23} = i\hbar(y \frac{\partial}{\partial x} - x \frac{\partial}{\partial y}) \ ,$$

and we can write corresponding expressions for the other generators. We can then work our the commutator

$$[J_{23}, J_{31}] = i\hbar\, J_{12} \,, \tag{23}$$

and cyclic permutations.

If we introduce the notation

$$M_1 = J_{23},\; M_2 = J_{31},\; M_3 = J_{12} \,,$$

and henceforth drop all factors of $\hbar$ (as we may do by a suitable choice of units), we can express these relations by

$$[M_k, M_\ell] = i\, \epsilon_{k\ell m}\, M_m \,. \tag{24}$$

From this, we can work out that

$$\vec{M}^2 = M_1{}^2 + M_2{}^2 + M_3{}^2 \,,$$

commutes with each of the M_i, i.e. it is an invariant of the group. Then, representations can be labelled by the value of $\vec{M}^2 = j(j+1)$, since the action of any of the generators M_i will not affect the value of $\vec{M}^2$. For a given value of j, the representation will be finite since it can be shown, by using Eq. (24), that the successive eigenvalues of M_3, which is customarily chosen to be diagonal, differ by integers, and cannot exceed j in absolute value.

At this point, we should emphasize that the relations (22a) and (24) will be taken to define the generators of infinitesimal rotations, even in those cases where we do not have an explicit representation of the state functions. In all cases, the generators G must be interpreted as linear operators

$$G = G_1 + G_2 + \dots$$

where G_1, G_2 ... act on the various arguments which may be affected by the transformation represented by G. This is particularly relevant for the case of the rotations since we often have the situation that the generators of rotations must be expressed as:

$$M_i = L_i + S_i ,$$

where L_i represents the changes of the state which result as a change of the angles occurring in the wave function, and S_i represents the changes which cannot be represented in this fashion, i.e. they correspond to changes in the internal state of the system, in this case, the spin angular momentum. Naturally, L_i should be taken as the sum of all such operators for the differnet angular arguments of the wave function while S_i must be the sum of the spin operators for all particles which are present in the state.

3. Inhomogeneous euclidean group

From the explicit representations for the generators of infinitesimal rotations, Eq. (22b) and the obvious corresponding representations for the generators of infinitesimal translations:

$$p_x = -i \frac{\partial}{\partial x} , \tag{25}$$

(note that we no longer include factors of $\hbar$), we can write down the commutation relations between the rotation and the translation operators:

$$[p_k, M_\ell] = [M_k, p_\ell] = i\, \epsilon_{k\ell m}\, p_m . \tag{26}$$

From these, we can show that the operators $\vec{p}^2 = p_1{}^2 + p_2{}^2 + p_3{}^2$ and $\vec{M}\cdot\vec{p} = \vec{p}\cdot\vec{M} = p_1 M_1 + p_2 M_2 + p_3 M_3$ commute with all M_k, p_ℓ and are therefore invariants under the group of displacements and rotations. Note, however, that $\vec{M}^2 = M_1{}^2 + M_2{}^2 + M_3{}^2$ is no longer, in general, an invariant.

$$[M_k M_k, p_\ell] = 2i\, \epsilon_{k\ell m} M_k\, p_m - 2p_\ell , \tag{27}$$

so that $\vec{M}^2$ commutes with displacements only if all components of p_ℓ are zero *). Thus, although $\vec{M}\cdot\vec{p}$, which is nothing other than the helicity, is

*) For eigenstates of momentum, the operators p_ℓ may be replaced by their eigenvalues.

invariant under translations, $\vec{M}^2$ is invariant only in co-ordinate frames in which the momentum vanishes, i.e. in the rest systems. The other invariant, $\vec{p}^2$, is related to the kinetic energy. Before we go on to discuss transformations which carry us into the rest system, i.e. Lorentz transformations, we first consider the group of real rotations in four dimensions.

4. Four-dimensional rotations

There are six independent rotation operators in four dimensions, corresponding to the six orthogonal co-ordinate planes in which we can make the rotations. We define

$$\begin{aligned} M_1 &= J_{23} \quad M_2 = J_{31} \quad M_3 = J_{12} \\ N_1 &= J_{41} \quad N_2 = J_{42} \quad N_3 = J_{43} \ , \end{aligned} \tag{28}$$

where the J_{ij} have been defined in Eq. (22). The commutation rules between the M_i have already been derived in Eq. (24). Those between the N_i, and between the M_i and the N_j can be obtained from those for the M_i, by relabelling the axes:

$$\begin{aligned} [M_i, N_j] = [N_i, M_j] &= i\ \epsilon_{ijk} N_k \\ [N_i, N_j] &= i\ \epsilon_{ijk} M_k \ . \end{aligned} \tag{29}$$

The invariants are

$$F = \frac{1}{4} J_{\ell m} J_{\ell m} = \frac{1}{2} (\vec{M}^2 + \vec{N}^2) \ , \tag{30}$$

and

$$G = \frac{1}{4} \epsilon_{k\ell mn} J_{k\ell} J_{mn} = \vec{M} \cdot \vec{N} = \vec{N} \cdot \vec{M} \ . \tag{31}$$

where $\epsilon_{k\ell mn}$ is antisymmetric in every pair of indices, and $\epsilon_{4123} = 1$. If we introduce new operators

$$K = \frac{1}{2} (\vec{M} + \vec{N}), \ \vec{L} = \frac{1}{2} (\vec{M} - \vec{N}) \ , \tag{32}$$

we find that they obey the commutation rules

$$[K_i, K_j] = i\,\epsilon_{ijk} K_k; \quad [L_i, L_j] = \epsilon_{ijk} L_k$$
$$[K_i, L_j] = 0\,. \tag{33}$$

Thus, the four-dimensional rotations may be represented by two independent groups of three-dimensional rotations, and irreducible representations of the four-dimensional rotation group may be characterized by two numbers j_1, j_2 corresponding to the eigenvalues of the invariants $\vec{K}^2$ and $\vec{L}^2$ for the two three-dimensional groups. In terms of these,

$$F = \vec{K}^2 + \vec{L}^2, \quad G = \vec{K}^2 - \vec{L}^2\,. \tag{34}$$

5. Lorentz transformations

Lorentz transformations can be regarded as rotations in four dimensions, except that rotations in planes containing the time axis will be through imaginary angles. We may retain the formalism of the preceding section and the generators will still be Hermitian provided we replace the N_j by iN_j, since the corresponding angles are now purely imaginary. We therefore take:

$$M_1 = J_{23},\; M_2 = J_{31},\; M_3 = J_{12}\,,$$
$$N_1 = J_{01},\; N_2 = J_{02},\; N_3 = J_{03}\,. \tag{35}$$

where $J_{0k} = 1/i\; J_{4k}$. The commutation rules between the M_i, and between the M_i and N_j are unchanged, while

$$[N_i, N_j] = -i\,\epsilon_{ijk} M_k\,. \tag{36}$$

The invariants are now*):

$$F = \frac{1}{2}(M^2 - N^2) = \frac{1}{4} J^{\kappa\lambda} J_{\kappa\lambda}$$
$$G = \vec{M}\cdot\vec{N} = \frac{1}{4}\epsilon^{\kappa\lambda\mu\nu} J_{\kappa\lambda} J_{\mu\nu} , \tag{37}$$

where we take $\epsilon^{0123} = 1$.

6. Inhomogeneous Lorentz group

To the pure Lorentz transformations we must add the generators of infinitesimal translations, which we have already discussed. The commutators between them can be found from the explicit representations:

$$[p_\lambda, J_{\mu\nu}] = i\,[g_{\lambda\mu} p_\nu - g_{\lambda\nu} p_\mu] , \tag{38}$$

and, in this notation, the commutators of the $J_{\lambda\mu}$ are

$$[J_{\kappa\lambda}, J_{\mu\nu}] = i\,[g_{\lambda\mu} J_{\kappa\nu} + g_{\kappa\nu} J_{\lambda\mu} - g_{\kappa\mu} J_{\lambda\nu} - g_{\lambda\nu} J_{\kappa\mu}] . \tag{39}$$

F and G are no longer invariant under the full group; instead, we have:

$$P = p^\lambda p_\lambda = p_0{}^2 - \vec{p}^2 , \tag{40}$$

and another which we shall introduce as follows. Define

$$\omega^\kappa = \frac{1}{2}\epsilon^{\kappa\lambda\mu\nu} p_\lambda J_{\mu\nu} , \tag{41}$$

which satisfies the commutation relations

$$[\omega^\kappa, p_\lambda] = 0$$
$$[\omega^\lambda, J^{\mu\nu}] = i(g^{\lambda\mu}\omega^\nu - g^{\lambda\nu}\omega^\mu) \tag{42}$$
$$[\omega^\lambda, \omega^\mu] = -i\,\epsilon^{\lambda\mu\nu\rho} p_\nu \omega_\rho .$$

---

*) We use the metric $g_{00} = -g_{11} = -g_{22} = -g_{33} = 1$, other components being zero.

Then the second invariant, which is called the Lubanski invariant, is

$$W = -\omega^{\nu}\,\omega_{\nu}\;. \tag{43}$$

If $P > 0$, we can interpret these invariants in the rest system. Then $\vec{p} = 0$, $p_0 = m$. Thus $P = m^2$. For the second, we have:

$$\omega_0 = 0,\; \omega_i = p_0 M_i\;, \tag{44}$$

therefore

$$W = m^2 \vec{M}^2; \quad \text{or} \quad \frac{W}{P} = s(s+1)\;, \tag{45}$$

where s is the spin, i.e. the angular momentum in the rest system. From the theory of the three-dimensional rotation group, we then know that there are $(2s+1)$ independent states corresponding to a given momentum vector. ω^{λ} is the relativistic operator describing the spin. In a general co-ordinate system

$$\omega_0 = \vec{p}\cdot\vec{M}; \qquad \vec{\omega} = -p_0\,\vec{M} + \vec{p}\times\vec{N}\;. \tag{46}$$

If $P = 0$, we have to consider the case of $W = 0$ and $W \neq 0$ separately. If we apply the theory for $P > 0$ and then allow P to approach zero, we see from Eq. (45) that $W \to 0$ for finite spin. Then $W = 0$ will correspond to the normal case, and we consider it first.

In this case, the invariants $P = W = 0$ do not suffice to specify the representation. However, since

$$\omega^{\mu}\omega_{\mu} = \omega^{\mu} p_{\mu} = p^{\mu} p_{\mu} = 0\;,$$

we must have

$$\omega^{\mu} = \lambda p^{\mu}\;,$$

where λ is a constant to be determined; it is essentially the magnitude of the spin. Using the general expression (46) for ω_0, we see that

$$\lambda = \frac{\vec{p}\cdot\vec{M}}{p_0} = \pm\,\frac{\vec{p}\cdot\vec{M}}{p}\;. \tag{47}$$

From the commutation relations of the inhomogeneous Euclidean group (in three dimensions), we could show that $s = |\lambda|$ represents the minimum j value possible in the given representation. For a given value of λ, there is just one state for a given value of the momentum. Under inversion of the space co-ordinates, λ changes sign. Therefore, if we include space reflections among our symmetry operations, we must include states with both signs of λ, $\lambda = \pm s$, corresponding to the right-handed and left-handed helicity states. For example, the electromagnetic interaction involves both polarization states with $\lambda = \pm 1$. On the other hand, if we do not require reflection invariance, the existence of one helicity state does not require the existence of the other, and this situation occurs in the case of the neutrino.

Now we remark briefly on the other possible representations.

$P < 0$ corresponds to imaginary masses. In this case, the energy can assume arbitrarily large positive or negative values, and it would appear that one could gain arbitrarily large amounts of energy from such particles, by pushing them to successively more negative energies. Such particles have never been observed.

For $P = 0$, $W > 0$ corresponds to massless particles of infinite spin. These representations do not seem to occur either.

7. Relation to usual spin description

Introduce an orthogonal set of space-like basis vectors $\vec{n}^k$ satisfying

$$(n^k)^\mu (n^\ell)_\mu = - \delta_{k\ell}; \quad (n^k)^\mu p_\mu = 0 , \tag{48}$$

for $k = 1,2,3$. Then

$$s^k = \frac{1}{m} \omega^\mu (n^k)_\mu , \tag{49}$$

are the components of the spin operator referred to the co-ordinate system specified by the n^k. They satisfy:

$$(S^1)^2 + (S^2)^2 + (S^3)^2 = \frac{1}{m^2} W = s(s+1) \ , \qquad (50)$$

and

$$[S^j, S^k] = i\,\epsilon_{jk\ell}\, S^\ell \ . \qquad (51)$$

II. DISCRETE SYMMETRY OPERATIONS

There are, in addition to the continuous symmetry transformations already discussed, certain discrete operations under which a large class of interactions is left invariant. Until a few years ago, it was considered self-evident that all the laws of physics should be separately invariant under the operations P of space inversion, T of time reversal (or more accurately, motion reversal), and C of charge conjugation (more precisely, particle-antiparticle conjugation) which are characteristic symmetries of the relativistic field theory of free particles. We now know that the weak interactions are certainly not invariant under the operations of C and P, and perhaps not even under the combined operation. Nonetheless, since these interactions are very much weaker than the strong interactions, it is meaningful to discuss the implications of invariance under these separate operations, since the conclusions will hold to high accuracy when strong interactions alone are involved*).

---

*) For weak interactions, it would be preferable to discuss directly those transformations which are actually invariance operations. However, what we shall do for convenience is to take over the transformation properties of free fields, for which C, P, and T are individually symmetry operations, and examine the transformation character of various interactions in terms of these. While this is not the most satisfactory approach from a logical viewpoint, it does cover the various possibilities.

Although the discontinuous transformations cannot be generated by infinitesimal steps, we have the simplifying feature that we have only one of each kind to deal with, instead of an infinity. Consider first the case of space inversion.

Corresponding to any given single-particle state $|\Psi\rangle$, we can define an inverted state $|\Psi_p\rangle$ such that the matrix elements of all spatially-odd operators change sign on going to the inverted states. In particular

$$\begin{aligned} \langle \Phi_p | x_i | \Psi_p \rangle &= -\langle \Phi | x_i | \Psi \rangle \\ \langle \Phi_p | p_j | \Psi_p \rangle &= -\langle \Phi | p_j | \Psi \rangle \ . \end{aligned} \tag{52}$$

We could define transformed operators x_i', p_j' such that

$$\begin{aligned} \langle \Phi_p | x_i' | \Psi_p \rangle &= \langle \Phi | x_i | \Psi \rangle \\ \langle \Phi_p | p_j' | \Psi_p \rangle &= \langle \Phi | p_j | \Psi \rangle \ . \end{aligned} \tag{53}$$

Obviously,

$$x_i' = -x_i, \quad p_j' = -p_i \ ,$$

and therefore

$$x_i'p_j' - p_j'x_i' = x_ip_j - p_jx_i \ ,$$

i.e. the primed operators obey the same commutation rules as the unprimed ones. This suggests that we may regard x_i' and p_j' as being obtained by unitary transformation of the x_i and p_j, that is to say, the states $|\Psi_p\rangle$ may be taken to belong to the same Hilbert space as $|\Psi\rangle$, and related by unitary transformation

$$|\Psi_p\rangle = P|\Psi\rangle \ . \tag{54}$$

Two inversions in seccession will bring us back to the original state, thus P^2 must be the identity operator, apart from a phase factor which we may set equal to unity without any loss of generality,

$$P^2 = \mathbb{1} \tag{55}$$

Together with the unitarity of P, this tells us that P is an Hermitian operator with eigenvalues ± 1. Furthermore, if the interactions are invariant under inversion,

$$PHP^{-1} = H \ . \tag{56}$$

P commutes with the Hamiltonian and is therefore a constant of motion. P is called the parity operator and its eigenvalue is the parity quantum number. The conservation of parity has no analogue in classical mechanics.

In quantized field theory*), a single particle state $|\Psi>$ is described by the operation on the vacuum state by the corresponding field operator φ^+. Under the unitary transformation P on the states, the operator φ will be correspondingly transformed. A scalar field φ corresponding to a spinless particle, will transform according to

$$\varphi' = P\varphi P^{-1} \ , \tag{57}$$

or

$$\eta_p \varphi(-\vec{r},t) = P\varphi(\vec{r},t)P^{-1} \ , \tag{58}$$

where we have allowed for the possibility that the field may acquire an additional phase factor η_p under inversion. This factor is conventional and can always be assigned the value ± 1 (see below). For Hermitian fields, however, the factor may not be changed arbitrarily since it has an absolute meaning. From Eq. (58) we find the transformation law for φ^+

*) In view of the difficulties encountered in quantum field theory, a certain school of thought advocates the avoidance of any reference to fields. We remark only that some of the most important concepts, especially in the domain of symmetry principles, have arisen directly from the microscopic, or field approach; as witnessed by the examples of charge conjugation and, more recently, the conserved vector current hypothesis.

$$P\varphi^+(\vec{r},t)P^{-1} = \eta_p^* \varphi^+(-\vec{r},t) \ . \tag{59}$$

If η_p is taken real, this implies that the antiparticle has the same intrinsic parity as the particle. This result is generally true for all bosons.

The choice $\eta_p = -1$ corresponds to the case of odd intrinsic parity and the π^o field is an example of such a case*). For such particles, the reflected state is described by a wave function which has the opposite sign of the wave function obtained by reflecting the co-ordinates in the original wave function. One may remark that the question of intrinsic parity arises only in processes where particles are created or destroyed. In processes where all particles remain unaltered, the same factors $\eta_a \eta_b \dots$ appear in the parities of both initial and final states, hence the consequences of parity conservation

$$P_{initial} = P_{final} \tag{60}$$

are the same as if we had ignored all factors $\eta_a \eta_b \dots$ completely. This also explains why the intrinsic parity of a particle described by a Hermitian field cannot be arbitrarily redefined. Such a particle**) can be created or destroyed singly without changing any of the other particles occurring in the reaction, consequently, its intrinsic parity has a definte meaning. Its value may be determined by any experiment in which this particle is created or destroyed, since in Eq. (60) either the right-hand side or the left-hand side will contain an extra factor η_H corresponding to this particle. From Eqs. (58) and (59) we see that it can only assume the values ± 1 .

---

*) It is interesting to note that this possibility was considered for pions by Kemmer long before pions were discovered.

**) Fermions described by Hermitian fields (none are known at present) would be created or destroyed only in pairs. For such particles only η_H^2 is measurable but it is natural to interpret the square root of this quantity as the intrinsic parity of the particle.

For other particles, we can only define relative intrinsic parities. Furthermore, the relative intrinsic parity between particles separated by a superselection rule (for example, neutron and proton) is unmeasurable in principle. It is therefore simplest to define certain intrinsic parities as + 1, and to determine the others by experiment. The number of particles with arbitrarily defined parities will be equal to the number of superselection rules which are operative, since we can assign intrinsic parity arbitrarily to one particle each time we introduce a superselection rule. As we have stated already, this choice is entirely arbitrary; nevertheless, it is customary to assign the same intrinsic parity to certain particles. For example, if we wish to describe the neutron and proton as an isotopic spin doublet, i.e. as differing only in some internal co-ordinate, it is much simpler to have them with the same external attributes and, therefore, with the same parity. Since the relative parity of the neutron and the proton is quite arbitrary, it could not change any physical results if we chose them to be opposite, but the formalism required to describe charge independence would become considerably more complicated.

For particles with spin, the different components of the fields may transform differently. For spin one, we have

$$P\varphi_k(\vec{r},t)\, P^{-1} = -\eta\, \varphi_k(-\vec{r},t) \quad \text{for } k = 1,2,3$$

$$P\varphi_0(\vec{r},t)\, P^{-1} = \eta\, \varphi_0(-\vec{r},t) \; .$$

$\eta = 1$ for the case of vector fields, $\eta = -1$ for the case of so-called pseudovector fields. For spinor fields, we have

$$P\psi(\vec{r},t)\, P^{-1} = \eta'\, \gamma_4\, \psi(-\vec{r},t) \; .$$

The presence of the factor γ_4 is necessary to guarantee the invariance of the free-field Lagrangian. A particular consequence is that the intrinsic parity of a Dirac particle is necessarily opposite to that of its anti-particle.

Now, if the interactions are invariant under space inversion, which is the only situation in which parity has a meaning, there will be a definite assignment of relative intrinsic parities for all participating particles whose intrinsic parity has not been established by convention. However, it is quite easy to write down interactions such that no choice of intrinsic parities will make the interaction invariant under reflection. For example, the coupling of a Dirac field ψ with a spinless field φ:

$$\psi^{+}\gamma_4\psi\,\varphi + \psi^{+}\gamma_4\gamma_5\psi\,\varphi \ , \qquad (61)$$

cannot be made invariant under space inversion, whichever way we choose the intrinsic parities of ψ and φ. Therefore, we shall say that Eq. (61) corresponds to a parity-violating interaction. Such an interaction will usually, though not necessarily always*), give rise to effects which are clearly not invariant under space inversion. For example, the interaction (61) will cause scattering between the fermions represented by the field ψ and the bosons represented by φ. Even if the fermions are initially unpolarized, they will, in general, be partially polarized after the scattering. Invariance under rotation and inversion requires that such polarization can occur only in a direction perpendicular to the plane of scattering, whereas the scattering due to Eq. (61) will, in general, give rise to a component in the scattering plane.

One of the mysteries of elementary particle physics is why strong and electromagnetic interactions conserve parity, while weak interactions do not.

---

*) A famous example in which parity is violated without any directly visible manifestation of non-invariance under space inversion, is the τ-Θ puzzle posed by the non-leptonic decays of the K meson. The 2π and 3π decay distributions of the spinless K-meson are forced, by rotational invariance alone, to be invariant under inversion. However, with the knowledge from other experiments that pions have odd parity, it was concluded that the observed 2π and 3π systems could not have the same parity.

1. Charge conjugation

The commutation relations for a spinless field φ

$$[\varphi(\vec{r}), \frac{\partial\varphi^+}{\partial t}(\vec{r}')] = i\ \delta(\vec{r}-\vec{r}') \ , \tag{62}$$

are left unchanged under the interchange of φ and φ^+. Therefore, there must exist a unitary transformation C which effects this operation. We take

$$\begin{aligned} \varphi_c &= C\ \varphi(\vec{r},t)\ C^{-1} = \eta_c \varphi^+(\vec{r},t) \\ \varphi_c^+ &= C\ \varphi^+(\vec{r},t)\ C^{-1} = \eta_c^* \varphi(\vec{r},t) \ , \end{aligned} \tag{63}$$

as the definitions of the charge conjugation (or particle conjugation) transformation. For a Hermitian field, the phase factor η_c is restricted to the values ± 1, but otherwise it is subject to the same type of arbitrariness as discussed in the case of the parity transformation. Under the transformations (63) the current operator

$$j_\mu = ie[\varphi^+\partial_\mu\varphi - (\partial_\mu\varphi^+)\varphi] \ , \tag{64}$$

changes sign, which is the historical reason for naming the transformations (63) as the charge conjugation transformation. This conclusion will hold for the currents of all kinds of charges which may be carried by the field, since these are represented by exactly the same operator (64); consequently, it is preferable to call the transformations (63) the transformations of particle conjugation.

Corresponding to the transformations on the field operators Eq. (63), the transformation on the states will be

$$|\Psi_c\rangle = C|\Psi\rangle \ . \tag{65}$$

Clearly C^2 must be a multiple of the unit operator. We take $C^2 = 1$. Now, since j_μ changes sign under charge conjugation, the total charge of a state will change sign under charge conjugation

$$Q_c = CQ_c\ C^{-1} = -Q \ . \tag{66}$$

Hence C is measurable only if Q = 0. For neutral systems, if the interactions are invariant under C,

$$CHC^{-1} = H \,, \tag{67}$$

C will be a measurable operator which will be conserved. The eigenvalue, which can have the value ± 1, is called the charge conjugation quantum number.

The electromagnetic field A_μ is coupled directly to j_μ; consequently, the charge conjugation invariance of electromagnetic interactions requires

$$CA_\mu C^{-1} = -A_\mu \,. \tag{68}$$

Other vector fields transform similarly to the scalar fields. For Dirac fields, the transformation of the fields can be quite complicated since the various components may be transformed into each other. However, we note that if we use the Majorana representation*) of the Dirac matrices, i.e. the one which makes all coefficients in the free Dirac equation

$$\gamma_\mu \partial_\mu \psi + m\psi = 0$$

purely real, ψ^+ satisfies the same equation as ψ and it is possible to choose the charge conjugation transformations as

$$\begin{aligned} \psi_c &= C\psi C^{-1} = \eta_c \psi^+ \\ \psi_c^+ &= C\psi^+ C^{-1} = \eta_c^* \psi \,, \end{aligned} \tag{69}$$

where it is understood that expressions involving Dirac fields will be properly antisymmetrized. With this condition we see that the current density corresponding to such a field,

*) Although all results concerning spinor fields must be independent of the choice of representation for the Dirac matrices, the Majorana representation is by far the most convenient for discussion of the space-time symmetry transformations.

$$j_\mu = \frac{ie}{2} (\psi^+ \gamma_4 \gamma_\mu \psi - \psi \gamma_4 \gamma_\mu \psi^+)$$

changes sign, as desired, under the transformations (69).

The original application of charge conjugation invariance was to prove that a system of an even number of photons cannot go over to an odd number. A n-photon state may be constructed by application of the electromagnetic field operator A_μ n times to the vacuum state, which is by hypothesis an eigenstate of charge conjugation with eigenvalue + 1. Then it follows from Eq. (68) that an n-photon state has a charge conjugation quantum number $(-1)^n$, and charge-conjugation invariance forbids odd-even transitions. Another famous application of charge conjugation invariance is to the selection rules for the annihilation of positronium. Using Eq. (69) and the fact that ψ^+ and ψ_c^+ anticommute, one may show that the charge conjugation quantum number for any state of positronium is given by $(-1)^{L+S}$, i.e. C = + 1 for any state which is allowed for two electrons, and C = -1 otherwise. This classification immediately tells us which states may annihilate into an even number of photons, and which may not.

The π^0 is known to decay into two photons. If interaction responsible for this decay is invariant under charge conjugation, the π^0 field must be even under charge conjugation, i.e. the factor η_c in Eq. (63) must be taken as + 1 in this case. On the other hand, if the π^0 were found to decay into three photons as well, we would be forced to conclude that the interactions responsible for the decay of the π^0 are not invariant under charge conjugation. Conversely, any interaction which would permit the π^0 to decay both into even and odd numbers of photons would necessarily be one which is not invariant under charge conjugation.

In the weak interactions, the violation of charge conjugation invariance has directly observable consequences. For example, whereas the μ^- emitted in the decay of a π^- is found to have its spin oriented parallel to its velocity, the μ^+ arising from a π^+ decay has the opposite helicity.

2. G parity

We have seen that C is a measurable operator only for neutral systems because, in general, C carries a state into the corresponding antiparticle state. However, states in which only the electric charge differs from zero can be treated on the same footing as neutral systems in the following manner. For any state whose charge conjugate state belongs to the same isospin multiplet as itself, the following operation, introduced by Michel and emphasized by Lee and Yang,

$$G = e^{i\pi T_2} C ,$$

which is just charge conjugation followed by 180° rotation round the y axis in isospace, carries the state back to itself. For charge independent interactions (which are invariant under isospin rotations), G must commute with the Hamiltonian; consequently, the G parity, which has eigenvalues ± 1, is conserved in strong interactions.

3. Time reversal

Following our discussion of space inversion, we first consider single-particle states $|\Psi>$ and define time-reversed states $|\Psi_T>$ such that matrix elements of all temporally odd operators change sign when evaluated between time-reversed states, for example

$$< \Phi_T | p_j | \Psi_T > = -< \Phi | p_j | \Psi >$$

but (70)

$$< \Phi_T | x_j | \Psi_T > = < \Phi | x_j | \Psi > .$$

If, as before, we define transformed operators for the time-reversed states

$$< \Phi_T | \vartheta' | \Psi_T > = < \Phi | \vartheta | \Psi >$$

we see that the commutator of x_i', p_j' has the opposite sign of that for x_i, p_j. Thus, the operation which carries a state to the corresponding time-reversed state, cannot be represented by a unitary transformation.

A more general (but equivalent) way to see this is that the Heisenberg equation

$$i\overset{\circ}{f} = [f, H] \tag{71}$$

is not left invariant under time reversal, whatever may be the transformation property of f, even when H is taken to be invariant under time inversion.

However, since we must retain the condition

$$|\langle \Phi_T|\Psi_T\rangle|^2 = |\langle \Phi|\Psi\rangle|^2$$

and unitary transformations cannot be used, we must employ an antiunitary transformation:

$$\langle \Phi_T|\Psi_T\rangle = \langle \Phi|\Psi\rangle^* , \tag{72}$$

which can also be written as

$$\langle \Phi_T|\Psi_T\rangle = \langle \Psi|\Phi\rangle . \tag{73}$$

The original method of describing time reversal, due to Wigner, is based on Eq. (72). One writes

$$|\Psi_T\rangle = U_T|\Psi\rangle^* . \tag{74}$$

where U_T is any unitary transformation and $|\Psi\rangle^*$ is to be interpreted in the following sense. We can always expand $|\Psi\rangle$ in terms of a complete set of states,

$$|\Psi\rangle = \sum_n |n\rangle\langle n|\Psi\rangle . \tag{75}$$

Then

$$|\Psi\rangle^* = \sum_n |n\rangle\langle n|\Psi\rangle^* . \tag{76}$$

An equally valid description of time reversal, due to Schwinger, is based on Eq. (73). Write

$$< \Psi_T| = \sum_n <n|\Psi><n|U_T^{-1} . \qquad (77)$$

Since this is just another way of writing Eqs. (74) and (76), it satisfies Eq. (72). Furthermore, since the time reversal transformation now carries bras to kets and vice versa, the implication is that operator expressions must now be read backwards, i.e. under time reversal a product of operators should be replaced by the product of the transformed operators in reversed order. This is just the change required to make Eq. (71) invariant under time reversal, assuming H is invariant.

This description has the advantage that it reminds us that under time reversal, the initial and final states of any process are interchanged. Also, c-numbers are not affected by the transformation. With these conventions, spinless fields must be transformed*) according to

$$\begin{aligned} \varphi'(\vec{r},t) &= \eta_T \varphi^+(\vec{r},-t) \\ \varphi'(\vec{r},t) &= -\eta_T \varphi^+(\vec{r},-t), \end{aligned} \qquad (78)$$

while vector fields must be transformed as

$$\varphi_0'(\vec{r},t) = -\eta_T' \varphi_0^+(\vec{r},-t)$$

$$\varphi_k'(\vec{r},t) = \eta_T' \varphi_k^+(\vec{r},-t) \text{ for } k = 1,2,3.$$

The factors η_T are relevant only for Hermitian fields; for non-Hermitian fields, these factors may be set equal to unity.

---

*) Transformations in which the φ^+ on the right-hand side of Eq. (78) are replaced by φ describe a different kind of time reversal in which particles are simultaneously transformed into antiparticles, as may be verified by examining the transformation of the charge density.

For Dirac fields, if we use the Majorana representation for the γ matrices, the appropriate transformation is

$$\psi'(\vec{r},t) = \gamma_4\gamma_5\ \psi^{+}(\vec{r},-t)\ . \tag{80}$$

Since the time reversal transformation is not a unitary one, we do not obtain conservation laws or selection rules on the basis of time reversal invariance alone. What we do obtain are relations between the amplitudes for processes and their inverses. In particular, for interactions which are invariant under time reversal, the S matrix is invariant under time reversal

$$< \Psi|S|\Phi > = < \Phi_T|S|\Psi_T> \ . \tag{81}$$

A breakdown of time reversal invariance would correspond to a situation where Eq. (81) was not satisfied in some instance.

4. TCP Theorem

We have discussed the various transformations T, C, P under which the free-field Lagrangians are invariant. We have also discussed the conditions imposed on the interaction terms if the interacting theory is to remain invariant under a particular transformation, and we have seen that it is relatively easy to construct examples in which any one of these ceases to remain an invariance operation for the total Lagrangian.

What the TCP theorem, due to Schwinger and Lüders, states is that it is very much harder to write down interactions which destroy invariance under the combined transformation of TCP. In fact, all local Lorentz invariant Lagrangian theories are automatically invariant under an antiunitary transformation Θ which may be identified with the product of the transformations TCP for free fields, provided they incorporate the spin statistics relation in the sense that boson fields satisfy commutation relations and fermion fields anticommute. The last condition can scarcely be considered a supplementary one, since it has been shown by Pauli that the use of commutation rules for fermions, or anticommutation relations for bosons, leads to physically unreasonable consequences *).

It seems essential to include the locality condition, by which we mean that the terms in the Lagrangian may only contain field operators or derivatives of field operators (of finite order) defined at the same space time point; i.e. terms like

$$\psi^+(x)\,\psi(x)\,\varphi(y)\,f\,[(x-y)^2]$$

are excluded.

The reason for the requirement of locality, or the introduction at some point of the concept of local fields, seems to be the following. If we do not introduce local fields, there is no necessity of introducing antiparticles into the theory. This does not conflict in any way with Lorentz invariance, and we may therefore consider a theory in which there are certain particles which interact with each other, but there are no antiparticles or, if one insists on having antiparticles, these antiparticles interact only very feebly with each other. Such a situation clearly violates TCP invariance.

The main consequence of TCP invariance is that the violation of one of the symmetries implies that at least one other is violated. Until very recently, the well-established lack of invariance under P in weak interactions was believed to be associated with a corresponding violation of C invariance, such that CP, and therefore also T, remained a valid symmetry operation. If it should be established that CP is indeed violated in K_2^0 decays, the immediate question would be whether T invariance also breaks down, as required by the TCP theorem. Should this, indeed be

---

*) Recently there has been some discussion as to whether one is confined to these possibilities. It is clear that if one restricts oneself to the usual interpretation whereby a state corresponding to given eigenvalues of the measurable operators of an n-particle system is represented by a single vector in Hilbert space, the only possibilities are the completely symmetric and antisymmetric ones, with respect to permutation of the particles.

found to be the case, we would have to seek an explanation of why one direction in time is preferred over the other; if not, we shall have to learn to live without the TCP theorem.

III. THE YANG-MILLS FIELD

We begin with a statement of Noether's theorem in the form in which we shall need it. If a Lagrangian theory characterized by the Lagrangian $\mathcal{L}(\psi^a, \psi^a_\mu)$ is invariant under the transformations

$$\psi^a \to \psi^a + \alpha\, F^a(\psi^b, \psi^b_\mu) \;, \tag{82}$$

where ψ^a_μ is $\partial\psi^a/\partial x_\mu$ and α is an infinitesimal parameter, we must have

$$\delta\mathcal{L} = \frac{\delta\mathcal{L}}{\delta\psi^a}\,\delta\psi^a + \frac{\delta}{\delta\psi^a_\mu}\,\delta\psi^a_\mu = 0$$

where summation over the repeated index a is also implied. Or

$$\frac{\delta\mathcal{L}}{\delta\psi^a}\,\alpha\, F^a + \frac{\delta\mathcal{L}}{\delta\psi^a_\mu}\,\alpha\, F^a_\mu = 0 \;.$$

Using the Euler-Lagrange equations, this may be written

$$\partial_\mu\left(\frac{\delta\mathcal{L}}{\delta\psi^a_\mu}\,\alpha\, F^a\right) + \frac{\delta\mathcal{L}}{\delta\psi^a_\mu}\,\alpha\, F^a_\mu = 0$$

or

$$\partial_\mu\left(\frac{\delta\mathcal{L}}{\delta\psi^a_\mu}\, F^a\right) = 0 \;. \tag{83}$$

A particular application is the group of transformations

$$\psi^a \to \psi^a + i\,\alpha q_a\,\psi^a \;, \tag{84}$$

which is just the infinitesimal form of the gauge transformations

$$\psi^a \to e^{i\alpha q_a}\,\psi^a \;. \tag{84'}$$

From Eqs. (82) and (83), we see that invariance under such transformations leads to the conservation law

$$\partial_\mu \left(q_a \frac{\partial \mathcal{L}}{\partial \psi^a_\mu} \psi^a \right) = 0 \ , \qquad (83')$$

which is a conservation law for the current

$$j_\mu = q_a \frac{\partial \mathcal{L}}{\partial \psi^a_\mu} \psi^a \ . \qquad (85)$$

The constant q_a is the charge associated with the field ψ^a. The conservation laws of electric charge, baryonic charge, leptonic charge, etc., which give rise to superselection rules, are all assumed to arise in this way. The transformations (84′) corresponding to different kinds of charges commute, as is required if we wish to have the different kinds of charge to be well defined for physically realizable states.

Now, in the case of the electric charge, we know that the gauge transformations (84′) can be generalized to include gauge functions $\alpha(x)$

$$\psi^a \rightarrow e^{iq_a \alpha(x)} \psi^a \ , \qquad (86)$$

which are functions of the co-ordinates provided we make corresponding transformations on the electromagnetic field. Under the transformation (84′),

$$\psi^a_\mu \rightarrow e^{iq_a \alpha} (\psi^a_\mu + iq_a \alpha_\mu \psi^a) \ . \qquad (87)$$

Thus, if we ensure that in the original Lagrangian, every ψ^a_λ appears in the combination $(\psi^a_\lambda - iq_a A_\lambda \psi)$, then the Lagrangian will be invariant under the generalized transformations (86), provided we simultaneously transform A_λ according to

$$A_\lambda \rightarrow A_\lambda + \alpha_\lambda \ . \qquad (88)$$

Thus, it appears that the generalization of the gauge function α from a constant to a function of space-time co-ordinates, requires the introduction of the electromagnetic field and specifies the manner of its coupling to the source fields ψ^a. This result may be interpreted in the following fashion.

The transformation (84′) appears at first sight to express the freedom of choice for the phase of ψ^a at any given point, implied by the superselection rule operating between states of different charge: since the action of ψ^a on any state is to change the charge by $\pm q_a$, its phase may be altered arbitrarily. However, Eq. (84′) requires that the phase at all other points be simultaneously changed by the same amount and it is difficult to understand from a dynamical viewpoint how a phase change at one point could, by itself, influence the choice of phase at another. But if we admit the existence of an intermediary field, in this case, the electromagnetic field, which recognizes the phase (because it interacts differently with ψ and ψ^+), there is no longer any mystery. In fact, we can, in that case, allow variations of the phase of ψ because this information can now be transmitted from point to point by suitable redefinition of the electromagnetic potentials. In fact, the change of the line integral

$$\int A_\lambda \, dx_\lambda \ ,$$

between any two points measures just the change of phase of ψ introduced by a generalized gauge transformation (86).

Thus, one may say that if one supplements the invariance principle (84′), which expresses the conservation of charge, by the principle of contiguity (no action at a distance), one is led to infer not only the existence of the electromagnetic field, but also the exact manner of its coupling to the charges which are its source*).

One may naturally ask whether other conservation laws generate corresponding vector fields. This question was raised and answered by

*) The deep connection between charge conservation and gauge invariance has been demonstrated in another way through a direct proof of the converse statement that the arbitrariness of the choice of gauge necessarily implies charge conservation. [E.P. Wigner, Proc.Am. Phil.Soc. 93, 521 (1949)].

Yang and Mills, who considered the particular case of isotopic spin. The gauge transformation on the nucleon field ψ, corresponding to isotopic spin rotations, is

$$\psi \to e^{i \underset{\sim}{\tau} \cdot \underset{\sim}{b}} \psi , \tag{89}$$

or

$$\psi \to \psi + i \underset{\sim}{\tau} \cdot b \psi , \tag{90}$$

for infinitesimal transformations, and leads to the conservation of the three components of the isotopic spin current,

$$\partial_\mu (\frac{\partial \mathcal{L}}{\partial \psi} \underset{\sim}{\tau} \psi) = 0 , \tag{91}$$

since the components of $\underset{\sim}{b}$ may be chosen arbitrarily. Now the whole idea of isotopic spin invariance was based on the notion that as far as the strong interactions are concerned, neutron and proton states are completely equivalent physically to any other pair of states obtained from them by a rotation in isotopic spin space. If it were not for the electromagnetic interactions which single out a particular direction in this space, we should be at perfect liberty to redefine any one of these pairs as the "neutron" and "proton" states. The question then is, if the interactions themselves show no preference for any direction in isospin space (we assume for the time being that it is possible to think of isospin invariance as an exact symmetry), why should it not be possible to adopt arbitrary local definitions of neutron and proton states at different points. Or, conversely, when we decide to redefine what we call a proton at one point, why must we simultaneously make the identical redefinition everywhere else, which is what is required by Eq. (89) if $\underset{\sim}{b}$ is taken to be a constant isovector.

Yang and Mills took the view that the "localized field concept" required that it should be possible to make independent isotopic spin rotations at different space-time points, i.e. the isospin vector gauge function $\underset{\sim}{b}$ should be allowed to vary with the co-ordinates

$$\psi \to e^{i \underset{\sim}{\tau} \cdot \underset{\sim}{b}(x)} \psi . \tag{92}$$

Exactly as in the case of the ordinary gauge transformation, we find that additional terms are generated by this transformation. In particular,

$$\Psi_\mu \rightarrow e^{i\,\underset{\sim}{\tau}\cdot\underset{\sim}{b}(x)}(\Psi_\mu + i\,\underset{\sim}{\tau}\cdot\underset{\sim}{b}_\mu\Psi)\ . \tag{93}$$

We can maintain invariance of the Lagrangian if Ψ_μ always appears in the "gauge-invariant" combination $(\Psi_\mu - ig\underset{\sim}{\tau}\cdot\underset{\sim}{B}_\mu)$ where the constant g plays a role analogous to that of electric charge, and it is understood that $\underset{\sim}{B}_\mu$ must undergo suitable transformations to maintain invariance. For infinitesimal transformations we require

$$\underset{\sim}{B}_\mu \rightarrow \underset{\sim}{B}_\mu + 2\underset{\sim}{B}_\mu \times \underset{\sim}{b} + \frac{1}{g}\underset{\sim}{b}_\mu\ . \tag{94}$$

The last term is exactly like the gauge term one obtained in Eq. (88) while the second expresses the change in the components of $\underset{\sim}{B}_\mu$ as a result of the rotation of the isotopic spin axes. The quantities

$$\underset{\sim}{f}_{\mu\nu} = \partial_\nu\underset{\sim}{B}_\mu - \partial_\mu\underset{\sim}{B}_\nu - 2g\,\underset{\sim}{B}_\mu \times \underset{\sim}{B}_\nu\ , \tag{95}$$

are the gauge-invariant analogues of the electromagnetic field tensor, and if we write the Lagrangian for the nucleon B-field system as

$$\mathcal{L} = -\frac{1}{4}\underset{\sim}{f}_{\mu\nu}\underset{\sim}{f}_{\mu\nu} - \Psi\gamma_\mu(\partial_\mu - ig\underset{\sim}{\tau}\cdot\underset{\sim}{B}_\mu)\Psi - m\bar{\Psi}\Psi \tag{96}$$

we obtain the equations of motion

$$\begin{aligned} \partial_\nu\underset{\sim}{f}_{\mu\nu} + 2g(\underset{\sim}{B}_\nu \times \underset{\sim}{f}_{\mu\nu}) + \underset{\sim}{J}_\mu &= 0 \\ \gamma_\mu(\partial_\mu - ig\underset{\sim}{\tau}\cdot\underset{\sim}{B}_\mu)\Psi + m\Psi &= 0\ , \end{aligned} \tag{97}$$

where $\underset{\sim}{J}_\mu = ig\Psi\gamma_\mu\underset{\sim}{\tau}\Psi$ is the isospin current of the nucleons. From Eq. (97) we find

$$\partial_\mu(\underset{\sim}{J}_\mu + 2g\,\underset{\sim}{B}_\nu \times \underset{\sim}{f}_{\mu\nu}) = 0\ .$$

This shows that the conserved isotopic spin current contains a contribution also from the B field. This is not surprising since the B field itself carries isotopic spin, and, according to the first of Eqs. (97), itself serves as the source of the $\underset{\sim}{f}_{\mu\nu}$ fields. As a result of this complication, Yang and Mills were unable to reach any conclusion concerning the mass of the B-field quanta, and since none were seen, either massive or massless, the question remained a more or less academic one until 1960.

The law of baryon conservation, on the other hand, is exactly similar to that of electric charge, so if we introduce the same arguments as one uses in the electromagnetic case, one infers the existence of a massless*) vector field, very similar to the electromagnetic field, which is coupled, however, to the baryonic charge. This would give rise to a long-range repulsion between two objects with like baryonic charge, whereas, at least, on the scale at which we are able to study the problem, the predominant long-range force between two pieces of neutral matter is an attractive one. Hence, we conclude that such a field, if it exists at all, interacts too feebly to be of interest in particle physics. At this point, one should make a remark about the strength of the coupling between a conserved current and its gauge field. Neither the original gauge principle (84) nor the generalized form (86) tells us anything about the magnitude of the charge carried by a given field (nor the even more striking fact that the charges carried by different fields are always multiples of a definite unit). However, we know that the electron is absolutely stable because there is no other charged particle into which it could decay. We also know that the charge on an electron must give rise to an electromagnetic field in the surrounding region, which necessarily contains energy (although we do not yet know how to calculate how much). Could it not be that the mass of the electron arises solely because of its charge? The electron mass is then, in some sense, a measure of the coupling strength between the charge and the electromagnetic field. If we assume a corresponding relation between the stability of the proton and the conservation of baryonic charge, we immediately conclude that the coupling constant of the baryonic charge to its

*) The usual argument is that mass terms of the form $m^2A^\lambda A_\lambda$ would not be invariant under the gauge transformation (88).

gauge field is very much greater than the electromagnetic constant. This distinction is pertinent because it has been argued that for coupling constants which are sufficiently large, a primary charge placed at a certain point may be completely shielded by the polarization of the vacuum*) so that there is not long-range interaction and no zero mass quanta of the field.

However, even before such arguments were advanced**) the concept of vector fields associated with the strongly conserved currents was revived and advocated by Sakurai, with remarkable success. He correctly ignored the mass problem as a technical one and asserted that the then known conserved currents - the three components of isospin, baryonic charge and hypercharge - must each give rise to a massive vector field which is strongly coupled to its generating current. Vector mesons corresponding to each of these fields have subsequently been found and the vector fields arising from the isospin current is found to couple to the isospin current of pions and nucleons with roughly the same constant, as predicted. The arguments advanced by Yang and Mills can be generalized to any other Lie group of internal symmetries. In SU_3, one predicts in addition to the fields predicted by Sakurai, two additional fields corresponding to the neutral and charged hypercharge-changing currents, and their Hermitian adjoints. These may be identified with the K^* mesons. Unfortunately, our inability to perform reliable calculations with strong couplings prevents us from obtaining anything more than semi-quantitative predictions of this theory, in certain simple situations. Attempts to associate gauge fields with lepton currents have not met with any great success. Nevertheless, since the concept has proved to be so fruitful in the case of the strong interactions, it is extremely likely that the idea of the Yang-Mills field will again find applications in the future.

---

*) For an electric charge we believe this effect occurs partially, giving rise to the charge renormalization, even though when we try to calculate it, the effective charge vanishes there also.

**) J. Schwinger, Theoretical Physics (Trieste 1962) I.A.E.A. Vienna.

BIBLIOGRAPHY

General : "Quantum Mechanics" by P.A.M. Dirac, Oxford University Press, London 1958.

Lorentz Group : E.P. Wigner, Annals of Mathematics 40, 149 (1939).
"Continuous groups in quantum mechanics" by W. Pauli, CERN report No. 56-31, Geneva 1956.
A.S. Wightman in "Relations de Dispersion et Particules Elementaires" Hermann, Paris 1960.
"Relativistic quantum field theory" by S.S. Schweber, Row, Peterson, Evanston 1961.

Discrete transformations : J. Schwinger, Phys.Rev. 82, 914 (1951).
G. Lüders, Dan.Mat-fys.Medd. 28, 5 (1954).
W. Pauli in "Niels Bohr and the Development of Physics", Pergamon Press, London, 1955.
R. Jost, Helv.Phys.Acta. 30, 409 (1957).

Yang-Mills fields : C.N. Yang and R.L. Mills, Phys.Rev. 96, 191 (1954).
R. Utiyama, Phys.Rev. 101, 1597 (1956).

ELEMENTS OF SU_3

S.M. Berman

Stanford Linear Accelerator Center
Stanford, California, U.S.A.

The purpose of this set of lectures is directed to the student who is unfamiliar with the use of the special unitary group, SU_3, in elementary particle physics. No knowledge of group theory is assumed, and therefore, certain general results about semi-simple Lie groups will be demonstrated, only in the context of SU_3. It is hoped that these lectures will serve as a brief introductory, but self-contained, treatment of this fascinating and timely subject. The author apologizes to his colleagues for the absence of references, and refers the reader to the paper by Behrends, Dreitlin, Fronsdal and Lee, Rev.Mod.Phys. 34, 1 (1962) and the forthcoming review article by Gasiorowicz and Glashow, for a survey of relevant literature.

The following topics will be covered in this course:

1) } The general idea of SU_3
2) }
3) Multiplet structure
4) Tensors
5) Mass differences in multiplets
6) Electromagnetism and currents in SU_3
7) Decay widths and cross-section relationships.

I. INTRODUCTION AND BASIC IDEAS

We first introduce O_3, the real three-dimensional orthogonal group. The most familiar matrix representation of O_3 is the group of matrices which transform the components of a three-dimensional vector in an initial co-ordinate system to its co-ordinates in a rotated co-ordinate system. From the properties of this representation we derive certain fundamental commutation relationships which define an algebra, the Lie algebra which "generates" the abstract group O_3.

Consider a position vector x with components x_i. (We do not distinguish between contravariant and covariant components.) Under an infinitesimal rotation the components transform according to

$$x_i' = x_i + \epsilon_{ij} x_j = (\delta_{ij} + \epsilon_{ij}) x_j , \tag{1}$$

where ϵ_{ij} is infinitesimal and we sum over repeated indices. Since the length of x is preserved under the rotation we must have

$$x_i' x_i' = x_i x_i . \tag{2}$$

From Eq. (1), dropping terms of the order of ϵ^2 we obtain

$$x_i' x_i' = (x_i + \epsilon_{ij} x_j)(x_i + \epsilon_{ik} x_k)$$

$$= x_i x_i + (\epsilon_{ij} x_j + \epsilon_{ik} x_k) x_i + O(\epsilon^2).$$

Therefore,

$$0 = \epsilon_{ij} x_j x_i + \epsilon_{ik} x_k x_i .$$

Now interchange i and k and replace k by j,

$$0 = (\epsilon_{ij} + \epsilon_{ji}) x_i x_j ,$$

therefore*)

$$\epsilon_{ij} = - \epsilon_{ji} . \tag{3}$$

Introduce an operator $U(\epsilon)$ which transforms $x \rightarrow x'$

$$x' = U(\epsilon) x .$$

---

*) Note Eq. (2) also permits the trivial case $\epsilon_{ij} = 0$.

An explicit operator representation for $U(\epsilon)$ is

$$U(\epsilon) = 1 - \frac{\epsilon_{\ell m}}{2}\left(x_\ell \frac{\partial}{\partial x_m} - x_m \frac{\partial}{\partial x_\ell}\right)_{\substack{\ell = 1.2.3 \\ m = 1,2,3}} \qquad (4)$$

which we verify by operating with $U(\epsilon)$ on a single component x_i

$$U(\epsilon)x_i = x_i - \frac{\epsilon_{\ell m}}{2}(x_\ell \delta_{mi} - x_m \delta_{mi})$$

$$= x_i + \frac{1}{2} \epsilon_{i\ell} x_\ell + \frac{1}{2} \epsilon_{im} x_m$$

$$= x_i + \epsilon_{i\ell} x_\ell$$

$$= x_i' \, .$$

In terms of the angular momentum operators**)

$$L_k \equiv L_{\ell m} = - i \left[x_\ell \frac{\partial}{\partial x_m} - x_m \frac{\partial}{\partial x_\ell}\right] (k\ell m \text{ cyclic}) \qquad (5)$$

which are known as the generators of O_3 and have

$$U(\epsilon) = 1 - \frac{i}{2} \epsilon_{\ell m} L_{\ell m} \, . \qquad (6)$$

To preserve the scalar product $x_i x_i$, $U(\epsilon)$ is required to be orthogonal or, equivalently, since $U(\epsilon)$ is real, unitary. Therefore,

$$1 = U^+ U = (1 + \frac{i}{2} \epsilon_{\ell m} L_{\ell m}^+)(1 - \frac{i}{2} \epsilon_{\ell m} L_{\ell m})$$

$$= 1 + \frac{i}{2} \epsilon_{\ell m} (L_{\ell m}^+ - L_{\ell m}) + O(\epsilon^2).$$

**) Note $L_{\ell m}$ is not the ℓm component of an operator L but the ℓ,mth operator.

Hence, $L_{\ell m}^{+} = L_{\ell m}$ or L is Hermitian. Recall that L_k satisfy the commutation rules:

$$[L_i, L_j] = iL_k \quad (i,j,k) \text{ cyclic.} \tag{7}$$

The commutation rules on L_1, L_2, and L_3 are called the Lie algebra of the group O_3.

We now give a brief review of angular momentum theory which follows entirely from the rules (7).

Any representation is classified by a non-negative integer or half-integer quantum number ℓ. For each ℓ there exist $2\ell + 1$ eigenstates $\psi_{\ell m}$ which satisfy

$$L^2\psi_{\ell m} = \ell(\ell+1)\psi_{\ell m}$$

$$L_3\psi_{\ell m} = m\psi_{\ell m} \qquad -\ell \leq m \leq \ell$$

where $$L^2 \equiv L_1{}^2 + L_2{}^2 + L_3{}^2 .$$

Raising and lowering operators may be constructed,

$$L_+ = L_1 + iL_2$$

$$L_- = L_1 - iL_2$$

which have the properties

$$L_i\psi_{\ell m} \sim \psi_{\ell, m\pm 1} .$$

Commutations rules equivalent to (7) are

$$[L_+, L_-] = 2L_3$$

$$[L_3, L_\pm] = \pm L_\pm .$$

Counting the representations present in a direct product of representations is simplified by the following device which we explain by way of example, in Figs. 1 and 2. Consider the direct product of two spin 1 representations.

We denote the one-dimensional space of m of the representations by points on a line:

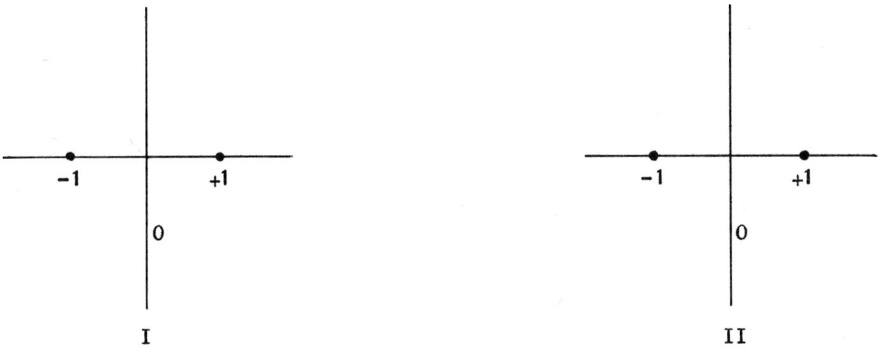

Fig. 1

Now superimpose one space on the other by placing the centre of I over each point of II:

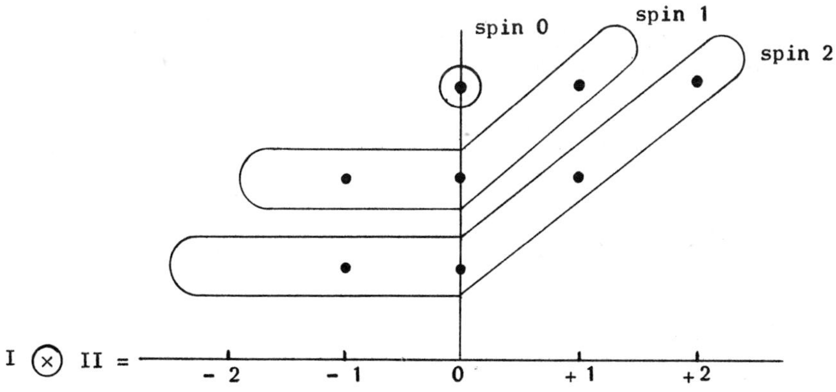

Fig. 2

This example decomposes to one spin 2, one spin 1, and one spin 0 representation. Although this construction may appear rather trivial in the case of O_3 it will be very useful in our treatment of SU_3.

The Unitary Group U_n

Consider x_μ and x^μ as abstract complex-valued covariant and contravariant co-ordinates in an n-dimensional space. These transform infinitesimally according to

$$x_\mu' = x_\mu + \Theta_\mu^\nu x_\nu \,, \tag{8}$$

and

$$x^{\mu\prime} = x^\mu + \bar{\Theta}_\nu^\mu x^\nu \tag{9}$$

where Θ and $\bar{\Theta}$ are infinitesimal.

Unitary transformations require that $x^{\mu\prime *} x_\mu' = x^{\mu *} x_\mu$ and that $g^{\mu\nu} = \delta^{\mu\nu}$, hence

$$\Theta_\nu^\mu = - (\Theta_\mu^\nu)^* \,. \tag{10}$$

Let us construct an operator that transforms $x \to x'$ primarily to the method employed for O_3. The transformation of the μth co-ordinate is of the form

$$x_\mu' = \left[1 + \Theta_\beta^\alpha A_\alpha^\beta \right] x_\mu \tag{11}$$

where Θ's are infinitesimal numbers and the A's are operators.

This reduces to Eq. (8) if we define

$$A_\alpha^\beta \equiv x_\alpha \frac{\partial}{\partial x_\beta} \,. \tag{12a}$$

because

$$x_\alpha \frac{\partial}{\partial x_\beta} x_\mu = x_\alpha \, \delta^\beta_\mu .$$

The commutation of A^μ_ν with A^σ_λ can be found by using the definition (12a) directly, i.e.

$$\left[A^\mu_\nu \, , \, A^\sigma_\lambda \right] = x_\nu \frac{\partial}{\partial x_\mu} x_\lambda \frac{\partial}{\partial x_\sigma} - x_\lambda \frac{\partial}{\partial x_\sigma} x_\nu \frac{\partial}{\partial x_\mu}$$

$$= x_\nu \, \delta^\mu_\lambda \frac{\partial}{\partial x_\sigma} + x_\nu x_\lambda \frac{\partial}{\partial x_\mu} \frac{\partial}{\partial x_\sigma} - x_\lambda \, \delta^\sigma_\nu \frac{\partial}{\partial x_\mu} - x_\lambda x_\nu \frac{\partial}{\partial x_\sigma} \frac{\partial}{\partial x_\mu} ,$$

and hence for twice continuously differentiable functions

$$\left[A^\mu_\nu , A^\sigma_\lambda \right] = \delta^\mu_\lambda A^\sigma_\nu - \delta^\sigma_\nu A^\mu_\lambda . \tag{12b}$$

Notice that the trace $\sum_\mu A^\mu_\mu$ commutes with all the operators:

$$\left[\Sigma_\mu A^\mu_\mu \, , \, A^\sigma_\lambda \right] = \delta^\mu_\lambda A^\sigma_\mu - \delta^\sigma_\mu A^\mu_\lambda = A^\sigma_\lambda - A^\sigma_\lambda = 0 .$$

It can be shown that $\Sigma_\mu A^\mu_\mu$ is the generator of a phase factor transformation on x_μ. Removal of the phase factor i.e., removal of $\Sigma_\mu A^\mu_\mu$ takes U_n to SU_n. In particular, consider U_2 where there are four linearly independent operators $A_1{}^1$, $A_1{}^2$, $A_2{}^1$, $A_2{}^2$. The sum $A_1{}^1 + A_2{}^2$ commutes with each A^ν_μ and generates a phase factor. SU_2 is the group U_2 with the phase factor removed.

A condition on the A^{ν}_μ's follows from the fact that the transformation is unitary.

Define

$$U = 1 + \Theta^\nu_\mu A^\mu_\nu . \tag{13}$$

Then the adjoint is

$$U^{+} = 1 + \Theta_{\mu}^{\nu *} A_{\nu}^{\mu +} \tag{14}$$

and we must have

$$1 = U^{+} U = 1 + \Theta_{\mu}^{\nu} A_{\nu}^{\mu} + \Theta_{\mu}^{\nu *} A_{\nu}^{\mu +} + 0(\Theta^{2}).$$

Using Eq. (10) we obtain

$$A_{\nu}^{\mu} = (A_{\mu}^{\nu})^{+}. \tag{15}$$

<u>U_2 and SU_2</u>

The group U_2 is generated by the four operators

$$A_1{}^1,\ A_1{}^2,\ A_2{}^1, \text{ and } A_2{}^2$$

which have the following algebra:

$$\begin{aligned}
&\left[A_1{}^1, A_2{}^2\right] = 0 && \left[A_2{}^2, A_1{}^2\right] = -A_1{}^2 \\
&\left[A_1{}^1, A_2{}^1\right] = -A_2{}^1 && \left[A_2{}^2, A_2{}^1\right] = A_2{}^1 \\
&\left[A_1{}^1, A_2{}^1\right] = A_1{}^2 && \left[A_1{}^2, A_2{}^1\right] = A_1{}^1 - A_2{}^2 .
\end{aligned} \tag{16}$$

To obtain SU_2 we remove $A_1{}^1 + A_2{}^2$ from the space of operators and define

$$\begin{aligned}
I_z &= \frac{1}{2}(A_1{}^1 - A_2{}^2) \\
I_{+} &= A_1{}^2 \\
I_{-} &= A_2{}^1
\end{aligned} \tag{17}$$

which span the remaining space. These operators have the commutation rules from Eq. (12b)

$$\left[I_z, I_\pm\right] = \pm I_\pm$$
$$\left[I_+, I_-\right] = 2I_z . \tag{18}$$

For any matrix representation of operators P and Q we have

$$Tr\ [P,Q]_- = 0 .$$

Then, since I_z, I_+, I_- are each equal to some commutator it follows they are all traceless.

Note that the algebra of the I's is identical to that of O_3. However, SU_2 and O_3 are homorphic, not isomorphic, i.e. there is not one-to-one correspondence. To every element in O_3 there are two elements in SU_2. Note that SU_2 is represented by complex 2×2 matrices, while O_3 is restricted to real matrices.

The device introduced previously to decompose products in O_3 by constructing a one-dimensional weight space for each representation applies equally well to SU_2. In fact, the simplest non-trivial representation, with two eigenvalues, is

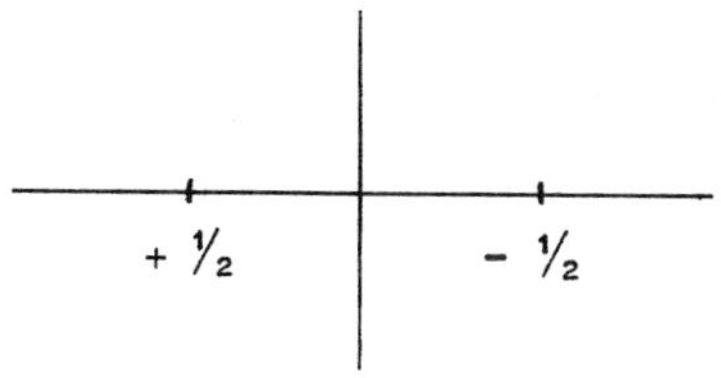

$\underline{SU_3}$

Instead of working with the A_μ^ν operators in SU_3, we define the following operators and new notation:

$$I_z = \frac{1}{2}\left[A_1{}^1 - A_2{}^2\right] \qquad I_+ = A_1{}^2 \qquad I_- = A_2{}^1$$

$$U_z = \frac{1}{2}\left[A_2{}^2 - A_3{}^3\right] \qquad U_+ = A_2{}^3 \qquad U_- = A_3{}^2 \tag{19}$$

$$V_z = \frac{1}{2}\left[A_3{}^3 - A_1{}^1\right] \qquad V_+ = A_3{}^1 \qquad V_- = A_1{}^3 \;.$$

Note that $I_z + U_z + V_z = 0$ so that there are really only eight independent operators. The space spanned by these operators does not contain the operator

$$\sum_{\mu=1}^{3} A^{\mu}_{\mu}$$

and therefore, we are in SU_3.

We list the 36 commutators of Eq. (19) as derived from the fundamental commutation rules of the A^{ν}_{μ}'s.

First note the I's among themselves, the U's and the V's, have the same algebra as SU_2.

$$\left[I_z, I_\pm\right] = \pm I_\pm \qquad \left[I_+, I_-\right] = 2I_z$$

$$\left[U_z, U_\pm\right] = \pm U_\pm \qquad \left[U_+, U_-\right] = 2U_z \tag{20}$$

$$\left[V_z, V_\pm\right] = \pm V_\pm \qquad \left[V_+, V_-\right] = 2V_z$$

The other commutators are

$\left[I_z , U_z \right] = 0$	$\left[I_z , V_z \right] = 0$
$\left[I_z , U_+ \right] = \frac{-1}{2} U_+$	$\left[I_z , V_+ \right] = \frac{-1}{2} V_+$
$\left[I_z , U_- \right] = \frac{1}{2} U_-$	$\left[I_z , V_- \right] = \frac{1}{2} V_-$
$\left[I_+ , U_z \right] = \frac{1}{2} I_+$	$\left[I_+ , V_z \right] = \frac{1}{2} I_+$
$\left[I_+ , U_+ \right] = V_-$	$\left[I_+ , V_+ \right] = - U_-$
$\left[I_+ , U_- \right] = 0$	$\left[I_+ , V_- \right] = 0$
$\left[I_- , U_z \right] = - \frac{1}{2} I_-$	$\left[I_- , V_z \right] = \frac{-1}{2} I_-$
$\left[I_- , U_+ \right] = 0$	$\left[I_- , V_+ \right] = 0$
$\left[I_- , U_- \right] = - V_+$	$\left[I_- , V_- \right] = + U_+$

$$[U_z, V_z] = 0 \qquad [U_+, V_z] = \frac{1}{2} U_+$$

$$[U_z, V_+] = -\frac{1}{2} V_+ \qquad [U_+, V_+] = I_-$$

$$[U_z, V_-] = +\frac{1}{2} V_- \qquad [U_+, V_-] = 0$$

$$[U_-, V_z] = -\frac{1}{2} U_-$$

$$[U_-, V_+] = 0$$

$$[U_-, V_-] = -I_+$$

While I_z, U_z and V_z all commute only two are linearly independent. Note that if we search for other sets of commuting operators they contain only two members. We define the rank of SU_n to be the maximal number of commuting, independent, diagonalizable operators. The rank of SU_2 is 1 since an SU_2 operator commutes only with itself and the rank of SU_3 is 2.

We choose to diagonalize the system with

I_z, corresponding to isotopic spin,

and

$Y = \frac{2}{3}(U_z - V_z)$, corresponding to hypercharge,

as the two commuting operators. The reason for the factor $2/3$ will become clear when we discuss applications to elementary particles.

The rank of the algebra is thus the dimension of the space of quantum numbers. The two-dimensional weight space is shown in Fig. 3.

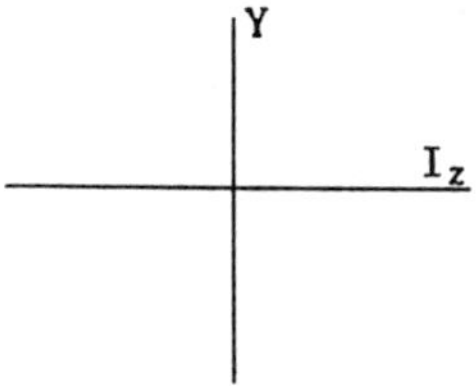

Fig. 3

We will next show what the representations of SU_3 look like in this two-dimensional weight space, with orthogonal co-ordinates Y and I_z.

Problems for Chapter I

1) Under what conditions is the law of transformations the same for covariant vector quantities F_μ and contravariant vector quantities F^μ?

2) Show that the operator $\sum_\mu A_\mu^\mu$ is equivalent to multiplying x_α a phase factor.

3) Is there any isomorphism between SU_3 and O_4? Explain.

4) What is the rank of the algebra of SU_n?

II. PROPERTIES OF SU_3 REPRESENTATIONS

A two-dimensional weight space has been introduced where a point in this space is represented by a value of I_z and $Y = \frac{2}{3}(U_z - V_z)$. These two operators commute and are hermitian so that they can be diagonalized simultaneously.

We wish to determine the complete set of eigenfunctions (denoted by a set of points in the weight space) which describes a given representation. First note that it may be convenient to draw the three axes I_z, U_z, and V_z in the weight space even though they are not independent co-ordinates.

$$I_z + V_z + U_z = 0. \tag{21}$$

That the axes must intersect at 120° immediately follows from Eq. (21) but let us demonstrate this fact by using the operators [Eq. (19)].

Let $|\alpha>$ be an eigenstate of I_z, U_z, and V_z with eigenvalues I_0, U_0, and $V_0 = - I_0 - U_0$.

$$\begin{aligned} I_z|\alpha> &= I_0|\alpha> \\ U_z|\alpha> &= U_0|\alpha> \\ V_z|\alpha> &= V_0|\alpha> \end{aligned} \tag{22}$$

Now, observe that $I_+|\alpha>$ is either zero or an eigenstate of I_z with eigenvalue $I_0 + 1$:

$$\begin{aligned} I_z I_+|\alpha> &= (I_+ I_z + I_+)|\alpha> \\ &= (I_0 + 1) I_+|\alpha> \end{aligned} \tag{23}$$

Hence, I_+, and U_+ and V_+ as well, are raising operators. Similarly, I_-, U_-, and V_- are lowering operators in that they either destroy an eigenstate or decrease the corresponding eigenvalue by one unit. In addition, we have relations such as

$$\begin{aligned} I_z U_\pm|\alpha> &= (I_0 \mp ½)U_\pm|\alpha> \\ I_z V_\pm|\alpha> &= (I_0 \mp ½)V_\pm|\alpha> \end{aligned} \tag{24}$$

which show that U_+ and V_+ are ½ - unit lowering operators for the quantum number I_z.

Consider the effect of the operator $V_+U_+I_+$ on the eigenstate $|\alpha>$. Let

$$|\beta> = V_+U_+I_+|\alpha>$$

then

$$I_z|\beta> = I_zV_+U_+I_+|\alpha>$$

$$= V_+I_zU_+I_+|\alpha> - \tfrac{1}{2}\,\beta$$

$$= V_+U_+I_zI_+|\alpha> - |\beta>$$

$$= V_+U_+I_+I_z|\alpha>$$

$$= I_0|\beta> .$$

Similarly, we obtain

$$U_z|\beta> = U_0|\beta>$$

$$V_z|\beta> = V_0|\beta> .$$

Thus $|\beta>$ ought to appear in the same position as $|\alpha>$ in the weight space. We have not proved these are the same state, only that they are located at the same point which could admit degeneracy. If we take three steps of equal length and return to the starting position we necessarily have stepped on the vertices of an equilateral triangle which suggests we take the I_z, U_z and V_z axes parallel to the sides of an equilateral triangle. The successive operations of I_+, U_+, and V_+ on $|\alpha>$ carry the state around a triangular path as shown on Fig. 4.

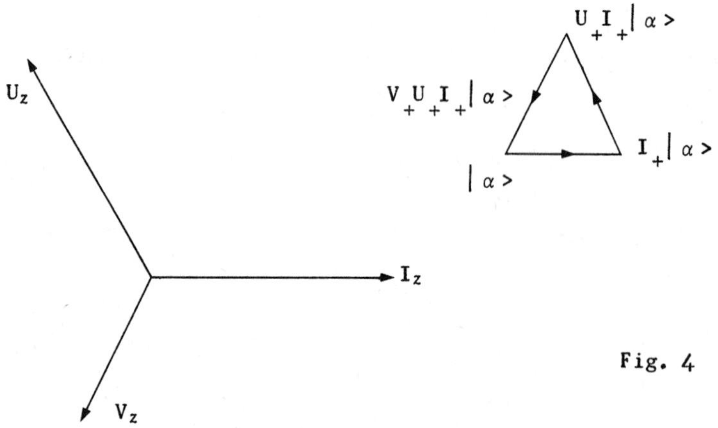

Fig. 4

Note that a displacement by I_+ of one unit in the I_z direction also decreases U_z and V_z by $\frac{1}{2}$ unit as expected from Eq. (24).

Consider a representation where a state $|\alpha>$ is both farthest to the right (positive I_z direction) and farthest to the left. Is such a representation permissible and if so what are its eigenvalues? All raising and lowering operators destroy the state since otherwise each moves $|\alpha>$ either to the right or to the left. Then we may write

$$(I_+I_- - I_-I_+)|\alpha> = 0$$

or

$$2I_z|\alpha> = 0.$$

Hence the state has $I_z = U_z = V_z = 0$ and all operators in Eq. (19) are represented by zeros. This representation trivially satisfies the commutation rules and hence is permissible. We call $|\alpha>$ in this trivial representation a singlet state.

Suppose there exist two adjacent states $|\beta>$ and $|\alpha>$ related by

$$I_-|\alpha> = |\beta> .$$

Then using $[U_+, V_+] = I_-$, we obtain

$$|\beta> = U_+V_+|\alpha> - V_+U_+|\alpha> .$$

At least one of the terms on the right-hand side must be non-zero and hence either $V_+|\alpha>$ or $U_+|\alpha>$ or both exist. Thus just a pure isospin doublet is not a representation of SU_3. This is an important point in that it means that isospin multiplets are not multiplets in SU_3 (at least for $I = \frac{1}{2}$ and it can be shown for all I in the same manner as above). Supposing $V_+|\alpha> \neq 0$, in the weight space we have the triangle shown in Fig. 5.

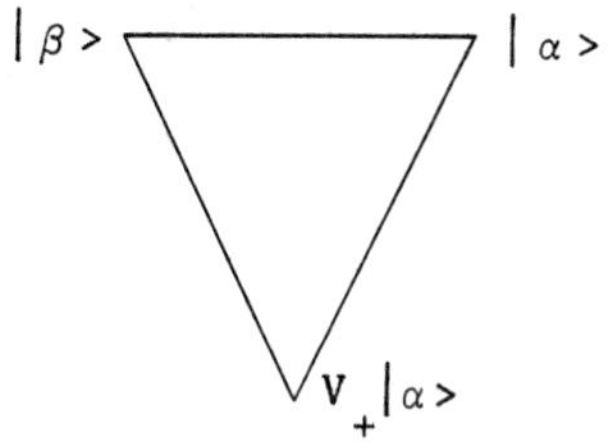

Fig. 5

Two adjacent states imply the existence of at least one more adjacent state. This is the simplest non-trivial representation and is called the `3' representation. If $V_+|\alpha> = 0$ and $U_+|\alpha> \neq 0$ we have the triangle shown in Fig. 6

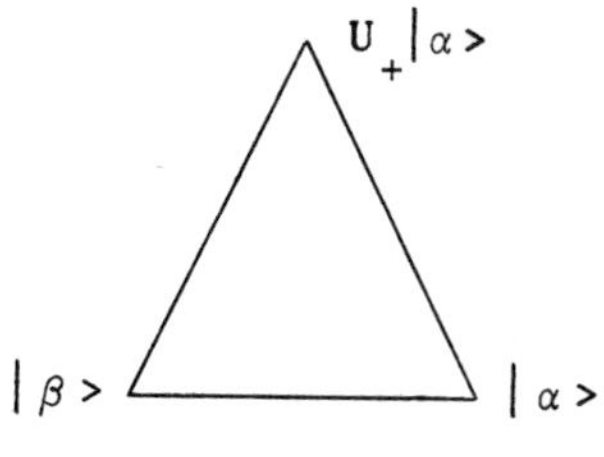

Fig. 6

called the `$\bar{3}$' representation.

Let us determine the position of the '3' representation in the weight space, i.e. determine the eigenvalues of the three states, $|\alpha>$, $|\beta>$ and $|\gamma>$

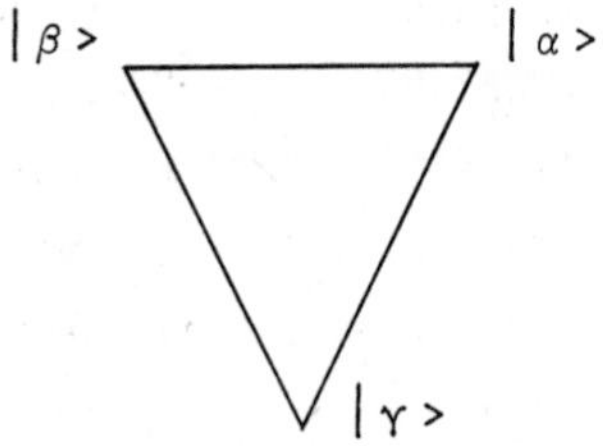

where we assume $I_{\pm}|\gamma> = 0$ and $V_-|\gamma> = |\alpha>$, $U_+|\gamma> = |\beta>$. Then $(I_+I_- - I_-I_+)|\gamma> = 0 = 2I_z|\gamma>$ and $|\gamma>$ is an isotopic singlet with $I_z = 0$.

Furthermore, $|\alpha>$ and $|\beta>$ are members of an isotopic doublet because

$$I_z|\alpha> = I_zV_-|\gamma> = V_-I_z|\gamma> + \tfrac{1}{2}V_-|\gamma> = \tfrac{1}{2}|\alpha>$$

and

$$I_z|\beta> = -\tfrac{1}{2}|\beta> .$$

Similarly, from $U_{\pm}|\alpha> = 0$ it follows that $U_z|\alpha> = 0$, $U_z|\beta> = \tfrac{1}{2}|\beta>$, $U_z|\gamma> = -\tfrac{1}{2}|\gamma>$ and from $V_{\pm}|\beta> = 0$ it follows that $V_z|\beta> = 0$, $V_z|\alpha> = -\tfrac{1}{2}|\alpha>$, $V_z|\gamma> = \tfrac{1}{2}|\gamma>$.

Labelling the states by isotopic spin I_z and hypercharge $Y = \tfrac{2}{3}(U_z - V_z)$ we have the eigenvalue shown in Fig. 7.

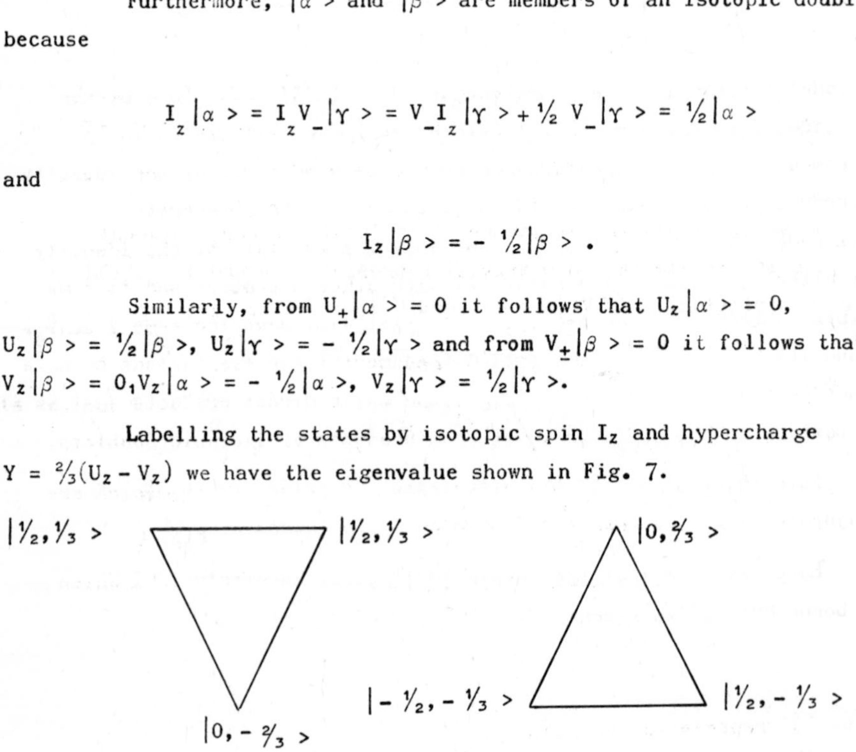

Fig. 7

where the labelling is I_z, Y >.

Note that $U_{\pm}$ and $V_{\pm}$ change Y by one unit which motivates the factor $\frac{2}{3}$ in the definition of Y. Also note that the scale of Y differs from the scale of I_z by a factor $\sqrt{3/2}$.

The Sakata model is based on the '3' and its conjugate '$\bar{3}$' representations as shown in the figure below.

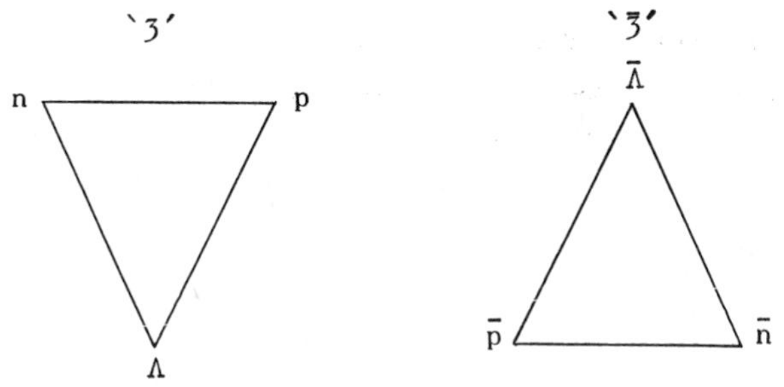

In this model the hypercharge is defined by $Y_s = (2/3)B + Y$. (B = baryon number) Since B is the same for all states in '3' and all states in '$\bar{3}$' it must commute with all operators and should be a multiple of the identity in an irreducible representation (Schur's Lemma). The apparently arbitrary redefinition of an operator by adding a multiple of the identity will not alter its commutation relations with other operators and is thus permissible. Members of an isotopic multiplet will have the same Y or Y_s. The '3' and its conjugate '$\bar{3}$' are called fundamental representations because all higher representations can be built from their direct products just as all representations in SU_2 could be built from products of isotopic doublets.

Note that '3' and '$\bar{3}$' are different. Representations which are self-conjugate exist and correspond physically to mesons.

Later we show that the Sakata model leads to conclusions which are not borne out by experiment.

Recall the proof that an isotopic doublet is not a representation of SU_3. We assumed two states existed such that

$$I_-|\alpha> = |\beta> ,$$

and replaced I_- by the commutator $[U_+, V_+]$

$$|\beta> = U_+V_+|\alpha> - V_+U_+|\alpha> .$$

Now suppose that neither term on the right-hand side vanishes so that there exist at least two other states $|\gamma>$ and $|\delta>$. Are these four states, as shown in Fig. 8, a representation of SU_3?

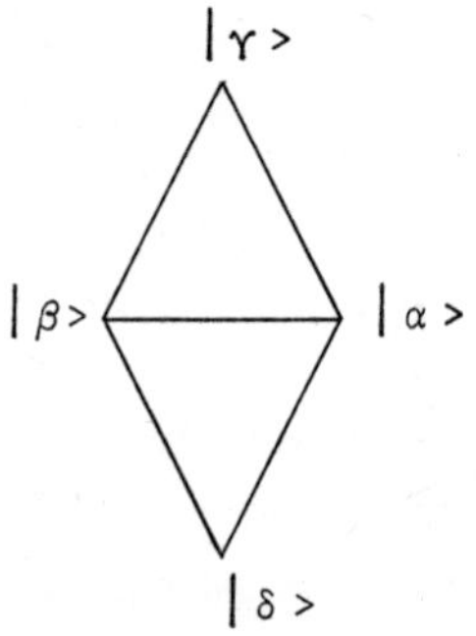

Fig. 8

To answer this question we try to determine the position of this representation in the weight space and appeal to the well-known result of SU_2 (or angular momentum theory): The facts that $|\beta> = I_-|\alpha>$ and $I_-|\beta> = I_+|\alpha> = 0$, and the existence of an operator $I^2 \equiv I_z^2 + \frac{1}{2}(I_+I_- + I_-I_+)$ that commutes with I_z, I_+, and I_- require that $|\alpha>$ and $|\beta>$ are members of an isotopic doublet with $I_z|\alpha> = \frac{1}{2}|\alpha>$ and $I_z|\beta> = -\frac{1}{2}|\beta>$. Similarly, we would find that $|\alpha>$ and $|\gamma>$ are a doublet along the U_z axis with $U_z|\alpha> = -\frac{1}{2}|\alpha>$ and $U_z|\gamma> = \frac{1}{2}|\gamma>$ while $|\alpha>$ and $|\delta>$ are doublet along the V_z axis with $V_z|\alpha> = -\frac{1}{2}|\alpha>$ and $V_z|\delta> = \frac{1}{2}|\delta>$.

Now note that this leads to $(I_z + U_z + V_z)|\alpha> = -\frac{1}{2}|\alpha>$ which is clearly wrong and the answer to the question is that the four states are not a representation of SU_3. We may state this more generally. If there exists a state at $I_z = I_0$, the commutation rules among the I's require that there exists a state at $I_z = -I_0$. Considering simultaneously all the commutators Eq. 20, if there exists a state at (I_0, U_0, V_0) then there must exist states (possibly not all different) at $(-I_0, -V_0, -U_0)$, (V_0, I_0, U_0), $(-V_0, -U_0, -I_0)$, (U_0, V_0, I_0), and $(-U_0, -I_0, -V_0)$. In other words the configuration of states must possess reflection symmetry about the lines $I_z = 0$, $U_z = 0$ and $V_z = 0$.

Assuming all representations are finite (not yet proved) so that it is meaningful to talk of the boundary of a representation we have a second general property, namely that the boundary is never concave. The proof is contained in a homework problem.

These two properties are combined in an important theorem of SU_3. The boundary of a representation is a regular hexagon specified by two lengths a and b.

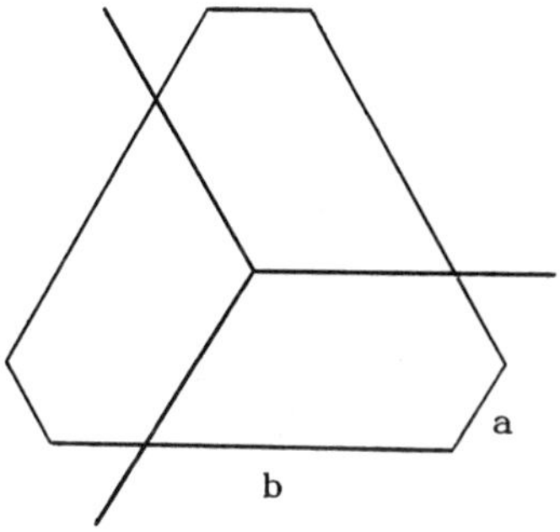

Fig. 9

The representation is completely determined by the lengths a and b. In particular, the number of states, including degeneracies, is determined by giving the boundary.

Problems for Chapter II

1) Show that there can be no hole (missing state) inside a boundary and thus, that the boundary must be convex.

2) Can the '6' or '$\bar{6}$' representation be realized by any particles or resonances thus far known?

III. DEGENERACY AND TENSORIAL METHODS

A representation of SU_3, determined by the regular hexagon slides a and b, is labelled by (a,b) or $D^n(a,b)$, where n is the number of states boundary and interior. Some examples are

$D^1(0,0)$ (singlet)

$D^3(1,0)$ (triplet)

$D^3(0,1)$ (triplet)

$D^8(1,1)$ (octet)

$D^6(0,2)$. (sextet)

Consider the representation shown in Fig. 10.

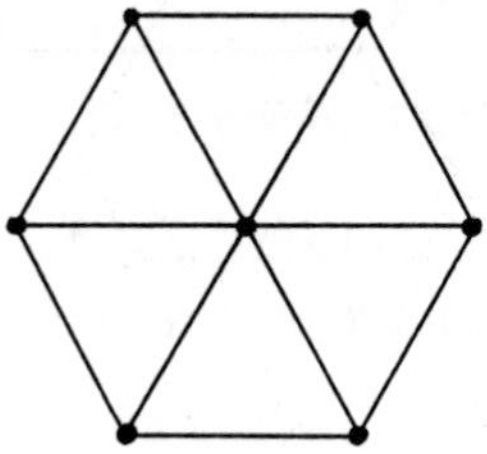

Fig. 10

where $|\alpha >$ is the state farthest to the right with eigenvalues $I_z = 1$, $V_z = -\frac{1}{2}$, $V_z = -\frac{1}{2}$. We assume that $|\alpha >$ is non-degenerate. The state $|\beta >$ in the centre may be constructed in various ways and we are now going to check for degeneracy, i.e. are there more than one state at $|\beta >$, by using Schwarz's Inequality. Define

$$|\beta_1 > = I_-|\alpha >$$

$$|\beta_2 > = V_+U_+|\alpha >.$$

Observe that no matter how we construct $|\beta>$ we obtain some linear combination of $|\beta_1>$ and $|\beta_2>$. For example,

$$U_+V_+|\alpha> = V_+U_+|\alpha> + I_-|\alpha>$$

$$= |\beta_2> + |\beta_1>.$$

and

$$U_-I_-U_+|\alpha> = |\beta_2> + |\beta_1>$$

and so on for every other way of constructing a state at the centre.

Schwarz's inequality states that

$$<\beta_1|\beta_1> \cdot <\beta_2|\beta_2> \geq |<\beta_1|\beta_2>|^2, \qquad (25)$$

where the equality is achieved if and only if the states $|\beta_1>$ and $|\beta_2>$ are linearly dependent. We have

$$<\beta_1|\beta_1> = <\alpha|I_+I_-|\alpha> = <\alpha|[I_+,I_-]|\alpha>$$

$$= 2<\alpha|I_z|\alpha> = 2<\alpha|\alpha>$$

$$<\beta_2|\beta_2> = <\alpha|U_-V_-V_+U_+|\alpha> = 2<\alpha|\alpha>$$

$$<\beta_1|\beta_2> = <\alpha|I_+V_+U_+|\alpha> = -<\alpha|\alpha>$$

or

$$|<\beta_1|\beta_2>|^2 = <\alpha|\alpha> \cdot <\alpha|\alpha> .$$

The equality in Eq. (25) is thus not attained and we have two linearly independent states $|\beta_1>$ and $|\beta_2>$ in the centre. We may identify one state as belonging to an isotopic triplet and the other as forming an isotopic singlet.

Similarly, it is possible to check for the degeneracy of boundary states (other than α) and it is found that they are non-degenerate.

The eight baryons correspond to the states of $D^8(1,1)$ as shown in Fig. 11.

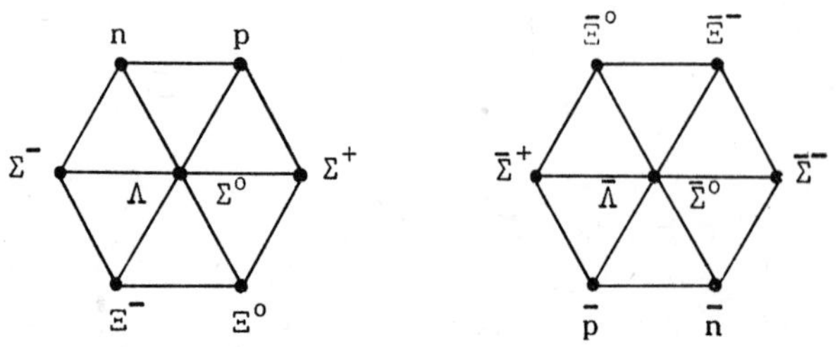

Fig. 11

and the $0^-(1^-)$ mesons correspond to the self-conjugate representation shown in Fig. 12.

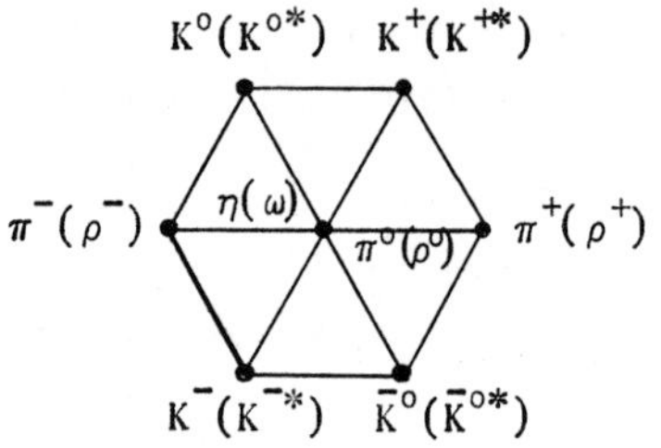

Fig. 12

Here we are using the principle that particles with the same space-time properties, i.e. spin and parity, can be grouped together in the same multiplet. Hence, we have assumed that the cascade particle has the same spin and parity as the proton which is as yet not definitely proven by experiments.

We next introduce a tensor notation for representations of SU_3 which provides a simple method for decomposing products of representations.

Consider the Sakata model where the basic representations are

$D^3(1,0) =$ 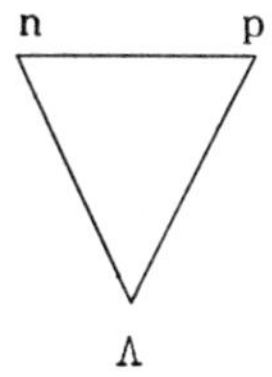

and $D^3(0,1) =$ 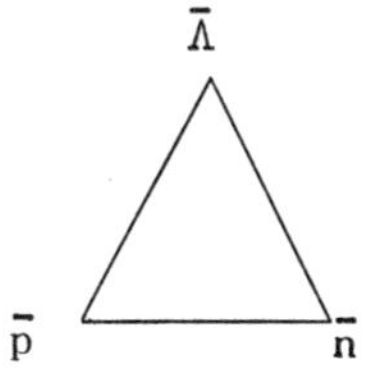

Since states connected by raising and lowering operators are orthogonal we have

$$\langle p|\Lambda\rangle = \langle p|n\rangle = \langle \Lambda|n\rangle = 0.$$

An arbitrary particle of spin and parity $\frac{1}{2}^+$, and baryon number unity could be represented by some vector in the three dimensional space spanned by the orthogonal vectors $|p\rangle$, $|n\rangle$, and $|\Lambda\rangle$. Let us denote a vector in this space by ψ^i $i = 1,2,3$, a contravariant tensor of first rank, where we may identify the components $\psi^1 = |p\rangle$, $\psi^2 = |n\rangle$, $\psi^3 = |\Lambda\rangle$. A vector in the conjugate representation is similarly denoted by a covariant first rank tensor ψ_i where now $\psi_1 = |\bar{p}\rangle$, $\psi_2 = |\bar{n}\rangle$, $\psi_3 = \bar{\Lambda}\rangle$.

There is no metric tensor connecting upper and lower indices here since the upper indices refer to particles and the lower to antiparticles.

Our goal is to represent the larger representations by building up higher rank tensors from these basic tensors and projecting out the irreducible components. The tensor formalism will be an algebraic method that corresponds to the geometric rules for taking direct products.

For example, using the technique outlined in Chapter I, the geometric rule for constructing the product $3 \otimes \bar{3}$ is to centre the $\bar{3}$ triangle over each vertex of the 3 and then identify the newly-formed representations as shown in Fig. 13.

$3 \times \bar{3} =$

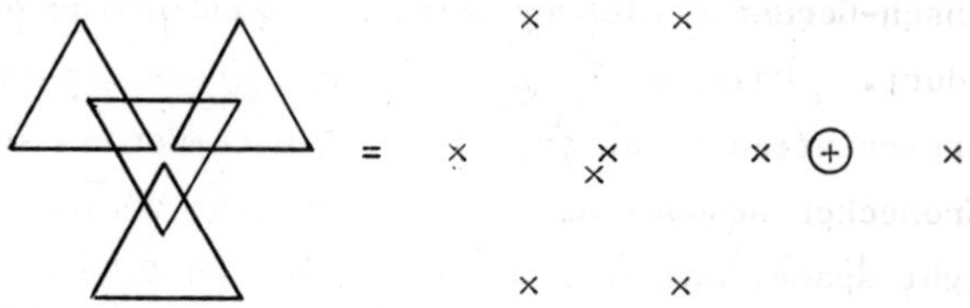

Fig. 13

There are 6 boundary states and 3 states in the centre. Two centre states belong to an 8 and the other forms a singlet. Thus

$$D^3(1,0) \otimes D^3(0,1) = D^8(1,1) \oplus D^1(0,0). \tag{26}$$

Again, the decomposition of the product $3 \otimes 3$ is shown in Fig. 14.

$3 \otimes 3 =$

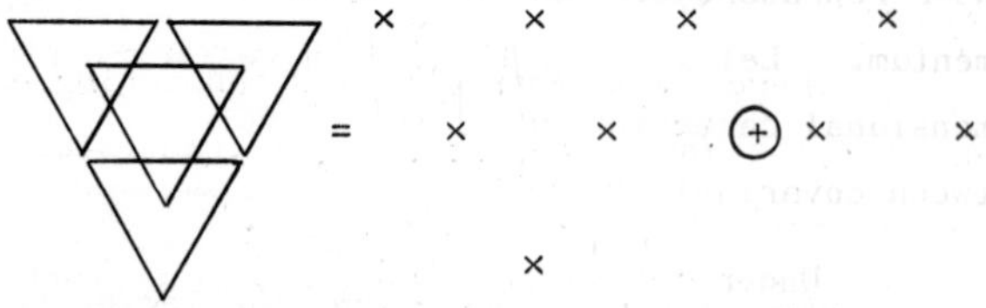

Fig. 14

Thus we have

$$D^3(1,0) \otimes D^3(1,0) = D^6(2,0) \oplus D^3(0,1). \tag{27}$$

A relation such as Eq. (26) or (27) is called a decomposition into a Clebsch-Gordan series or sum of irreducible representations of a Kronecker product. Raising and lowering operators cannot connect one irreducible representation to another in a Clebsch-Gordan series. Note that states in a Kronecker product are obtained by the vectorial addition of weights in the weight space, and in these notes we can take this addition as the definition of multiplying two representations.

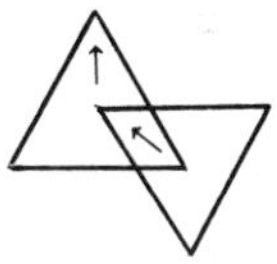

Fig. 15

Vector addition of two weights yielding their product weight.

Before developing the tensor formalism in SU_3 let us recall the tensor representation of spin states in the familiar theory of angular momentum. Let x_i, i = 1,2,3 be a vector or first rank tensor in a three-dimensional cartesian co-ordinate system. (No distinction made here between covariant and contravariant components.)

Under rotational transformations through an angle Θ we find there are three eigenvectors belonging to eigenvalues $e^{i\Theta}$, 1, $e^{-i\Theta}$ and hence we associate x_i with spin 1. The second rank tensor $x_{ij} = x_i x_j$ decomposes into a spin 2, spin 1, and spin 0 tensor as follows:

$$x_{ij} = \left[\frac{x_{ij} + x_{ji}}{2} - \frac{1}{3}\,\delta_{ij}\,x_{\alpha\alpha}\right] + \left[\frac{x_{ij} - x_{ji}}{2}\right] + \left[\frac{1}{3}\,\delta_{ij}\,x_{\alpha\alpha}\right].$$

The term in the first bracket is a traceless, symmetric second-rank tensor with five independent elements which transform among themselves under rotations as the base vectors of a spin 2 representation; i.e. it is possible to decompose this term further into five linearly independent eigentensors belonging to eigenvalues $e^{2i\Theta}$, $e^{i\Theta}$, 1, $e^{-i\Theta}$, $e^{2i\Theta}$.

The second bracket contains an antisymmetric second tensor whose three linearly independent elements transform identically as the first rank tensor

$$y_i = \frac{x_{jk} - x_{kj}}{2} ,$$

where i,j,k, are in cyclic order, and hence is associated with spin 1.

The third bracket, a multiple of the identity, is clearly an invariant or scalar under rotation and is to be associated with spin 0.

The numerical tensors δ_{ij} and ϵ_{ijk} (antisymmetric in all indices with $\epsilon_{123} = +1$) are used in projecting out of tensors of arbitrary rank the various spin components. Note that they are invariants under proper rotations.

$$\delta'_{ij} = a_{ik} a_{j\ell} \delta_{k\ell} = a_{ik} a_{jk} = \delta_{ij}$$

$$\epsilon'_{ijk} = a_{i\ell} a_{jm} a_{kn} \epsilon_{\ell mn} = \epsilon_{ijk} \det|a| = \epsilon_{ijk}$$

and are the only possible invariant tensors.

For example, consider an arbitrary fifth rank tensor and ask what spins are present? To obtain spin 0 tensors we must reduce the rank to 0 by the numerical tensors. There are a number of distinct ways to do this corresponding to the number of spin 0's:

$$x_{ijk\ell m} \epsilon_{ijk} \delta_{\ell m}$$

$$x_{ijk\ell m} \epsilon_{ij\ell} \delta_{km} , \quad \text{etc.}$$

The spin 2 tensors are obtained by reducing the number of indices to 2 and removing the other irreducible components, the trace and the antisymmetric part. Other spins are obtained in a similar way: the general rule is first to reduce the number of indices to some desired rank and then subtract off all possible irreducible components until only one irreducible component remains.

Further, suppose $x_{ijk\ell m}$ is constructed from the product of x_{ijk} and $x_{\ell m}$, where x_{ijk} is a completely symmetric third rank tensor corresponding to spin 3 and $x_{\ell m}$ is a symmetric second rank tensor corresponding to spin 2. Is there a spin 0 in

$$x_{ijk\ell m} = x_{ijk}x_{\ell m}?$$

We already know the answer from the geometric rules for addition of angular momentum, that is, there is no spin 0. We also obtain this result in the tensor formalism since every possible reduction to a zero rank tensor gives 0. For example

$$x_{ijk}x_{\ell m}\epsilon_{i\ell m}\delta_{jk} = 0$$

since $x_{\ell m}$ is symmetric and $\epsilon_{i\ell m}$ is antisymmetric in ℓ and m.

We shall now apply these same familiar techniques to the problem of decomposing Kronecker products in SU_3. Consider the product $3\otimes\bar{3} = \psi^i\psi_j$ in SU_3 which has already been treated geometrically. The numerical tensors in SU_3 have both contravariant and covariant components and are δ_i^j, ϵ_{ijk}, ϵ^{ijk}.

The decomposition of $3\otimes\bar{3}$ is as follows

$$\psi^i\psi_j = \left[\psi^i\psi_j - \frac{1}{3}\,\delta_j^i\,\psi^k\psi_k\right] + \left[\frac{1}{3}\,\delta_j^i\,\psi^k\psi_k\right].$$

The first bracket is traceless, has 8 components and corresponds to $D^8(1,1)$ while the second bracket is a multiple of the identity with one component, and corresponds to $D^1(0,0)$.

The product $\bar{3}\otimes\bar{3} = \psi_i\psi_j$ decomposes as follows:

$$\psi_\ell\psi_m = \psi_\ell\psi_m - \frac{1}{2}\psi_i\psi_j\,\epsilon^{ijk}\epsilon_{k\ell m} + \frac{1}{2}\psi_i\psi_j\,\epsilon^{ijk}\epsilon_{k\ell m}$$

$$= \frac{\psi_\ell\psi_m + \psi_m\psi_\ell}{2} + \frac{1}{2}\psi^k\epsilon_{k\ell m} \;.$$

The first bracket is symmetric, with 6 components, corresponding to $D^6(0,2)$. Note there is no trace removal since it is not permitted to sum over two lower indices. The second bracket is an antisymmetric covariant tensor which transforms like a first rank contravariant tensor and corresponds to $D^3(0,1)$. A general decomposition can hence be performed just as in SU_2 by using the SU_3 numerical tensors δ^i_j, ϵ^{ijk} and ϵ_{ijk}.

We now list the lowest rank tensors and their corresponding representations.

$$D^3\,(1,0) = \psi^i$$

$$D^3\,(0,1) = \psi_i$$

$$D^6\,(2,0) = \psi^{[i,j]}$$

$$D^6\,(0,2) = \psi_{[i,j]}$$

$$D^8\,(1,1) = \psi^i_j \text{ with } \delta^j_i\,\psi^i_j = 0$$

$$D^{10}(3,0) = \psi^{[i,j,k]}$$

$$D^{10}(0,3) = \psi_{[i,j,k]}$$

$$D^{15}(4,0) = \psi^{[i,j,k,\ell]}$$

$$D^{15}(2,1) = \psi_k^{\;[i,j]} \text{ with } \delta^k_i\,\psi_k^{\;[i,j]} = 0$$

$$D^{27}(2,2) = \psi^{[k,j]}_{[k,\ell]} \text{ with } \delta^k_i\,\psi^{[i,j]}_{[k,\ell]} = 0$$

The bracket notation $[i,j,\dots,\ell]$ signifies that the indices are symmetrized. Note that in general we have

$$D\,[a,b] = \psi\,\begin{matrix}[a \text{ indices}]\\ [b \text{ indices}]\end{matrix}$$

and the trace, where meaningful, is zero.

IV. THE MATRICES FOR BARYONS AND MESONS AND YUKAWA COUPLINGS

We shall now identify the physical particles with particular components of the tensors that are used to describe a given representation. Consider the eight-dimensional representation $D^8(1,1)$. This representation is made from the fundamental representations by the product '8'= $3\times\bar{3}$. The traceless 3 by 3 matrix φ^i_j describes this eight-dimensional representation and is related to simple one-dimensional tensors ψ^i and ψ_j which describe the 3 and $\bar{3}$ representations by the relation

$$\varphi^i_j = \psi^i\psi_j - \frac{1}{3}\,\delta^i_j\,\psi^k\psi_k\ .$$

As we have noted before, the representation $D^8(1,1)$ in the weight space is constructed by laying the '$\bar{3}$'labelled by

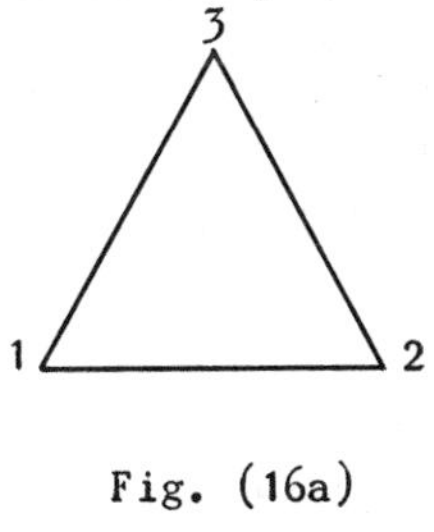

Fig. (16a)

over each state of the '3' labelled by

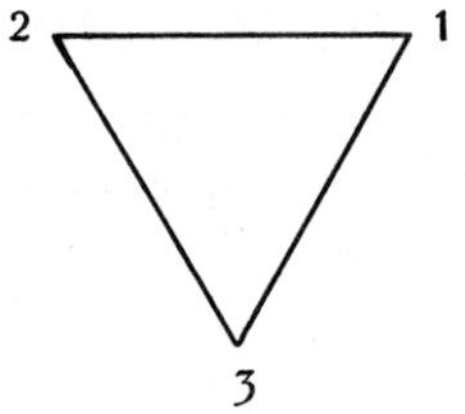

Fig. (16b)

Thus the boundary states of φ^i_j can be immediately identified from the rub for constructing products and are shown in Fig. 17.

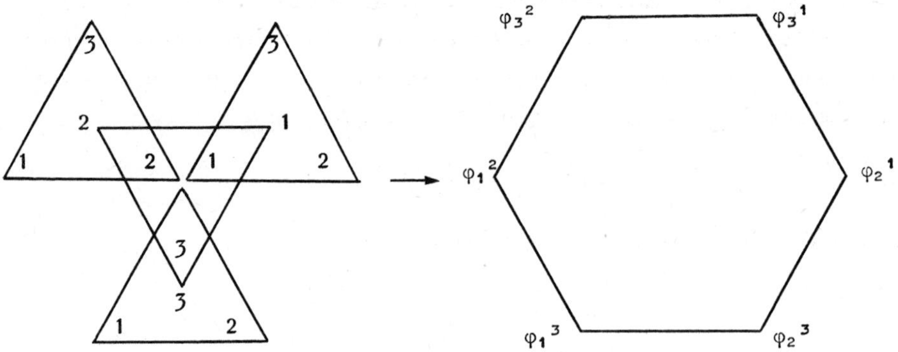

Fig. 17

The identification of the two interior states requires a bit more care and we consider this problem now.

From the isotope and hypercharge values of the eight-dimensional representation, we know that $\varphi_3{}^2$ and $\varphi_3{}^1$ are an isospin doublet with unit hypercharge. This follows directly from the definition of the `8' in terms of laying the `$\bar{3}$' on the `3'. The I_z and Y of $\varphi_3{}^1$ must be the sum of the I_z and Y of ψ^1 and ψ_3, respectively, and from Chapter II this gives

$\varphi_3{}^1$: $I_z = \frac{1}{2}$ and $Y = 1$. Thus we can identify $\varphi_3{}^2$ and $\varphi_3{}^1$ with n and p. Similarly, $\varphi_1{}^3$ and $\varphi_2{}^3$ can be identified with Ξ^- and Ξ^0, respectively. The two states $\varphi_1{}^2$ and $\varphi_2{}^1$ have $I_z = -1$ and $+1$, respectively, and can be identified with Σ^- and Σ^+. The remaining problem is to find which combinations of $\varphi_1{}^1$, $\varphi_2{}^2$ and $\varphi_3{}^3$ should be identified with Σ^0 and Λ. Since $\sum_i \varphi_i^i = 0$ only two of the three diagonal states are independent. To find Σ^0 we note that by definition Σ^0 is proportional to $(I_+\Sigma^-)$ then

$$I_+\varphi^2_1 = I_+(\psi^2\psi_1) = (I_+\psi^2)\,\psi_1 - \psi^2(I_+\psi_1)$$

$$= \psi^1\psi_1 - \psi^2\psi_2 \;.$$

Thus, the normalized state

$$\frac{1}{\sqrt{2}}\left[\psi^1\psi_1 - \psi^2\psi_2\right] = -\frac{1}{\sqrt{2}}\left[\varphi_2{}^2 - \varphi_1{}^1\right]$$

is the correct combination of the diagonal terms to be identified with Σ^0. The state Λ can now be readily determined since it must be orthogonal to the state Σ^0. Hence, Λ is proportional to $(\varphi_1{}^1 + \varphi_2{}^2)$ or since $\varphi_1{}^1 + \varphi_2{}^2 + \varphi_3{}^3 = 0$ it is also proportional to $\varphi_3{}^3$. To find the constant of proportionality we normalize the state Λ to unity, i.e.

$$|\Lambda|^2 = C^2|\varphi_3{}^3|^2 = C^2\left[\psi^3\psi_3 - \frac{1}{3}\,\psi^i\psi_i\right]^2 = 1$$

and therefore $C = \pm\sqrt{\frac{3}{2}}$.

The sign of C is arbitrary as long as the condition $\psi^i\psi_i = 0$ is assured and we take C negative in order to make a definite choice.

From the conditions

$$\Sigma^0 = \frac{1}{\sqrt{2}}\,(\varphi_1{}^1 - \varphi_2{}^2),\; \Lambda = -\sqrt{\frac{3}{2}}\,\varphi_3{}^3 \text{ and } \sum_1 \varphi_1{}^1 = 0$$

we can solve back for diagonal terms and hence have that

$$\varphi_1{}^1 = \frac{\Sigma^0}{\sqrt{2}} + \frac{\Lambda}{\sqrt{6}} \; ; \quad \varphi_2{}^2 = \frac{-\Sigma^0}{\sqrt{2}} + \frac{\Lambda}{\sqrt{6}} \; ; \quad \varphi_3{}^3 = -\frac{2}{\sqrt{6}}\Lambda \; .$$

The baryon matrix B_j^i is then

$$B_j^i = \begin{pmatrix} \frac{\Sigma^0}{\sqrt{2}} + \frac{\Lambda}{\sqrt{6}} & \Sigma^+ & p \\ \Sigma^- & \frac{-\Sigma^0}{\sqrt{2}} + \frac{\Lambda}{\sqrt{6}} & n \\ \Xi^- & \Xi^0 & \frac{-2}{\sqrt{6}}\Lambda \end{pmatrix}$$

Note that all particles in B_i^j have the same space-time properties, i.e. spin = ½, parity = + , baryon number = 1.

Similarly, we would have the meson matrix

$$m_j^i = \begin{pmatrix} \frac{\pi^0}{\sqrt{2}} + \frac{\eta}{\sqrt{6}} & \pi^+ & K^+ \\ \pi^- & \frac{-\pi^0}{\sqrt{2}} + \frac{\eta}{\sqrt{6}} & K^0 \\ K^- & \overline{K^0} & \frac{-2\eta}{\sqrt{6}} \end{pmatrix}$$

and the vector meson matrix

$$V_j^i = \begin{pmatrix} \frac{\rho^0}{\sqrt{2}} + \frac{\omega^0}{\sqrt{6}} & \rho^+ & K^{+*} \\ \rho^- & \frac{-\rho^0}{\sqrt{2}} + \frac{\omega^0}{\sqrt{6}} & K^{0*} \\ K^{-*} & \overline{K^{0*}} & \frac{-2\omega^0}{\sqrt{6}} \end{pmatrix}$$

In identifying the ω^0 as the iso-singlet belonging to the octet we have ignored the fact that the 1020 MeV $K\bar{K}$ resonance referred to as φ has the same quantum numbers as the ω^0 and hence one is faced with the problem of which particle, the φ or the ω, belongs in the octet. The non-octet particle is then supposedly a singlet which is, of course, an equally valid representation of SU_3.

We next introduce the baryon-meson coupling scheme.

In addition to the baryon matrix B^i_j, the 0^- meson matrix M^i_j and the vector meson matrix V^i_j given here, we also require the antibaryon matrix $\bar{B}^i_j$:

$$\bar{B} = \begin{pmatrix} \frac{\bar{\Sigma}^0}{\sqrt{2}} + \frac{\bar{\Lambda}}{\sqrt{6}} & \bar{\Sigma}^- & \bar{\Xi}^- \\ \bar{\Sigma}^+ & \frac{-\bar{\Sigma}^0}{\sqrt{2}} + \frac{\bar{\Lambda}}{\sqrt{6}} & \bar{\Xi}^0 \\ \bar{p} & \bar{n} & \frac{-2\bar{\Lambda}}{} \end{pmatrix} \qquad (28)$$

Recall that in field theory, the charge independent pseudoscalar coupling between meson (φ) and nucleon (N) fields is described by the Lagrangian of the form

$$L = |\bar{N}\,\gamma_5\,\vec{\tau}\,N| \cdot \vec{\varphi}\ ,$$

where $\vec{\tau}$ is isotopic spin. We now wish to generalize this coupling to a unitary symmetric Lagrangian, i.e. construct some scalar linear in B, $\bar{B}$, and M which is invariant under SU_3 transformations. Linearity is desired because in the three-point coupling between baryons and mesons one describes creation and destruction of one meson, one baryon, and one antibaryon. Since the only invariant of a tensor depending linearly on its components is its trace, the obvious construct is the trace of the matrix product of $\bar{B}$, B, and M. There are only two linearly independent products which we combine with two coupling constants

$$L = a\ \mathrm{Tr}\ [\bar{B} B M] + b\ \mathrm{Tr}\ [\bar{B} M B], \tag{29}$$

where the space-time properties (pseudoscalar nature) of M has been suppressed. An alternate combination, conforming to the literature, is

$$L = f\ \mathrm{Tr}\left[\bar{B}\ [B,M]_-\right] + d\ \mathrm{Tr}\left[\bar{B}\ [B,M]_+\right], \tag{30}$$

where $a = f + d$, $b = d - f$ and where $[B,M]_- = BM - MB$ and $[B,M]_+ = BM + MB$. Explicitly, we have from

$$\begin{aligned} \mathrm{Tr}\ [\bar{B}\ BM] = \Big\{ & \frac{-2}{\sqrt{6}} (\bar{N}N)\ \eta + \frac{1}{\sqrt{2}} \bar{\Sigma} \cdot (\bar{K} \vec{\tau} N) + \frac{1}{\sqrt{2}} (\bar{N} \vec{\tau} K) \cdot \vec{\Sigma} \\ & + \frac{1}{\sqrt{6}} (\bar{N} K) \Lambda + \frac{1}{\sqrt{6}} \bar{\Lambda} (\bar{K} N) - \frac{1}{\sqrt{6}} (\bar{\Lambda}\Lambda)\ \eta + (\vec{\pi} \cdot \Sigma) \frac{\bar{\Lambda}}{\sqrt{6}} \\ & + (\Xi \vec{\tau} \Xi) \cdot \vec{\pi} + \frac{1}{\sqrt{6}} (\bar{\Xi}\Xi)\ \eta + \frac{2}{\sqrt{6}} (\bar{K}\bar{\Xi})\ \Lambda \\ & - \frac{2}{\sqrt{6}} \bar{\Lambda} (\Xi K) + (\vec{\bar{\Sigma}} \cdot \vec{\Sigma})\ \eta + \frac{(\vec{\bar{\Sigma}} \cdot \vec{\pi})}{\sqrt{6}} - i\ \vec{\bar{\Sigma}} \times \vec{\Sigma} \cdot \pi \Big\} \end{aligned} \tag{31}$$

$$\begin{aligned} \mathrm{Tr}\{\bar{B}\ MB\} = \Big\{ & - \frac{2}{\sqrt{6}} (\bar{N} K)\ \Lambda + \frac{1}{\sqrt{2}} \vec{\bar{\Sigma}} \cdot (\Xi \vec{\tau} K) + \frac{1}{\sqrt{2}} \bar{N} \vec{\tau} N \cdot \vec{\pi} \\ & + \frac{1}{\sqrt{6}} (NN)\ \eta + \frac{1}{\sqrt{6}} \bar{\Lambda} (\Xi K) - \frac{1}{\sqrt{6}} (\bar{\Lambda}\Lambda)\ \eta + \frac{1}{\sqrt{6}} (\bar{\Xi}\bar{K})\ \Lambda \\ & + \frac{\bar{K} \vec{\tau} \bar{\Xi} \cdot \pi}{\sqrt{2}} - \frac{2}{\sqrt{6}} (\bar{\Xi}\Xi)\ \eta - \frac{2}{\sqrt{6}}\ {}^{-}(\bar{K}\Xi) + (\vec{\bar{\Sigma}} \cdot \vec{\pi}) \frac{\Lambda}{\sqrt{6}} \\ & - \frac{i}{\sqrt{2}} (\vec{\bar{\Sigma}} \times \vec{\pi}) \cdot \vec{\Sigma} + (\vec{\bar{\Sigma}} \cdot \vec{\Sigma}) \frac{\eta}{\sqrt{6}} + \frac{\bar{\Lambda}}{\sqrt{6}} (\vec{\pi} \cdot \vec{\Sigma}) \Big\}. \end{aligned} \tag{32}$$

A vector notation has been used in Eqs. (31) and (32) to save space: i.e.,

$$\Sigma = \begin{pmatrix} \frac{\Sigma^+ + \Sigma^-}{2} \\ \\ \frac{\Sigma^+ + \Sigma^-}{2i} \\ \\ \Sigma^0 \end{pmatrix} \quad \bar{\Sigma} = \begin{pmatrix} \frac{\bar{\Sigma}^+ + \bar{\Sigma}^-}{2} \\ \\ \frac{\bar{\Sigma}^+ - \bar{\Sigma}^-}{2i} \\ \\ \bar{\Sigma}^0 \end{pmatrix} \quad \pi = \begin{pmatrix} \frac{\pi^+ + \pi^-}{2} \\ \\ \frac{\pi^+ - \pi^-}{i2} \\ \\ \pi^0 \end{pmatrix}$$

Other definitions are as follows:

$$N = \begin{pmatrix} p \\ n \end{pmatrix} \qquad \bar{N} = (\bar{p}\ \bar{n})$$

$$K = \begin{pmatrix} K^+ \\ K^0 \end{pmatrix} \qquad \bar{K} = (\bar{K}\ \bar{K}^0)$$

$$\tau_x = \begin{pmatrix} 0 & 1 \\ 1 & 0 \end{pmatrix} \qquad \tau_y = \begin{pmatrix} 0 & -i \\ i & 0 \end{pmatrix} \qquad \tau_z = \begin{pmatrix} 1 & 0 \\ 0 & -1 \end{pmatrix}$$

Some statements can be made about the relative values of a and b. Note that if a = − b the Λ, Σ, π coupling terms cancel out, or if b = 0, there would be no direct π-nucleon coupling since this term appears only in Tr $[\bar{B}\ MB]$.

Cabibbo[1)] and Cutkosky[2)] give theoretical arguments suggesting that d is 2 or 3 times larger than f.

V. THE MASS FORMULA: MEDIUM STRONG SPLITTINGS

Mass splittings among the particles of nature occur in three ways which we may understand as follows:

i) Some strong force separates all particles into groups of multiplets.

ii) In a given multiplet, a weaker force causes mass splittings for particles having different hypercharge Y.

iii) An even weaker force causes mass splitting in I_z.

The third type of splitting, the most nearly understood, is attributed to the virtual photon field and results from the operator $1 + \tau_z$ which we note has definite transformation properties in isotopic spin space but is not invariant. By analogy to electromagnetism we will construct some operator in SU_3 to explain mass splittings in Y which will be assumed to have definite transformation properties in SU_3 but is also not invariant.

Before undertaking this topic it is necessary to discuss some mechanics which are relevant in the subsequent discussion on mass splitting.

The hypercharge in the fundamental `3' representation must be a 3×3 matrix Y such that

$$Y^i_j \psi^j = Y \begin{pmatrix} p \\ n \\ \Lambda \end{pmatrix} = \begin{pmatrix} p \\ n \\ 0 \end{pmatrix}$$

Thus we must have

$$Y = \begin{pmatrix} 1 & 0 & 0 \\ 0 & 1 & 0 \\ 0 & 0 & 0 \end{pmatrix} .$$

Similarly, the hypercharge in the fundamental `3' representation must be a 3×3 matrix $\bar{Y}$ such that

$$\psi_j Y^j_i = (\bar{p}\ \bar{n}\ \bar{\Lambda})\ \bar{Y} = (-\bar{p}\ -\bar{n}\ 0) ,$$

requiring

$$\bar{Y} = - Y .$$

We now would like to know the form of the hypercharge operator Y in the '8' representation. Letting $\psi^j = \psi$, $\psi_j = \bar{\psi}$, we must have

$$\begin{aligned} Y(B) &= Y(\psi\bar{\psi} - \tfrac{1}{3} \operatorname{Tr} \psi\bar{\psi}) \\ &= Y\psi\bar{\psi} - \psi\bar{\psi}Y - \tfrac{1}{3} \operatorname{Tr} [Y\psi\bar{\psi} - \psi\bar{\psi}Y] \\ &= [Y,B] . \end{aligned}$$

Note that if we write $Y = \tfrac{2}{3} I + \tfrac{1}{3} Y^1$, where Y^1 is the traceless matrix

$$Y^1 = \begin{pmatrix} 1 & 0 & 0 \\ 0 & 1 & 0 \\ 0 & 0 & -2 \end{pmatrix}, \tag{33}$$

and I is the unit matrix, then the unit matrix part of Y does not contribute in the commutator of [Y,B] so that we have

$$Y(B) = \tfrac{1}{3} [Y^1, B] . \tag{34}$$

Similarly, for the antibaryon matrix B we have

$$Y(\bar{B}) = \tfrac{1}{3} [Y^1, \bar{B}] . \tag{35}$$

Recall that in trying to explain the mass splitting in isotopic spin it is assumed that the splitting is the result of the operator τ_3 which has definite transformation properties in isotopic spin space but it is not invariant; i.e. it is a vector which picks out a special direction in the space. The analogue of the isospin mass splitting transforming as a component of a vector τ_z in SU_2 is that the

SU_3 splitting "thing" transforms as a component of an '8'. The hypercharge Y transforms as a component of an '8' and picks out a special direction in the eight-dimensional space of SU_3, and as we shall next see is the is the right direction to give the observed masses.

Let us construct a Lagrangian containing Y that causes the mass splitting as we did before for the meson baryon coupling. In place of the meson matrix M we put Y' and obtain

$$H' = f \,\mathrm{Tr}\, \bar{B}\, [B,Y']_- + d \,\mathrm{Tr}\, \bar{B}\, [B,Y']_+ . \qquad (36)$$

While the anticommutator appears out of place in the light of Eqs. (34) and (35), it will be seen that this term is necessary to give the Σ, Λ mass splitting. The f and d are coupling constants independent of the ones introduced for meson baryon coupling and are the coupling constants associated with the mass splitting type force.

We justify the form (36) by the following considerations:

i) It is the most general coupling that is linear in $\bar{B}$, B, and Y.

ii) The part of Y which is proportional to the identity cannot give rise to mass splittings (since Tr $\bar{B}$ B is an invariant) and would correspond to a constant term in H'. This is why we chose to subtract off the identity and introduce the traceless component Y' into the Lagrangian.

iii) Since we are looking for baryon self-energy terms in the Lagrangian and not couplings between baryons of different type, Y' must be diagonal.

iv) Finally, we note that there is another restriction on Y' since there is to be no splitting between p and n or between Ξ^- and Ξ^0. Y' must be of the form

$$\begin{pmatrix} a & 0 & 0 \\ 0 & a & 0 \\ 0 & 0 & -2a \end{pmatrix},$$

i.e. the matrix has to be diagonal in the indices 1 and 2, otherwise, particles in the same isotopic multiplet will have different masses.

We say that the above Hamiltonian H^1 transforms like a component of an '8' because under transformations in unitary space B^i_j and $\bar{B}^k_i$ transform as irreducible tensors but Y^i_j does not transform, i.e. Y^i_j picks out a special direction. (Of course, if Y^i_j also transformed as an irreducible tensor then H^1 would be an SU_3 invariant.) Thus, in H^1, Y picks out a special combination of the indices i, j in the bilinear forms,

$$[\bar{B},B]_-{}^i_j \quad \text{and} \quad [B,B]_+{}^i_j \, .$$

If we think of the eight independent members of the traceless three by three matrices of $[\bar{B},B]_-$ and $[\bar{B},B]_+$ as making up the axes of an eight-dimensional space then Y picks out a special direction in this space and the combination of $\{f\ [\bar{B},B]_- + d\ [\bar{B},B]_+\}$ along Y is a component of an eight-dimensional vector. Since Y^1 is traceless the Tr $[\bar{B},B]_+$ contributes no mass splitting and is ignored.

Using the explicit form of Y^1 already given, we obtain

$$H^1 = f\left[-\frac{3}{\sqrt{6}}\,\bar{N}N + \frac{3}{\sqrt{6}}\,\bar{\Xi}\Xi\right] + d\left[-\frac{1}{\sqrt{6}}\,\bar{N}N - \frac{2}{\sqrt{6}}\,\bar{\Lambda}\Lambda - \frac{\bar{\Xi}\Xi}{\sqrt{6}} + \frac{2}{\sqrt{6}}\,\bar{\Sigma}\Sigma\right] . \tag{37}$$

Absorbing the $\sqrt{6}$ into the coupling constants we have

$$M_N = M_0 - 3f - d$$

$$M_\Lambda = M_0 - 2d$$

$$M_\Sigma = M_0 + 2d$$

$$M_\Xi = M_0 + 3f - d,$$

where M_0 is identified as the bare baryon mass. Since there are three unknowns and four equations we may eliminate the unknowns to obtain the Gell-Mann - Okubo mass formula for the baryon 8-dimensional representation

$$\frac{M_{\Xi} + M_N}{2} = \tfrac{3}{4} M_{\Lambda} + \tfrac{1}{4} M_{\Sigma} \tag{38}$$

which is satisfied to an accuracy of about 1% by the actual baryon masses. Compare this to the 35% difference between N and Ξ masses. The unknowns are approximately d = 18, f = 63, M_0 = 1140, which suggests that first order perturbation theory might not be far off.

In the case of the 0^- mesons the mass formula is

$$M_k^2 = \tfrac{3}{4} M_{\eta}^2 + \tfrac{1}{4} M_{\pi}^2 \tag{39}$$

which, except for the squares of masses, is obtained from Eq. (38) by making the substitutions Ξ, $N \to K$; $\Lambda \to \eta$; $\Sigma \to \pi$. Note that from Eq. (37) there can be no f-type couplings with these substitutions.

That the squares of masses appear in Eq. (39) is more difficult to understand. A possible reason for this difference is suggested if we inspect the propagators for a fermion which are linear in m

$$\frac{1}{\not p - m}$$

while for mesons the propagator is quadratic in m,

$$\frac{1}{p^2 - m^2} .$$

Adding the self-energy mass correction from the two denominators results in an additive correction to m for fermions and to m^2 for mesons. This is not a very convincing reason for the m^2 meson mass formula and the problem is not well understood at this time.

The two unknowns in the meson case, d and M_0^2, are related by $d = -\tfrac{1}{2} M_0^2$ which seems to be too large a correction to be determined reliably from first order perturbation theory. However, the two sides of Eq. (39) still agree to within a few per cent.

The fact that the (mass)^2 law works so well for the 0^- mesons and that the perturbation is so large that first order perturbation theory is not reliable, means that we do not have a good understanding of the mass law. The situation might be something like the case of strong Zeeman splitting in atoms where the level splittings are the same for weak magnetic fields as for strong magnetic fields although the levels cross at some intermediate field region.

The general mass formula for all representations was derived by Okubo. In tensor notation we may formulate the problem in the following way. The coupling that produces the mass splitting is to be linear in the representation

$$\psi^{[i,j,\ldots,k]}_{[m,n,\ldots,p]} ,$$

its conjugate representation

$$\psi^{[m,n,\ldots,p]}_{[i,j,\ldots,k]}$$

and the hypercharge tensor Y^r_s which, as we have discussed before, is a fixed tensor in SU_3 space so that the coupling transforms as a component of an '8'. In general, there are two such terms and we have

$$H' = a\psi^{[m,n,\ldots,p]}_{[i,j,\ldots,k]}\psi^{[i,j,\ldots,k]}_{[r,n,\ldots,p]}Y^r_m + b\psi^{[m,n,\ldots,p]}_{[i,j,\ldots,k]}\psi^{[r,j,\ldots,k]}_{[m,n,\ldots,p]}Y^i_r . \tag{40}$$

As before, we may replace Y by the traceless Y' since the trace of Y^r_m corresponds to a contraction with δ^r_m giving no mass splitting.

In the case of triangular representations there is only one term of the form

$$H \sim \psi_{[r,n,\ldots,p]}\, \psi^{[s,n,\ldots,p]}\, Y^{r}_{s} \,. \qquad (41)$$

Rather than carry out explicitly*) the summations indicated in Eq. (41), we note that Eq. (41) is just the matrix element of the hypercharge evaluated in the representation under consideration.

Recalling that in terms of the infinitesimal operators, hypercharge Y is proportional to $U_z - V_z$, we see that the mass formula for triangular representation is immediately obtained by taking the expectation value of $U_z - V_z$ for each state. The difference between the masses of succeedingly higher isotopic multiplets is clearly a constant for the representation.

Consider some triangular representation shown below.

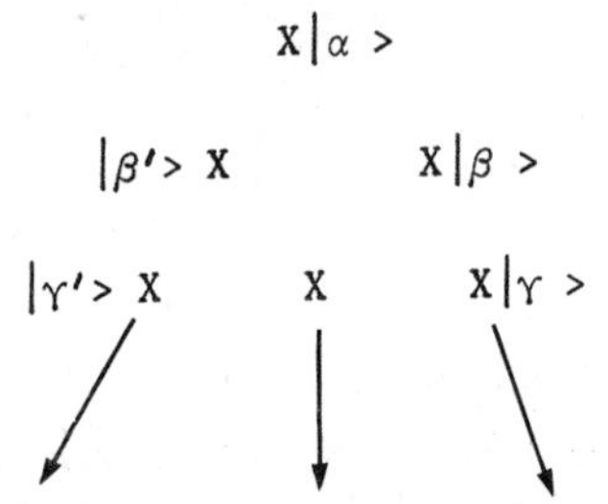

States $|\alpha>$, $|\beta>$, $|\gamma>$ decrease in U_z stepwise by one unit; states $|\alpha>$, $|\beta'>$, $|\gamma'>$ increase in V_z stepwise by one unit.

---

*) The sums are actually quite easy. Let a particular particle in the representation of N indices can be characterized by x 2's and y 3's while all other indices are 1's. Focusing attention on this particle we note it occurs $t(N;\ x,y) = N!/(x!y!(N-x-y)!)$ times in the sum. Weighting each occurrence with the value of Y^{r}_{s}, we have $H' = t(N-1;\ x,y)\, Y_1{}^1 + t(N-1;\ x-1,y)\, Y_2{}^2 + t(N-1;\ x,y-1)\, Y_3{}^3$. Normalizing by dividing by $t(N;\ x,y)$ we obtain $H' = 1 - 3y/N$, independent of x (indepemdent of isotopic spin as we expect) and linear in y and therefore linear in hypercharge.

Evaluating $U_z - V_z$ for the state $|\alpha>$ and using the fact that $|\alpha>$ is an isosinglet and $I_z + U_z + V_z = 0$ we have

$$< \alpha|(U_z - V_z)|\alpha> = 2 < \alpha|U_z|\alpha> = 2U_{z\alpha} .$$

For the state $|\beta>$, $V_z = -(U_z + I_z) = -(U_z + \frac{1}{2}) = -(U_{z\alpha} - \frac{1}{2})$ and $U_z - V_z = U_{z\alpha} - 1 + (U_{z\alpha} - \frac{1}{2}) = 2U_{z\alpha} - \frac{3}{2}$ for the state $|\beta'>$; $U_z = -(V_z + I_z) = -(V_{z\alpha} + \frac{1}{2}) = U_{z\alpha} - \frac{1}{2}$ and $U_z - V_z = 2U_{z\alpha} - \frac{3}{2}$. Similarly, for $|\gamma>$ and $|\gamma'>$ we find for $< U_z - V_z> = U_{z\alpha} - \frac{5}{2}$. Thus the mass splitting operator which is proportional to the expectation value of the operator $(U_z - V_z)$ gives equal mass splittings between any two adjacent hypercharge multiplets. For triangular representations shown below the mass would increase with increasing Y as indicated in Fig. 18.

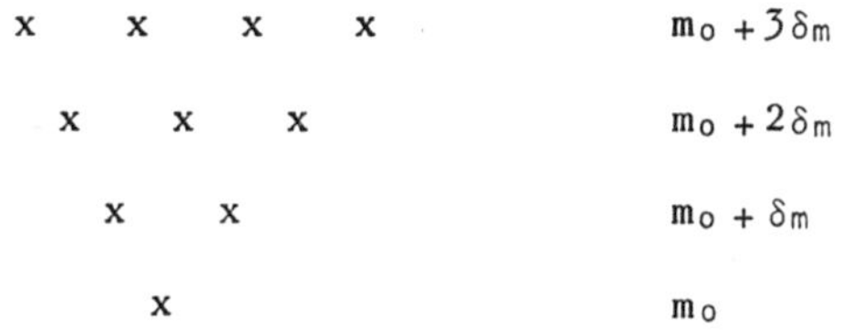

x	x	x	x	$m_0 + 3\delta m$	
	x	x	x	$m_0 + 2\delta m$	The representation
		x	x	$m_0 + \delta m$	$D^{10}(0,3)$.
			x	m_0	

Fig. 18

The ten-dimensional representation $D^{10}(0,3)$ is shown in Fig. 18 above. This representation has the nice property that a number of spin $\frac{3}{2}^+$ resonances seem to fit well into this representation. These are

Name	I spin	Y	Mass
N^*	$\frac{3}{2}$	1	1238
Y^*	1	0	1385
Ξ^*	$\frac{1}{2}$	-1	1530
Ω^-	0	-2	1676

The existence of Ω^-, an isosinglet with S = - 3, is a necessary consequence of SU_3 symmetry. The lowest mass it could have which would still allow a strong decay is 1815 MeV for the $\Xi^- + \bar{K}^0$ mode. Any other modes such as $\Sigma^- + 2\bar{K}^0$ or $p + 3\bar{K}^0$ require an even larger mass. If the Ω^- mass is less then 1815 it would appear as a relatively stable member of the multiplet, decaying via weak interactions through the channels

$$\Omega^- \rightarrow \Xi^- + \pi^0$$

$$\rightarrow \Xi^0 + \pi^- \ .$$

Consider now the mass formula prediction. Given the N^* and Y^* masses, the Ξ^* mass is predicted to be 1532 which is in fantastic agreement with the observed 1530, while the Ω^- mass would be $\sim$ 1680, well below the critical mass 1815. Thus, if we believe the mass formula, SU_3 with symmetry breaking predicts a stable spin $3/2$ baryon.

Discovery of the particle*) with an observed mass of 1676 MeV gives a remarkable confirmation of one of the outstanding predictions in particle physics. In fact, it is (Ω^-) the first stable baryon discovered since the Ξ in 1952. Note, however, that until the spin and parity is confirmed to be $3/2^+$ we are not absolutely sure that the particle is the SU_3 predicted one.

VI. THE ELECTROMAGNETIC MASS SPLITTINGS

We will now derive the electromagnetic mass splittings, which outside of the multiplet structure, is probably one of the best tests of SU_3 for the following two reasons:

---

*) The Ω^- has been discovered (see New York Times 19 February, 1964) at Brookhaven with an observed mass of 1686 ± 12 MeV.

i) The SU_3 transformation properties of the electromagnetic current operator is completely defined unlike the ad hoc assumption for the strong mass splittings.

ii) Perturbation theory should be more satisfactory since the electromagnetic mass splittings are much smaller than the strong mass splittings.

The basic assumption is that a particle's electromagnetic self-energy, giving rise to electromagnetic mass splittings, is entirely due to its charge and its resultant SU_3 invariant coupling to other particles, i.e. we assume that the particles have no bare anomalous moments although such physical moments are allowed as a result of SU_3 invariant couplings.

If we define Q by the matrix

$$Q = \begin{pmatrix} 1 & 0 & 0 \\ 0 & 0 & 0 \\ 0 & 0 & 0 \end{pmatrix} \tag{42}$$

then, similarly, to the hypercharge, the eigenvalue equation for the electric charge is

$$Q(B) = [Q,B]_- = \begin{pmatrix} 0 & \Sigma^+ & p \\ -\Sigma^- & 0 & 0 \\ -\Xi^- & 0 & 0 \end{pmatrix} \tag{43}$$

To find the current operator for a bare baryon we apply gauge invariance to the free particle Lagrangian which is

$$L_0 = \sum_{i,j} B_j^i \, (i\partial_\mu \gamma_\mu + m) \, B_i^j \, .$$

(Note that the Lagrangian is an SU_3 scaler.) Gauge invariance requires that $\partial_\mu \rightarrow \partial_\mu - ieA_\mu$ for each charged particle. In the SU_3 space this results in adding to the free Lagrangian L_0 above the electromagnetic Lagrangian

$$L_{elec} = e\ \mathrm{Tr}\left\{\bar{B}\ \gamma_\mu A_\mu [Q,B]_- \right\} \qquad (44)$$

or

$$= e\ \mathrm{Tr}\left\{Q\ [\bar{B}\ \gamma_\mu A_\mu, B]_- \right\} . \qquad (44')$$

One can readily verify by explicitly writing out L_{elec} that it is the usual coupling of photons to bare charged baryons. The Lagrangian, L_{elec}, gives rise to diagrams as shown below in Fig. 19.

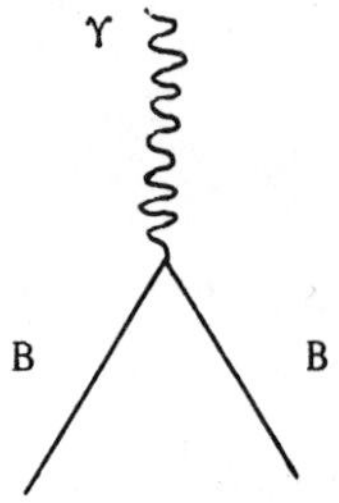

(Photon interacting with bare charged baryon by E_{elec}.)

Fig. 19

If the electromagnetic Lagrangian is thought of as the product of the electromagnetic field with a current, i.e. $L_{elec} = eA_\mu J_\mu$ then for bare baryons the current is

$$J_\mu^S = \mathrm{Tr}\left\{Q\ [\bar{B}\gamma_\mu, B]_- \right\} .$$

Similarly, we have for mesons

$$J_\mu^M = \mathrm{Tr}\left\{Q\ [\bar{M}, \partial_\mu M]_- \right\} .$$

Including baryon and meson couplings as well as the electromagnetic current couplings can give rise to diagrams as shown in Fig. 20

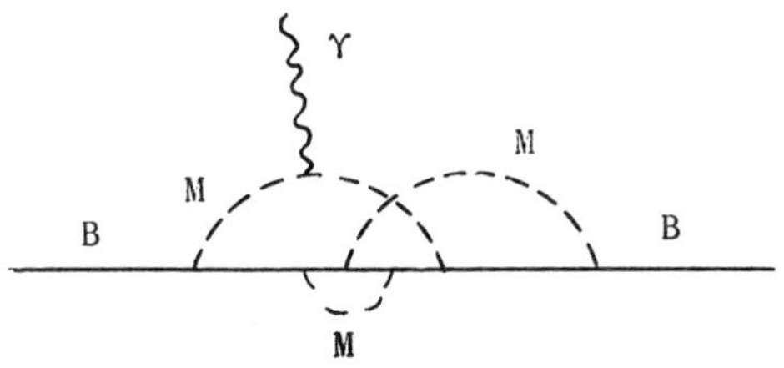

Fig. 20

Electromagnetic mass splittings will arise from diagrams like those shown in Fig. 21.

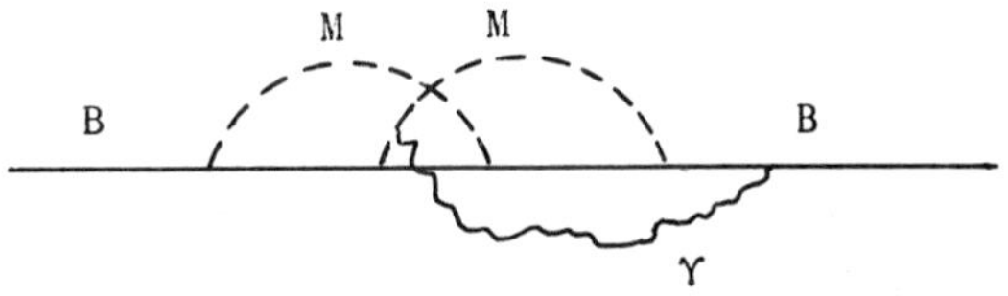

Fig. 21

Since the interaction involves emission and absorption of one virtual photon the perturbation mass δm which results from electromagnetic interactions wull be quadratic in the matrix Q. The most general coupling involving initial and final baryons and which is quadratic in Q is

$$(\delta M)_{elec} = a_1 \, Tr\,[\bar{B}QBQ] + a_2 \, Tr\,[\bar{B}BQQ] + a_3 \, Tr\,[\bar{B}QQB] + a_4 \, [\bar{B}Q] \, Tr\,[BQ] + a_5 \, Tr\,[\bar{B}QB] \, Tr\,[Q] + a_6 \, Tr\,[\bar{B}BQ] \, Tr\,[Q] \,. \tag{45}$$

(Terms like Tr $[\bar{B}B]$ Tr $[Q^2]$ are not considered since they would not give any mass splitting.)

Since $Q^2 = Q$ the terms a_5 and a_6 are the same as a_3 and a_2, respectively, the Lagrangian reduces to four terms and $(\delta M)_{elec}$ can be taken to be of the form

$$(\delta M)_{elec} = a\ \mathrm{Tr}\ [\bar{B}QBQ] + b\ \mathrm{Tr}\ [\bar{B}BQQ] + c\ \mathrm{Tr}\ [\bar{B}QQB] + d\ \mathrm{Tr}\ [\bar{B}Q]\ \mathrm{Tr}\ [BQ]\ . \tag{46}$$

Carrying out the traces we obtain

$$(\delta M)_{elec} = (a + b + c + d)\left(\frac{\bar{\Sigma}^0}{\sqrt{2}} + \frac{\bar{\Delta}}{\sqrt{6}}\right)\left(\frac{\Sigma^0}{\sqrt{2}} + \frac{\Delta}{\sqrt{6}}\right)$$
$$+ b(\bar{\Sigma}^-\Sigma^- + \bar{\Xi}^-\Xi^-) + c(\bar{\Sigma}^+\Sigma^+ + \bar{p}p)\ . \tag{47}$$

Also, note that Ξ^0 and n do not appear in the expression so that we may take the masses of these particles to be equal to their electromagnetically bare masses (i.e. bare including SU_3 invariant forces and forces that cause the strong mass splittings).

Denoting, then, M_Σ as that bare Σ mass we have

$$c = M_p - M_n = M_{\Sigma^+} - M_\Sigma$$

$$b = M_{\Sigma^-} - M_\Sigma = M_{\Xi^-} - M_{\Xi^0}$$

and upon eliminating M_Σ

$$M_p - M_n + M_{\Sigma^-} - M_{\Sigma^+} = M_{\Xi^-} - M_{\Xi^0}\ . \tag{48}$$

Putting in the observed masses, we get remarkably good agreement:

$$+ 6.7 \pm 0.5 \text{ MeV} = + 6.1 \pm 1.6 \text{ MeV}\ .$$

Equation (48), the electromagnetic mass formula, may be taken as constituting a profound test of SU_3.

We consider now the possible relations among the baryon magnetic moments as a consequence of SU_3.

Recall that the nucleon electromagnetic form factors are defined by the equation

$$\bar{u}(p_2)(F_1^S + F_1^V \tau_3)\ \gamma_\mu\ u(p_1) + \bar{u}(p_2)(F_2^S + F_2^V \tau_3)\ \sigma_{\mu\nu}\ q_\nu\ u(p_1)\ . \qquad (49)$$

This equation is valid to all orders in strong coupling and to first order in the electromagnetic interaction. We want the generalization of this equation which covers all the eight baryons.

Typical diagrams that contribute to the baryon magnetic moments are shown in Fig. 22.

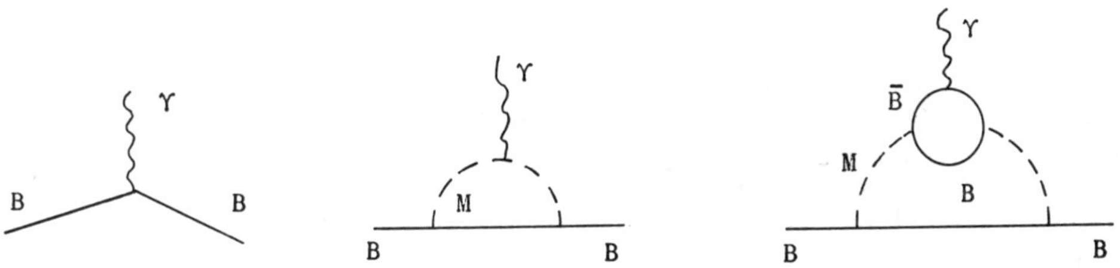

Fig. 22

The expression for this kind of electromagnetic interaction should be valid to all orders in SU_3 invariant interactions and first order in electromagnetism which means linear in the matrix Q.

Rather than Eq. (49), we could express the first order electromagnetic interaction in terms of the effective current operator to be sandwiched between nucleon spinors

$$j_\mu^{eff} = \bar{\psi}(F_1{}^s + F_1{}^v \tau_3)\, \gamma_\mu \psi + \psi(F_2{}^s + F_2{}^v \tau_3)\sigma_{\mu\nu} q_\nu \psi \, . \tag{50}$$

The isotopic spin conditions are taken care of by τ_3 and the unit matrix (not expressly written in Eq. (50); ψ is the nuclear field operator. The extension of Eq. (50) to include the charge and hypercharge degrees of freedom takes the form

$$\begin{aligned} J_\mu^{eff} &= a_1 \, Tr(\bar{B}Q\gamma_\mu B) + b_1 \, Tr(\bar{B}\gamma_\mu BQ) + c_1 \, Tr(\bar{B}\gamma_\mu B) \, Tr \, Q \\ &\quad + a_2 \, Tr \, \bar{B}Q\sigma_{\mu\nu}Bq_\nu + b_2 \, Tr \, \bar{B}\sigma_{\mu\nu}BQq_\nu + c_2 \, Tr \, \bar{B}\sigma_{\mu\nu}B \, Tr \, Qq_\nu , \end{aligned} \tag{51}$$

where the subscript 1 refers to the charge part, and the subscript 2 to the magnetic moment part.

Suppressing subscripts and Dirac matrices, and taking traces, we have

$$\begin{aligned} J^{eff} &= a\left[\left(\frac{\bar{\Sigma}^0}{\sqrt{2}} + \frac{\bar{\Lambda}}{\sqrt{6}}\right)\left(\frac{\Sigma^0}{\sqrt{2}} + \frac{\Lambda}{\sqrt{6}}\right) + \bar{\Sigma}^- \Sigma^- + \bar{\Xi}^- \Xi^-\right] \\ &\quad + b\left[\left(\frac{\bar{\Sigma}^0}{\sqrt{2}} + \frac{\bar{\Lambda}}{\sqrt{6}}\right)\left(\frac{\Sigma^0}{\sqrt{2}} + \frac{\Lambda}{\sqrt{6}}\right) + \bar{\Sigma}^+ \Sigma^+ + \bar{p}p\right] \\ &\quad + c\left[\left(\frac{\bar{\Sigma}^0}{\sqrt{2}} + \frac{\bar{\Lambda}}{\sqrt{6}}\right)\left(\frac{\Sigma^0}{\sqrt{2}} + \frac{\Lambda}{\sqrt{6}}\right) + \left(\frac{-\bar{\Sigma}^0}{\sqrt{2}} + \frac{\bar{\Lambda}}{\sqrt{6}}\right)\left(\frac{-\bar{\Sigma}^0}{\sqrt{2}} + \frac{\bar{\Lambda}}{\sqrt{6}}\right)\right. \\ &\quad + \frac{2}{3}\bar{\Lambda}\Lambda + \bar{\Sigma}^+\Sigma^+ + \bar{\Sigma}^-\Sigma^- + \bar{n}n + \bar{p}p \\ &\quad \left. + \bar{\Xi}^-\Xi^- + \bar{\Xi}^0\Xi^0\right] . \end{aligned} \tag{52}$$

If the electromagnetic coupling of all particles involves only commutators of Q, as is the case for the baryons, pseudoscalar and vector mesons in the eight-dimensional representation, then all electromagnetic interactions would be invariant under the transformation

$$Q \rightarrow Q + aI \qquad (53)$$

where a is a constant and I is the unit matrix. This invariance is true likewise for the ten-dimensional representation as well as any representation which can be generated starting from octets. However, if one envisions a model like the Sakata model where the interaction of baryons and photons does not involve the commutator of B and Q, then the invariance expressed by Eq. (53) would not hold.

We can derive relations among the baryon magnetic moments under both conditions [i.e. with and without supposing Eq. (53)]. If Eq. (53) is true then

$$a + b + 3c = 0$$

and we have the relations

$$\mu_n = -2a - 2b \qquad \mu_{\Sigma^0} = a + b$$

$$\mu_p = -2a + 4b \qquad \mu_{\Sigma^-} = 4a - 2b$$

$$\mu_\Lambda = -a - b \qquad \mu_{\Xi^0} = -2a - 2b$$

$$\mu_{\Sigma^+} = -2a + 4b \qquad \mu_{\Xi^-} = 4a - 2b \; .$$

These may all be rewritten in terms of μ_n and μ_p:

$$\mu_\Lambda = \tfrac{1}{2} \mu_n$$

$$*\mu_{\Sigma^+} = \mu_p$$

$$\mu_{\Sigma^0} = -\tfrac{1}{2} \mu_n$$

$$\mu_{\Sigma^-} = -\mu_p - \mu_n \qquad (54)$$

$$*\mu_{\Xi^0} = \mu_n$$

$$\mu_{\Xi^-} = -\mu_p - \mu_n$$

$$*\mu_{\Xi^-} = \mu_{\Sigma^-} \qquad (54)$$

$$*\mu_\Lambda = \tfrac{1}{3}\,\mu_{\Sigma^0} + \tfrac{2}{3}\,\mu_n .$$

(The relations marked * are those which still survive if the invariance condition (53) is relaxed.)

Note that the charges as well as magnetic moments must and do satisfy these same relations. The only experimental test of Eq. (54) is the measurement of μ_Λ which gives -0.66 ± 0.35 and which is in some kind of agreement with theory (at least the probability that μ_Λ is negative is higher than the probability that it is positive). Another experimental consequence, observable in e^+e^- colliding beam experiments, is that the process $\gamma \to \Sigma^+ + \bar{\Sigma}^+$ should proceed at the same rate (except for phase space differences) as $\gamma \to p + \bar{p}$ since both charge and magnetic moment form factors are the same for p and Σ^+. Another experimental consequence seens from Eq. (53) is a relation between the $\Sigma^0 \to \Lambda$ transition rate and μ_n. The decay is caused by a transition magnetic moment interaction with a strength

$$\mu_{\Sigma^0\Lambda} = -\frac{\sqrt{3}}{2}\,\mu_n .$$

VII. DECIMET DECAY WIDTHS AND SUMMARY

Another of the experimental consequences of SU_3 is the set of relations among the decay rates (or widths) of the $\tfrac{3}{2}^+$ baryon resonances which fit into the representation $D^{10}(0,3)$ as previously observed. These $\tfrac{3}{2}^+$ particles decay into the $\tfrac{1}{2}^+$ baryons $D^8(1,1)$ and pseudoscalar mesons $D^8(1,1)$. Thus, we need to construct an SU_3 invariant coupling between these three representations. The easiest way to do this is to first construct a '10' from the two '8' 's in terms of the normalized tensors

$$T^{[ijk]} = B^i_m M^j_n \frac{\epsilon^{mnk}}{\sqrt{s}} \text{ (symmetrized over } i,j,k), \qquad (55)$$

where s is the number of terms in the sum, second, then contract this '10' with the '10' for the $3/2^+$ baryons represented by the tensor $\psi^{[ijk]}$, obtaining the invariant interaction

$$H = \psi_{[ijk]} \cdot T^{[ijk]} .$$

(Note [ijk] means symmetrized in i,j,k.)

The tensor components of the $3/2^+$ baryons are readily identified as follows: (We use the fact that there is only one '10' in $3\times 3\times 3$.)

N^*	$\psi^{[222]}$	$\psi^{[221]}$	$\psi^{[211]}$	$\psi^{[111]}$
Y^*	$\psi^{[223]}$	$\psi^{[123]}$	$\psi^{[311]}$	
Ξ^*	$\psi^{[233]}$	$\psi^{[331]}$		
Ω^-	$\psi^{[333]}$			

Consider the decay of the $\psi^{[111]}$ component of N^*. This is coupled with the component $T^{[111]}$ which we construct according to Eq. (55)

$$T^{[111]} = \frac{1}{\sqrt{2}}\left[B^1_j M^1_\ell \epsilon^{j\ell 1}\right]$$

$$= \frac{1}{\sqrt{2}}\left[B^1_2 M^1_3 - B^1_3 M^1_2\right]$$

$$= \frac{1}{\sqrt{2}}\left[\Sigma^+ K^+ - p\,\pi^+\right].$$

Since the decay to $\Sigma^+ K^+$ is not energetically possible for $N^*(1238)$, the only relevant final state is $p\,\pi^+$. Thus

$$T^{[111]}_{p\pi^+} = -\frac{1}{\sqrt{2}}\, p\pi^+ .$$

The transition rate, containing all phase space factors, is given by

$$\Gamma_{N^* \to p\pi^+} = \frac{g^2\, q^3_{p\pi^+}}{M^2_{N^*}}\, |T^{[111]}_{p\pi^+}|^2\, \frac{(E_p + M_p)}{M_{N^*}} \qquad (56)$$

where g^2 is a coupling constant that is the same for the entire multiplet of $\frac{3}{2}^+$ baryons, $q_{p\pi^+}$ is the c.m. momentum of the π^+ and p, and M_{N^*} is the N* mass. E_p and M_p are the energy and mass of the decay proton. The decay

$$\tfrac{3}{2}^+ \to 0^- + \tfrac{1}{2}^+$$

proceeds via p wave (conservation of parity and angular momentum) which is the reason for the factor q^3. The factor $(E_p + M_p)/M_{N^*}$ multiplying the expression given in Eq. (56) arises because of the spin $\frac{3}{2}$ character of the decaying N*. (In general, this factor varies very little among the various decays and was not included in the numerical values calculated below.)

The experimental width of N* is 100 MeV. Thus g^2 can be determined and we may now predict other widths in terms of this coupling constant.

Consider the decay of the $\psi^{[113]}$ component of Y* (i.e. Y^{*+})

$$Y^* \to \Lambda\pi, \Sigma\pi$$

which is coupled to $T^{[113]}$

$$T^{[113]} = \frac{1}{\sqrt{6}}\left[B_j^{\,1} M_\ell^{\,1}\,\epsilon^{j\ell 3} + B_j^{\,1} M_\ell^{\,3}\,\epsilon^{j\ell 1} + B_j^{\,3} M_\ell^{\,1}\,\epsilon^{j\ell 1}\right]$$

$$= \frac{1}{\sqrt{6}}\left[B_1^{\,1} M_2^{\,1} - B_2^{\,1} M_1^{\,1} + B_2^{\,1} M_3^{\,3} - B_3^{\,1} M_2^{\,3} + B_2^{\,3} M_3^{\,1} - B_3^{\,3} M_2^{\,1}\right]$$

$$= \frac{1}{\sqrt{6}}\left[\left(\frac{\Sigma^0}{\sqrt{2}} + \frac{\Lambda}{\sqrt{6}}\right)\pi^+ - \Sigma^+\left(\frac{\pi^0}{\sqrt{2}} + \frac{n}{\sqrt{6}}\right) + \Xi^0 K^+ + \frac{2\Lambda}{\sqrt{6}}\pi^+ - \frac{\Sigma^+ 2n}{\sqrt{6}} - p\,\bar{K}^0\right].$$

Excluding those terms not energetically possible we have

$$T^{[113]} = \frac{1}{\sqrt{6}}\left[\frac{\Sigma^0\pi^+}{\sqrt{2}} - \frac{\Sigma^+\pi^0}{\sqrt{2}} + \sqrt{\frac{3}{2}}\,\Lambda\pi^+\right].$$

Hence,

$$|T^{[113]}_{\Lambda\pi^+}|^2 = \frac{1}{4}$$

$$|T^{[113]}_{\Sigma^0\pi^+}|^2 = |T^{[113]}_{\Sigma^+\pi^0}|^2 = \frac{1}{12}$$

and

$$\Gamma_{Y^* \to \Lambda\pi^+} = \frac{g^2}{4}\,\frac{q^3_{\Lambda\pi^+}}{M_{Y^*}}\left(\frac{E_\Lambda + M_\Lambda}{M_{Y^*}}\right)$$

$$\Gamma_{Y^* \to \Sigma^+\pi^0} = \Gamma_{Y^* \to \Sigma^0\pi^+} = \frac{g^2}{12}\,\frac{q^3_{\Sigma\pi}}{M^2_{Y^*}}\left(\frac{E_\Sigma + M_\Sigma}{M_{Y^*}}\right).$$

Finally, consider the decay of the $\psi^{[331]}$ component of Ξ^*. This component is coupled to $T^{[331]}$

$$T^{[331]} = \frac{1}{\sqrt{6}}\left[B_i^{\,3} M_j^{\,3}\, \epsilon^{ij1} + B_i^{\,3} M_j^{\,1}\, \epsilon^{ij3} + B_i^{\,1} M_j^{\,3}\, \epsilon^{ij3}\right]$$

$$= \frac{1}{\sqrt{6}}\left[B_2^{\,3} M_3^{\,3} - B_3^{\,3} M_2^{\,3} + B_1^{\,3} M_2^{\,1} - B_2^{\,3} M_1^{\,1} + B_1^{\,1} M_2^{\,3} - B_2^{\,1} M_1^{\,3}\right]$$

$$= \frac{1}{\sqrt{6}}\left[\frac{-2}{\sqrt{6}}\,\Xi^0 n + \frac{2}{\sqrt{6}}\,\Lambda\,\bar{K}^0 + \Xi^-\pi^+ - \Xi^0\left(\frac{\pi^0}{\sqrt{2}} + \frac{n}{\sqrt{6}}\right) + \left(\frac{\Sigma^0}{\sqrt{2}} + \frac{\Lambda}{\sqrt{6}}\right)\bar{K}^0 - \Sigma^+ K^-\right].$$

Excluding those not energetically possible we have

$$T^{[331]} = \frac{1}{\sqrt{6}}\,\Xi^-\pi^+ - \frac{1}{\sqrt{12}}\,\Xi^0\pi^0 .$$

Hence,

$$|T^{[331]}_{\Xi^-\pi^+}|^2 = \frac{1}{6}, \quad |T^{[331]}_{\Xi^0\pi^0}|^2 = \frac{1}{12}$$

and

$$\Gamma_{\Xi^* \to \Xi^-\pi^+} = \frac{g^2}{6}\,\frac{q^3_{\Xi\pi}}{M^2_{\Xi^*}}\left(\frac{E_\Xi + M_\Xi}{M_{\Xi^*}}\right)$$

$$\Gamma_{\Xi^* \to \Xi^0\pi^0} = \frac{g^2}{12}\,\frac{q^3_{\Xi\pi}}{M^2_{\Xi^*}}\left(\frac{E_\Xi + M_\Xi}{M_{\Xi^*}}\right).$$

For the Ω^- decay we would find it coupled to

$$T^{[333]} = \frac{1}{\sqrt{2}}\left[\Xi^-\bar{K}^0 - \Xi^0 K^-\right]$$

but recall that by the mass formula we expect it to be stable against strong decay.

The following table shows how the predicted widths compared with the experimental ones*). [Compare with Glashow and Rosenfeld[3]).]

Decay	q(MeV)	Experimental width	Theoretical width
$N^* \to \pi p$	231	100	100 (by definition)
$Y^* \to \Lambda\pi$	210	-	42
$\to \Sigma\pi$	119	< 2	5
$\to$ total	-	50	47
$\Xi^{0*} \to \Xi^- \pi^+$	148	-	9
$\to \Xi^0 \pi^0$	148	-	4.5
$\to$ total	-	8.0	13.5

SU_3 predicts the dominant Y* rate rather well but the agreement is not very good for the Ξ^* as well as the $\Lambda\pi$ mode of the Y*. Note that the relative rates within an isotopic multiplet are given purely by isotopic spin Clebsch-Gordan coefficients. It is the relative rates between different isotopic multiplets that is the prediction of SU_3.

Let us summarize some of the consequences of SU_3.

1) Multiplet structure

a) Baryons

The eight stable baryons ($\frac{1}{2}^+$) seem to fit into the representation

---

*) In these calculations a possible form factor at the decay vertices which depends on the decay momentum [which might be of the form $\Lambda^2/(\Lambda^2 + q^2)$] has not been used. Such a form factor could be used to improve the agreement on the Ξ^*.

$D^8(1,1)$. The ten-dimensional representation $D^{10}(0,3)$ is filled by the spin $\frac{3}{2}^+$ particles N*, Y*, Ξ*, and Ω^-(if the Ω^- spin turns out to be $\frac{3}{2}^+$). However, note that there is the well-established Y*(1660) which now appears to be $\frac{3}{2}^-$ and has isospin unity and so may fit in an octet with the N*(1512) which is also $D_{3/2}$. Furthermore as far as baryon resonances are concerned there are a great many others which as yet have not been grouped together in SU_3 multiplets. Understanding this problem (similarly for the extra mesons) is one of the most important problems in the application of SU_3.

b) Mesons

The eight 0^- mesons fit into the eight-dimensional representation $D^8(1,1)$. For the vector (1^-) mesons seven of the eight make up the $I = \frac{1}{2}$ and $I = 1$ components of the octet but there is the question of whether the ω or φ is the isosinglet. In any case, one of the two (or a linear combination) can fit as the isosinglet while the other (or orthogonal linear combination) can be a singlet representation $D^1(0,0)$. Other mesons with $I = 0$ which may fit into singlet representations are the f_0 at 1250 MeV with spin parity 2^+ and the $\eta\pi\pi$ at 958 MeV with spin parity 0^-. This gives a total of 20 mesons which are easily accommodated in SU_3 multiplets.

Besides these 20 mesons there are at least the following 15 other mesons or meson resonances which at the present time are not fitted into some SU_3 multiplet structure (the exact number depends on the isospin assignments which are not completely known).

Particle	Mass	Particle	Mass
K_1K_1	1000	$KK\pi$	1410
$\pi\omega$(Buddha)	1220	$K\pi\pi$	1175
$\pi\rho(A_1)$	1080	κ	730
$\pi\rho(A_2)$	1310	2π	381

2) Strong mass formula

This is an interesting consequence of SU_3 but it is not clear that it is really a test because of the ad hoc assumption of the form and transformation property of the mass operator.

3) Electromagnetic mass formula

Here we must emphasize that the transformation property of the charge is not an ad hoc assumption and this the electromagnetic mass formula is a valid test of SU_3. Furthermore, we obtained good agreement with experiment. (Remember that cross terms with SU_3 violating forces were neglected in deriving this expression.)

4) Decay widths - $(10 \rightarrow 8+8)$

These predictions are in fairly good agreement with SU_3.

In summary, it appears that emerging from the jungle of strong interaction physics is some semblance of order which is sufficiently manifest that Gell-Mann and Ne'man have been able to penetrate the camouflage presented by both the symmetry violating interactions as well as the morasses of data. Surely physicists will accept this invitation of nature and commence with increased vigour to discover even more of her symmetries.

REFERENCES

1) N. Cabibbo, Phys.Rev.Letters 10, 531 (1963).

2) R. Cutkosky (to be published).

3) S. Glashow and A. Rosenfeld, Phys.Rev.Letters 10, 192 (1963).

CONSEQUENCES OF SU_3 SYMMETRY IN WEAK INTERACTIONS

R.P. Feynman,
California Institute of Technology.

Introduction

1st LECTURE

These lectures will cover the relationship of SU_3 and the weak interactions. The lectures will be geared for experimental people so that they may get an idea of how our theoretical predictions arise. At first, I will speak a little bit about how calculations are made for the weak decays, then we shall consider SU_3, and finally the effects of unitary symmetry upon the weak interactions. The subject matter is split in this way so that one may get a clearer idea of the origins of the various problems in the theory of weak interactions. Not all of our difficulties arise from SU_3 nor do all of the successes, and it is important to realize this.

The theory of weak decays is very unsatisfactory except that it agrees with experiment. To understand that remark let us consider the muon. A muon is a particle which has exactly the same properties as the electron except that its mass is 207 times the mass of the electron. This statement completely describes our experiments with the muon, but such a comment is also unsatisfactory for a true theorist. Experimentalists find a beautiful and simple thing which is easy for the theorists to describe. Nevertheless, we must be unhappy about this situation because we have no idea of why this particle exists. Similarly, the theory of weak decay, up to the point where we encounter strangeness changing interactions, is accurate but unsatisfactory. There are various mysterious properties which I shall mention as I go on, but I should like to remind you that the most mysterious aspect of the weak decays is that they exist at all. It seems so much simpler just to forget them. There is no clue from electromagnetism, from gravity, or from nuclear forces that the weak interactions must exist. They seem to have no connection with the rest of the world.

Form of the four-fermion weak interaction

The theory of the weak decays was originated by Fermi. Fermi tried to describe mathematically an idea of Pauli's concerning the neutrino. For example, in K capture an orbital electron in the K shell is eaten by a proton in the nucleus with the result that a neutron plus a neutrino is created. Fermi attempted to write down an abstract description of this process. He assumed that there was a Hamiltonian which contained a term of the form

$$Q^*_\nu \, Q^*_n \, Q_e \, Q_p \; .$$

In this form the Q^*_n is an operator which creates a neutron, Q_p is an operator which destroys a proton, Q^*_ν creates a neutrino, and Q_e destroys an electron. Such a term is present in a Hamiltonian of the world with a certain strength characterized by a coupling constant G, and gives rise to a certain amplitude for the K-capture reaction, but no mechanism is described by it. Another way of describing the reaction is to draw a diagram with a four-point coupling

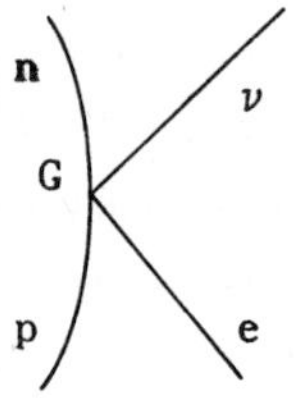

and to associate with that diagram the strength constant G, together with certain well-defined rules for calculating the amplitude. The decay amplitude is proportional to G and the amplitude for finding the proton and the electron together. Given the amplitude for the process, the rate at which the reaction proceeds is given by a Golden Rule of the form

$$\text{Rate} = 2\pi |\text{Amp}|^2 \text{ (Density of final states)}.$$

Actually things are a bit more complicated. A fermion, described by the Dirac equation, is represented by <u>four</u> amplitudes, two spin possibilities times two charge possibilities. The product of four such Q's will produce 4^4 possible terms, each of which might have its own characteristic coupling constant. Actually such a horrible mess is simplified by requiring relativistic invariance of the amplitude. This reduces the number of possible coefficients to ten. Mathematically, if we represent the four-component spinor wave function of a particle by its name, the possible forms for the coupling can be represented as

$$(\bar{\nu}1e)\,(\bar{n}1p),\ (\bar{\nu}\gamma_\alpha e)\,(\bar{n}\gamma_\alpha p),\ (\bar{\nu}1e)\,(\bar{n}\gamma_5 p)\ ,$$

and so on. Fermi, however, was not satisfied with writing down all the possibilities. He made a guess that the interaction was vector

$$(\bar{\nu}\gamma_\alpha e)\,(\bar{n}\gamma_\alpha p)\ .$$

Having limited the form of the amplitude by this guess, he was then able to calculate the properties of the beta decay.

Parity non-conservation

The most prominent feature is the shape of the spectrum, which depends almost wholly on the density of final states. Early experiments failed to confirm this spectrum, but those experiments were incorrect because of rescattering in the foils. The subsequent history of beta-decay investigations is beclouded by two decades of inaccurate observations and poor theoretical suggestions, which I shall not discuss. The final resolution of the puzzle is simply to multiply each wave function of a particle by the left-handed helicity operator,

$$a = (1 + i\gamma_5)/2\ .$$

This prescription reduces to one the number of independent coupling constants in beta decay.

The helicity operator has certain properties, namely

$$aa = a,\ \bar{a}\bar{a} = \bar{a},\ a\bar{a} = 0\ .$$

Using this helicity operator in the interaction also results in a violation of parity conservation in the weak interaction, which was found in 1957. The final form for the beta-decay coupling in the Lagrangian may then be written as

$$\sqrt{8}\ G(\bar{a}\bar{\nu}\gamma_\alpha ae)\ (\bar{a}\bar{n}\gamma_\alpha ap)\ .$$

With such a coupling, the particles are emitted polarized along the direction of their motion. They are spinning to the left with a probability of $(1 + v)/2$, and to the right with a probability of $(1 - v)/2$, where v is the particle velocity in units of c. The opposite polarization holds for the antiparticles. For beta decay the above Lagrangian may be written in the form

$$\frac{1}{\sqrt{2}}\ G\left[\bar{\nu}\left(\gamma_\alpha + i\gamma_\alpha\gamma_5\right)e\right]\cdot\left[\bar{n}\left(\gamma_\alpha + i\gamma_\alpha\gamma_5\right)p\right]$$

and it is common today to identify the various terms in this formula with current-density operators. People like to define the vector current of the leptons to be $J^{\bar{\nu}e}_{V\alpha} = (\bar{\nu}\gamma_\alpha e)$, and the axial vector current of the leptons as $J^{\bar{\nu}e}_{A\alpha} = (\bar{\nu}\gamma_\alpha i\gamma_5 e)$, together with similar definitions of the nuclear vector and axial vector currents. With this symbolism the beta-decay interaction takes the form

$$\frac{G}{\sqrt{2}}\left[J^{\bar{\nu}e}_{V\alpha} + J^{\bar{\nu}e}_{A\alpha}\right]\left[J^{\bar{n}p}_{V\alpha} + J^{\bar{n}p}_{A\alpha}\right]\ .$$

To discuss the decay of the muon we need only replace the proton spinor by a neutrino spinor and the neutron spinor by a muon spinor in the above coupling. I shall not go through the calculation of the spectrum and polarization properties of the decay on the basis of this proposed theory, but shall only comment on the results. This spectrum agrees very well with the experiments which I have seen. In fact the agreement between experiment and theory today is so detailed that one has to take into account the radiative corrections to the spectrum. The absolute value of the coupling constant G_μ, can be determined from the rate of the decay of the muon, and the result is $G_\mu M_p^2 = 1.01 \cdot 10^{-5}$. (I use natural units in which $\hbar = c = 1$.)

Strong interaction modification of weak decay matrix elements, and the conserved vector current theory

Let us return to the beta decay of the neutron. In this case we have two kinds of currents, vector and axial vector, which couple to the leptons. In beta decay the nucleons are non-relativistic and we can simplify the calculation of matrix elements. The four-dimensional vector current for a non-relativistic particle is dominated by its time component, which is just the operator 1, while the axial vector current is dominated by its space-like terms, which are just the spin operators. The vector term does not change the spin of the nucleon and is called the Fermi coupling, while the axial vector term, called Gamow-Teller coupling, flips the spin of the nucleon. Because each type of coupling leads to distinctive selection rules it was known quite early that both types of coupling are present. In the muon decay the ratio of the axial-vector term to the vector term is unity, but from experiments on the disintegration of the neutron and O^{14} it was shown that the ratio in nuclear-beta decay differs substantially from unity. If we calculate the properties of neutron decay using the coupling

$$\frac{1}{\sqrt{2}}\left[\bar{\nu}\left(\gamma_\alpha + i\gamma_\alpha\gamma_5\right) e\right] \cdot \left[\bar{n}\left(G_V\gamma_\alpha - iG_A\gamma_\alpha\gamma_5\right) p\right] ,$$

we come to the conclusion that for polarized neutrons if $G_A = - G_V$, the electron is emitted isotropically, but the neutrino is much more likely to come out along the direction of the neutron spin than opposite. The recoil proton is also anisotropic, but the electron is not. Actually the electron is slightly unsymmetric in its emission direction. From measurements on the decay of polarized neutrons one can then find that the ratio of the coupling constants is negative and approximately 1.2. What a destruction of the beautifully simple theory! $(1 + i\gamma_5)/2$ is very pretty because its square equals itself, and it projects out a certain helicity component, but $(1 + 1.2\, i\gamma_5)/2$ is dirty. However, this situation is really not unexpected, because the nucleons are fairly complicated particles due to strong interactions about which we know little. Indeed, in the sense of perturbation theory, it would be expected that a fundamental simple-type of coupling would no longer be simple. In other words, it is still possible that in the ddep heart of matter the coupling formula for the nucleons involves the helicity projection operator, but that the spinors which entered do not represent the real proton and neutron but rather some kind of idealized p and n. In calculating matrix elements for the real nucleons, corrections would then have to be made for pions and other strongly interacting particles which would renormalize the relative coefficient of the vector and axial vector current.

Strong interactions in fact would be expected to renormalize not only the axial current but also the vector current. After some mental effort one can see, however, that it is quite possible that the vector current need not be renormalized at all, as experimental clues hinted, when it was found that the muon coupling constant was the same as the Fermi coupling constant to within a few per cent. The extraction of the Fermi constant from the rate of O^{14} beta decay involves an additional assumption about nuclear forces unless the vector current for the weak interactions is not renormalized. In the decay the parent nucleus contains eight protons and six neutrons, while the daughter nucleus contains seven protons and seven neutrons. Now, there is a state in N^{14} which is the same as the ground state in O^{14} in the sense of isotopic spin. The nuclear forces are independent of whether the nucleons are protons or neutrons, and therefore in every system of seven protons and seven neutrons there is a state which has essentially the same character as any state that exists for eight protons and six neutrons. (The inverse is not true because of the exclusion principle.) The sister state of the ground state of N^{14}, which has isotopic spin 1, lies lower in energy than that state and so the nitrogen nucleus does decay to its sister state. Since the kinematic features of the wave functions of the initial and final states are the same, the matrix element of the integral of the beta-decay charge density involves simply an isotopic spin Clebsch-Gordan coefficient, which is just $\sqrt{2}$. The calculation is not exact because the violation of isotopic spin invariance by electromagnetism destroys the perfect overlap of the wave functions, but this effect is at most a half per cent.

This matrix element is almost the sole example of an accurate calculation in nuclear physics, because one does not have to know any nuclear physics to calculate it. This trick is possible only at very low momentum transfer where the integral of the fourth component of the charge density becomes the operator for the total charge. Since the isotopic spin is conserved by the strong interactions we have therefore no renormalization of such matrix elements.

The assumption that the vector part of the beta-decay current is a component of the isotopic-spin current, implies also that two pions must have a well-defined weak coupling to two leptons. It is quite easy to see how strong the coupling is by using our electricity analogue. Since the isotopic spin of the pion is the same as that for O^{14}, namely one, we again get a factor of $\sqrt{2}$ for the matrix element. Similarly, there will be matrix elements of the currents between two kaons, two Σ hyperons, and so on. We propose that this, in fact, is the way the world works and, consequently, that the vector part of the beta-decay coupling which conserves hypercharge is not renormalized.

Electromagnetic corrections to weak interaction matrix elements

When the coupling constants for the Fermi beta decay and that for the muon beta decay are determined in the manner indicated, they turn out not to be equal as we had expected, but to differ by a few per cent. To be more accurate, the vector coupling constant determined from the rate of decay of O^{14} is 0.985 times the muon beta-decay constant, whereas, that determined from the decay of Al^{26} is 0.975 G_{μ}. In doing calculations we have a problem with certain relativistic electromagnetic corrections. We are trying to investigate a difference of a few per cent and the order of magnitude of electromagnetic effects is the same. Because the agreement between the two coupling constants is so close, one is reluctant to guess that the idea of equality is wrong ... . One would prefer to speculate that the discrepancy may be due to something else, such as a misunderstanding in the calculation of the electromagnetic corrections. It is therefore worth while to discuss the question of how accurately we know such corrections. In computing them for the decay of the muon we have no problem; the electromagnetic structure of the muon is well known and it has no other anomalous moments. The calculation goes through straightforwardly. However, in calculating proton corrections to the disintegration of the neutron we get into difficulties because the integrals diverge. The divergence is due to the anomalous magnetic moment of the nucleons. Now, when we have to compute such integrals, frankly we do not get completely satisfactory answers; depending on where one puts the cut-off one might at first be able to account for any discrepancy. However, in spite of this apparent uncertainty, it turns out that the answer is not very sensitive to the cut-off. In fact, the analysis is not uncertain by more than about ± ½ per cent. Even though the electromagnetic effects are larger than this, the biggest part of them can be understood without serious ambiguity.

The uncertainty in the radiative correction is expected to be quite small because it is really a correction to a correction. Let me explain the origin of the major part of the correction by referring to the oxygen decay. In this case we would have the following types of diagrams

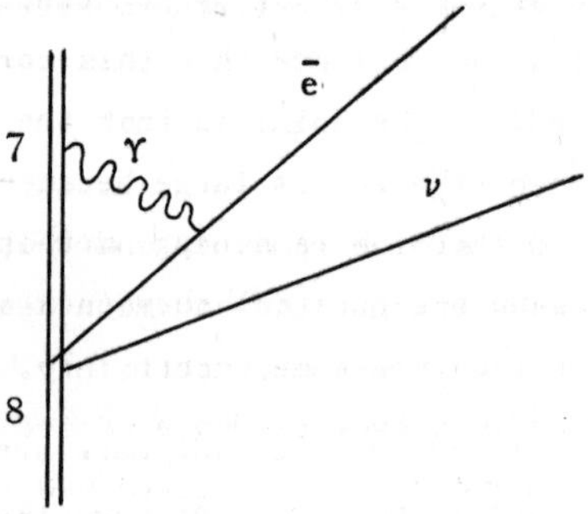

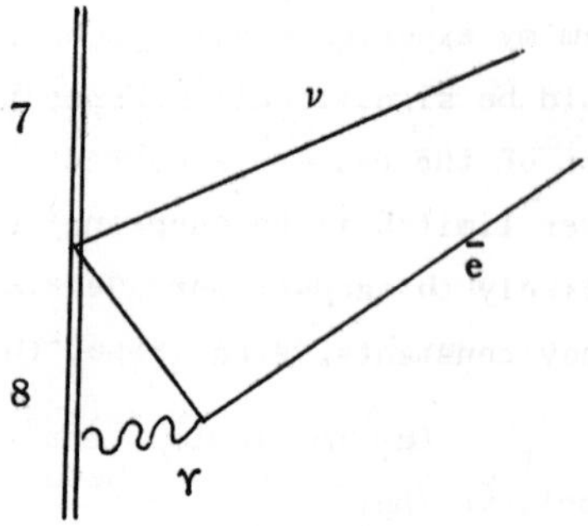

In these diagrams we see that the virtual photon interacts both with an object of charge 7 and one of charge 8. The usual procedure would be to use a Coulomb wave function for the outgoing positrons (that is, for a field of a nucleus with charge 7). This results in a well-known correction to the f value. But the second diagram is not included correctly in this procedure. The approximation actually includes the following diagram

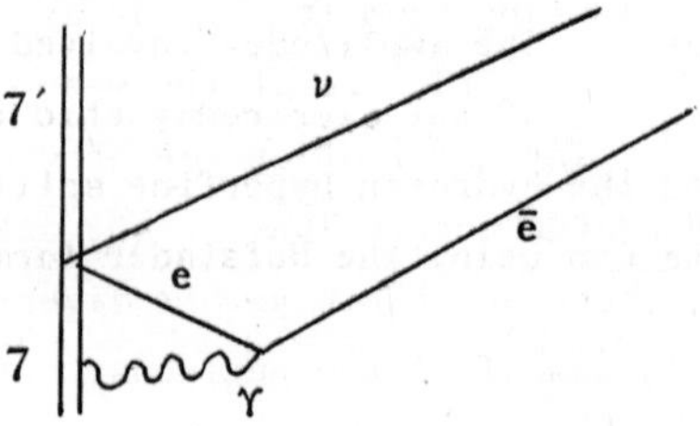

in which, outside the nucleus, an electron-positron pair is created by the virtual photon which interacts with a charge of seven units. These two diagrams A and B have to be added, and are comparable in strength for a relativistic positron. In fact, f accounts for the sum of A and C. The error is the difference of diagram B and C, which is a diagram like C but with charge 1 on the nucleus. When this is calculated, disregarding recoil of the nucleus, one obtains $(e^2/2\pi)\ \ln (X/E)$ where E is the positron energy and X is ∞. Actually, the result should be modified for recoil and magnetic-moment corrections etc., the result being to replace X by some unknown of the order M_p. If I stop the integral at about $2M_p$, I will then have to add an unknown amount to account for the high energy piece of the integral. It is this unknown amount that is estimated to be of the order of ½ per cent. From my experience with such calculations I do not believe that this correction could be significantly larger than ½ per cent. The point is that the major part of the radiative correction is well known (the log is large because the lower limit E is so much smaller than M_p) and that the remaining part is very unlikely to account for the discrepancy between the nuclear and muon weak decay constants, even though the calculation involves some uncertainty.

Can the radiative correction calculation ever be made more precisely? I believe that it can and would like to propose a programme for theorists. What is really needed is an evaluation of the accuracy of the approximation of keeping only a one-particle intermediate state in the calculation of matrix elements for the product of two currents. Many theorists profess to believe that such an approximation is quite good, but they really lack any reason to support their stand. It is not possible to compute the degree of validity of this approximation, but if we analyse suitable experiments, we ought to be able to obtain a very good answer to our problem. One should conduct a careful investigation of high-energy Compton scattering off a proton, and of the hyperfine structure of hydrogen. The amplitudes involved in these phenomena are matrix elements of the square of the electromagnetic current. Now Platzman and Iddings have computed the hydrogen hyperfine splitting, keeping only the proton intermediate state and using the Hofstader form factors at each vertex, and their result disagrees with experiment. However, their work is valuable because it provides an evaluation of the accuracy of this type of approximation, and it is on this basis that I believe our estimate of the radiative correction to nuclear beta decay is good to ½ per cent. It would be useful to have another check on this approximation by studying Compton scattering, and it is likely that such a study will provide additional substantiation for our estimate of the ½ per cent accuracy.

Strangeness changing weak decays 2nd LECTURE

The beta decay of nucleons and the decay of the muon are only two examples of the weak decays. There are many more and it is now our task to outline the possible terms which are required in the weak interaction coupling in order that all types of decays may be accounted for, at least qualitatively. To do this let us use a more convenient symbolism. Let us abbreviate the V-A current term $[\bar{A}\gamma_\alpha(1 + i\gamma_5)B]$ by $(\bar{A}B)$. In this language, to describe nuclear beta decay, we need a coupling term of the form $(\bar{\nu}e)(\bar{n}p)$, together with its Hermitian conjugate. In our discussion of neutron decay we have seen that such a form is correct only qualitatively. Indications are that the vector current is not renormalized and, consequently, that additional terms for other strongly interacting particles such as pions, K's, etc. must be present.

We have speculated that the vector beta-decay current which is strangeness preserving is a suitable component of the isotopic spin current, which is conserved. For that reason the theory we have discussed is called the conserved vector current (CVC) theory. (It is well to remind ourselves that our main requirement was that the vector coupling constant should not be modified by the strong interactions. An easy way to guarantee this is to propose that the vector current is conserved, but that may not be the only way.) The axial vector coupling constant differs from its ideal value [1.26 instead of 1*)]. Some people consider this a small deviation so that they are tempted

*) Bernardini has told me that Miss Wu now finds the ratio of the axial vector to the vector nuclear beta-decay coupling constants to be 1.16.

to supply some reason for such a relatively small renormalization. Many attempts have been made to construct a conserved axial current, but all have failed because of mass terms. However, it is by no means self-evident that we cannot set up the axial current so that its coupling is essentially unchanged by renormalization, even though such a current will not be conserved.

The decay of the muon shows that the weak coupling must contain a term of the form $(\bar{\nu}e)(\bar{\mu}\bar{\nu}_\mu)$, and today it is known definitely that ν_μ, which we might call the neutretto, is distinct from ν, the neutrino. Since bound muons disappear faster than free ones, we also know that there must be a term like $(\bar{\nu}_\mu\mu)(\bar{n}p)$. By measuring the degree to which the muon lifetime is shortened in various nuclei, we can get a pretty fair idea of the strength of the muonic lepton coupling to nucleons. The experimental evidence allows one to assume that the strength of this coupling is the same as the electron beta-decay coupling strength, which is also the same as G to a few per cent.

These three terms are sufficient to give rise to many other observed decays. For example, the modes $\pi \to \mu + \nu_\mu$ and $\pi \to e + \nu$ would be expected qualitatively because they can proceed through an intermediate $\bar{N}N$ state which is coupled to leptons*). In fact, all weak decays which conserve hypercharge are predicted by the three types of weak coupling already considered. But to account for the observed strangeness changing decays we need to postulate at least three more types of weak coupling. Consider the following three decays of the K meson: $K \to \mu + \nu_\mu$, $K \to \pi + e + \nu$, and $K \to \pi + \pi$. We see that we need a strangeness changing term, which, without prejudice as to its true nature, we shall abbreviate by $(\bar{\Lambda}p)$, coupled to both types of the leptons, and to strongly interacting particles with zero strangeness: $(\bar{\nu}_\mu\mu)(\bar{\Lambda}p)$, $(\bar{\nu}e)(\bar{\Lambda}p)$, and $(\bar{p}n)(\bar{\Lambda}p)$. These three terms are sufficient because all the strangeness changing weak decays, about which there is no dispute experimentally, obey the selection rule that the change in strangeness equals the change in the charge $\Delta S/\Delta Q = +1$. Now one would guess that the strength of the last three types of

*) For example, π^+ goes virtually to p and antineutron via strong interactions. The proton then goes to N, e^+ and ν, the neutron and antineutron annihilating.

weak coupling might be the same as the first three which conserve hypercharge, but it turns out that this is not the case. The strangeness changing decay rates are weaker by an order of magnitude from what would be expected if the strength G were universal.

The current-current theory

These six terms are somewhat messy and the question is whether things can be organized in a more pleasing way. One idea that pops into view is to combine the four currents into one grand weak interaction current

$$J_\alpha = (\bar{\nu}e) + (\bar{\nu}_\mu \mu) + a(\bar{p}n) + b(\bar{p}\Lambda) ,$$

with the coefficients, a and b, to be determined by some symmetry principles, and to suggest that the weak coupling is simply a current-current interaction $1/\sqrt{2}\, G\bar{J}_\alpha J_\alpha$. In the cross-products one finds the six types of terms that are required experimentally. Such a proposal automatically eliminates neutral lepton currents, for which there is no evidence experimentally. One may ask why we write charged currents. The answer is that if we rewrite for example $(\bar{\nu}e)(\bar{\mu}\nu_\mu)$ as $-(\bar{\nu}\nu_\mu)(\bar{\mu}e)$, and then pursue the idea of a current-current coupling the decay $K^0 \rightarrow \mu + \bar{e}$ would be predicted. Since such a decay is definitely not seen, we feel that the charged current hypothesis is much to be preferred.

The current-current interaction not only leads to the six desired cross terms from the four basic types of current, but also predicts four new types of parity non-conserving interactions, which are the diagonal terms in the product. Three of them will be extremely difficult to observe; for example, the diagonal term $(\bar{\nu}e)(\bar{e}\nu)$ leads to a direct parity non-conserving scattering cross-section between neutrinos and electrons, but since the cross-section is so tiny and neutrinos are so hard to detect, the existence of such a term has not yet been verified experimentally. However, experiments in nuclear physics can be designed which are extremely sensitive to the existence of a parity-violating contribution to the nuclear forces. Recently, Felix Boehm at Caltech has measured the circular polarization of the gamma rays produced in a partially forbidded M1 transition in a heavy ellipsoidal nucleus. This polarization can be non-zero only through an admixture of the parity forbidden

El matrix element. Boehm found good evidence for a small parity violation in the nuclear forces. Such an effect is predicted by the $(\bar{n}p)(\bar{p}n)$ diagonal term in the current-current theory. Because of strong renormalizations which are not calculable, it is impossible to state whether or not the size and sign of the experimental effect agree with the prediction of the current-current theory of weak interactions. The order of magnitude of the effect nevertheless, is correct, and hence this does constitute a qualitative verification of the hypothesis.

If the weak interaction does have the current-current form an appealing theoretical possibility is that a new vector meson exists, which mediates the interaction in the same way that the photon mediates the interaction between two charge currents. Such a new field will give rise through the following type of diagram

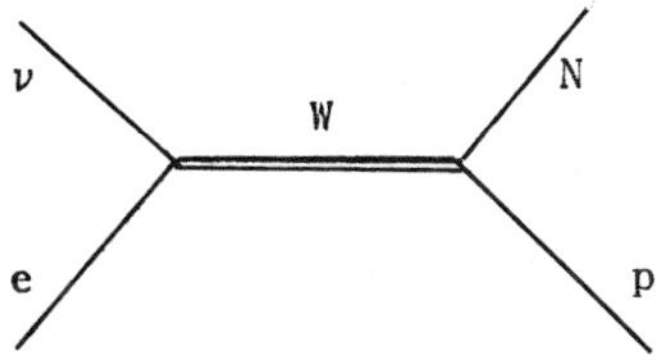

to a weak interaction between two currents of the form

$$4\pi\ e_W^2\ \bar{J}_\alpha \left(\delta_{\alpha\beta} - q_\alpha q_\beta/m_W^2\right) J_\beta/(q^2 - m_W^2)\ .$$

In this formula, m_W is the mass of the intermediate boson, and e_W is its coupling to the weak interaction current. For $q << m_W$, the interaction reduces to our current-current form once we identify $4\pi\, e_W^2/m_W^2$ with $g/\sqrt{2}$!

The charged vector meson theory, like the four-fermion point interaction theory, is not renormalizable, but this never bothers me. All of our theories are wrong at high energies, and renormalizability only refers to whether this universal disease can be swept under the rug for the analysis of low-energy phenomena. I personally have felt no particular favour for renormalizable theories, and will just as well accept one that is unrenormalizable as one that is renormalizable. It has never been proved that renormalizable theories are superior because they are consistent; indeed, it seems to me likely that renormalizable theories suffer from ghost difficulties at high energies. I make a point of this because in my later analysis I shall continue to discuss non-renormalizable theories, thus opposing the conventional practice, and shall make no apology for doing so.

From the size of the weak-boson coupling constant e_W, one can estimate the production rate of these particles. Once threshold energy has been passed sufficiently, they should be produced copiously enough to be seen readily if they exist at all.

Pion decay

Let us now turn to the question of the extension of the idea of non-renormalizability from the vector current to the axial current. At the same time we will study the treatment of another prominent non-strangeness changing decay, the decay of the pion. To clarify the ideas involved, we stick to a model of the universe in which nucleons and pions are the only strongly interacting particles. As already explained, one expects the pion to decay into leptons just because of the existence of the following type of diagram:

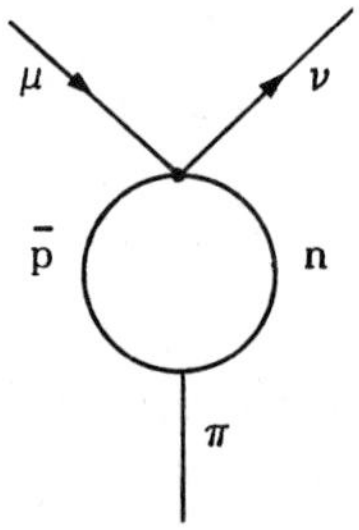

In the coupling of the pion to the nucleon loop one usually sees the Dirac matrix $g\gamma_5$. However, we shall come back later and discuss an alternate form for the vertex, which I prefer. The nucleon loop is coupled to leptons by both a γ_μ matrix and a $\gamma_\mu\gamma_5$ matrix. For this problem only the $\gamma_\mu\gamma_5$ term contributes, since the pion is a pseudoscalar particle. This loop cannot be calculated because it is divergent. Even if it were not, one would not believe the answer because pion corrections to it would be very important.

However, the form it gives for the matrix element

$$\sqrt{8\pi}\; q_\alpha F_\pi (\bar{\psi}_\mu \gamma_\alpha a \psi_\nu) ,$$

where q is the momentum of the pion, is the only possible invariant form for the amplitude. The number F_π is the result of all possible diagrams. We do not know it nor do we know how to calculate it.

Given this form for the amplitude we can calculate the decay rate using the Golden Rule given in the first lecture. It turns out to be

$$\frac{1}{\tau_\pi} = \left(F_\pi m_\pi\right)^2 \frac{m_\pi\; m_\mu^2}{2\; m_\pi^2} \left[\frac{m_\pi^2 - m_\mu^2}{m_\pi^2}\right]^2 .$$

Using the known decay rate of the charged pion, one finds that

$$F_\pi m_\pi = 5.95\times 10^{-8} .$$

Incdientally, the same mathematics hold for the decay of kaons into leptons, in which case $F_k m_k = 5.55\times 10^{-8}$.

To describe the decay of $\pi \rightarrow e+\nu$, the amplitude would have the same invariant structure. You will note that if the coupling constants are of the same order for both $(\bar{e}\nu)$ and $(\bar{\mu}\nu_\mu)$ the rate for decay into $(\bar{e}\nu)$ is severely inhibited. The inhibition is due to the fact that the charged lepton must come out with its spin aligned along its direction of motion. This is very difficult for electrons since their velocity is quite high and, in the weak interactions, particles prefer to be polarized in the opposite sense. The probability of right-hand polarization goes as I - V/2. The muons, on the other hand, are not highly relativistic and, consequently, not so greatly inhibited. Theoretically one finds the ratio:

$$\frac{\pi \rightarrow e+\nu}{\pi \rightarrow \mu+\nu_\mu} = 1.36\times 10^{-4} ,$$

where this theoretical estimate includes some radiative corrections.

The theoretical estimate for the ratio of the decay rates assumes that the coupling of $(\bar{e}\nu)$ and $(\bar{\mu}\nu_\mu)$ is the same for weak interactions. Experiment agrees with that result to within two per cent; that means that within one per cent the electron and muon couple in the same way in the weak interactions. The pion decay experiment thus provides the best check of the hypothesis that the strength of the muon coupling is the same as the electron coupling in the weak interactions. This is a much better result than is obtained from studying μ capture in complicated nuclei. Note that this check is entirely independent of the value of F_π which is not calculable.

Is there some theoretical argument for determining the pion decay amplitude F_π? It is a delightful problem because it is apparently hopeless. However, there appeared a paper by Goldberger and Treiman, who found a formula for F_π. The argument given by Goldberger and Treiman is inadequate since they ignored terms of the same order as the ones that were kept. Similar formulae had also been discovered before by several other people who had not pursued them because they did not agree well with experiment. Goldberger and Treiman's contribution was to put renormalized constants into the formula, thus obtaining much better agreement with experiment.

In this lecture I should like to describe my first approach to a derivation of the Goldberger-Treiman relation. In the next lecture I shall discuss Gell-Mann's refinement of this approach.

To understand the ideas involved in this derivation, let us recall our attempt to construct the vector beta-decay current in such a way that it was not modified by renormalization. In our model universe of pions and nucleons one can show that if the coefficient A of the pion current, in the combination $(\bar{\psi}_\rho \gamma_\alpha \bar{\psi}_n) + A(\pi^- \partial_\alpha \pi^0 - \pi^0 \partial_\alpha \pi^-)$ is suitably chosen, the renormalized vector beta-decay coupling constant is the same as the bare vector-coupling constant. An obvious question is whether or not one can write the axial vector current in such a way that there is no renormalization. The answer to that, generally speaking, is that we cannot. Furthermore, there is some renormalization effect. Nevertheless, because the renormalization is small, one is tempted to construct the axial vector current in such a way that only a small renormalization would result. To study this question let us write a possible Lagrangian for our model universe

$$\mathcal{L} = \tfrac{1}{2}\,[(\nabla\varphi)^2 - m_0^2\varphi^2] + \bar{\psi}\,\not{\partial}\,\psi - \bar{\psi} M_0\,\psi$$
$$+ a_0\,\bar{\psi}\,\tau(\gamma_5 \not{\nabla}\,\Phi)\,\psi + e_W\left[\bar{\psi}\gamma_\mu\left(\frac{1+i\gamma_5}{2}\right)\tau_4\,\psi\right]W_\mu\ .$$

For the purpose of this lecture we neglect complications due to isotopic spin. The essential point is to get an idea, with the aid of a single model, which might be true in a more realistic description of nature. The first three terms in the above Lagrangian are those characterizing free meson and nucleon fields. The a_0 term describes the coupling of the nucleon field to the pseudoscalar mesons. The final term describes the coupling of the nucleon fields to intermediate vector bosons. It may be noted that in the pseudoscalar meson-nucleon coupling I have used a gradient form, which is called pseudovector coupling. For single pion interactions at low pion momenta, this form is equivalent to the conventional pseudoscalar coupling $\bar{\psi}\gamma_5\,\psi\varphi$, providing that one identifies the coefficient $2m_N a_0$ with the conventional coupling constant g_0. For two pion interactions there is a great distinction between pseudovector and pseudoscalar coupling. The absence of low-energy s wave scattering is compatible with the prediction of pseudovector coupling and very difficult to explain with pseudoscalar coupling. For this and other reasons I prefer the pseudovector form, and I do not care in the least that the pseudovector form belongs to the class of interactions called unrenormalizable. It is very difficult to check which of these couplings is more correct because calculations cannot be made for strong interactions, except possibly by noting the following fact. If, in any amplitude, we can extrapolate the pion four-momentum off the mass shell down to the point where it is zero (zero momentum and zero energy), then that amplitude should vanish in the case of pseudovector coupling. This is an interesting principle which should aid in developing good trial formulae for pion interactions, but it has not been used very much up to now.

In electricity we have the coupling of charged particles to the electromagnetic field A, in such a way that if one adds to A a pure gradient

$$A_\alpha \to A_\alpha + \partial_\alpha \lambda$$

it makes no difference. Let us pursue the idea of constructing the coupling for the weak interaction such that if we add a pure gradient $\nabla\lambda$, to the vector boson field W_α, then there is also no effect. For the vector part of the coupling there is no change if we have the W meson coupled to a current which is conserved, as we have already assumed. For the axial vector term the addition of the gradient leads to an extra term in the Lagrangian of the form

$$e_W[\psi_i \nabla\lambda \gamma_5 \tau_+ \psi] \ .$$

Can we cancel this? It turns out that we can, partially, if we use the pseudo-vector coupling. Suppose that when we change the W field by adding the gradient, we also change the pion field by

$$\varphi \to \varphi - \frac{e_W}{a_0} \lambda \ .$$

In that case the $a_0[\bar{\psi}\tau_+ \gamma_5 \not{\nabla}\varphi\psi]$ term will be modified in a way that exactly compensates the change in the weak interaction Lagrangian. The compensation is not exact because of the mass term in the pion field, and it is impossible to produce an exact compensation. However, having lived under the influence of Gell-Mann, who likes to suggest that if all the masses were zero there would be much greater symmetry in the Lagrangian, I shall disregard the mass term. Thus, neglecting the mass squared term in the free-pion field Lagrangian, the change is $-e_W/a_0 \partial_\alpha \varphi \partial_\alpha \lambda$ to the first order and this is compensated if we add a term $(e_W/a_0)\, \partial_\alpha \Phi W_\alpha$ to the Lagrangian. It is in this way that we obtain a definite prescription for the direct coupling of the pion to the weak-vector boson, or equivalently to lepton currents. Combining terms, it is seen that the axial vector current which is coupled to the W field is $e_W(\frac{1}{2} \psi \gamma_\alpha i\gamma_5 \psi + 1/a_0\, \partial$

The result of these considerations is to predict that there is a direct bare coupling of pions to leptons with a strength

$$F_{\pi}\ (\text{theoretical}) = \frac{G}{\sqrt{8\pi}\ a_0} = \frac{m_p G}{\sqrt{2\pi}\ g_0}$$

This would be the famous Goldberger-Treiman relation if G and g_0 were renormalized. G and g_0, which are coupling constants before renormalization, are unknown. Thus the problem is: what can be done with this formula? If, without justification, at this point one inserts for G the axial vector coupling constant for nuclear beta decay and for g_0 the experimental pion-nucleon coupling constant, then one finds for F_{π} (theoretical) the value 5.5×10^{-8}. This value is not very different from the experimental result (5.95×10^{-8}). The difference may have something to do with inaccurate analysis of the effects of renormalization.

We now have to discuss why it is legitimate to replace these bare-coupling constants in the Goldberger-Treiman relation by their renormalized experimental values. To do this we shall have to inquire as to how higher order diagrams with many pions lead to a renormalization of the coupling constants. There is a clever way to do this, by which one can prove the theorem in a few lines. However, since the ideas of renormalization are not self-evident to everyone here, we shall study a more detailed treatment.

We begin by defining some terms. First, the unrenormalized axial vector beta-decay coupling to nucleons, which is $G_V \bar{n} \gamma_{\mu} \gamma_5 p$, (where we have assumed that $G_{A(\text{bare})} = -G_{V(\text{bare})} = -G_V$), and which is represented by

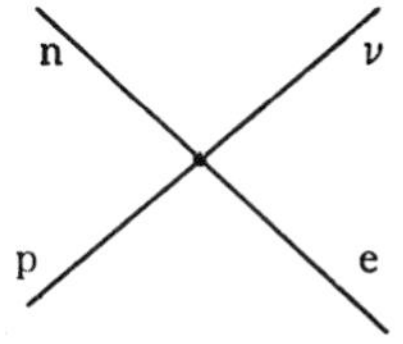

is modified by pion corrections, for example

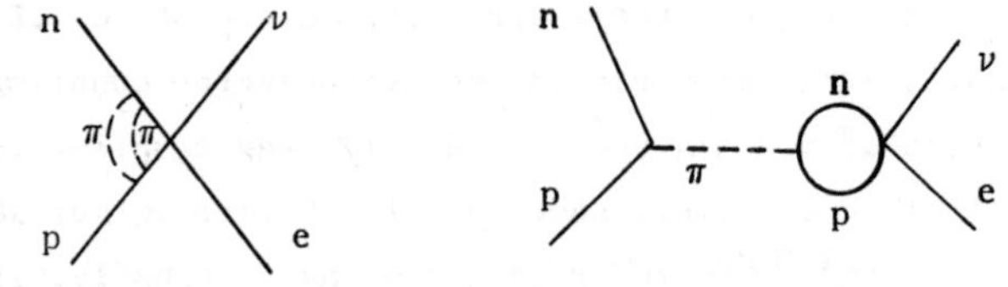

so that the resultant effective beta-decay coupling is $G_A \bar{n} \gamma_\mu \gamma_5 p$. The effective coupling constant is G_A only in those cases where the leptons effectively carry off zero momentum. When the momentum transfer becomes large, the strength of the coupling will be modified. We may indicate this by a function $G_A(q^2)$; $G_A(0) \hat{=} G_A$. Theoreticians call the ratio of the bare-coupling constant to the experimental one a renormalization constant Z_A. That is $G_A/G_{A(bare)} = 1/Z_A$.

In our subsequent considerations we shall encounter the following nucleon loop

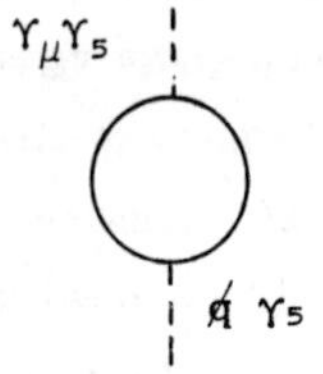

together with all the pion correction diagrams, e.g.

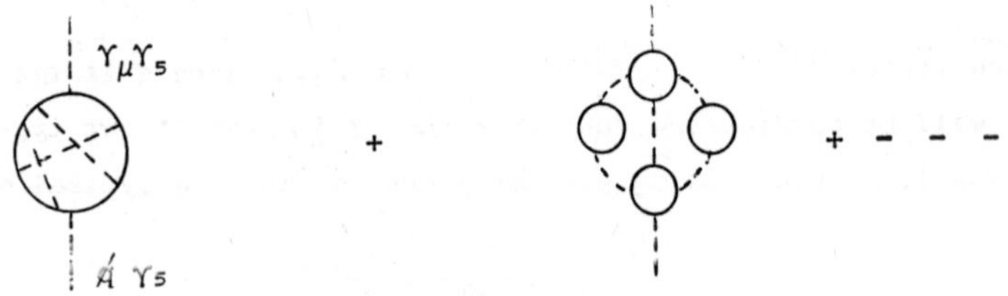

The sum of all these loop diagrams must be a vector. Since the only vector around is q_μ, the momentum transfer at each of the two vertices, then the sum must be represented mathematically by $q_\mu K(q^2)$. $K(q^2)$ does not blow up as $q^2 \to 0$

One would expect that $K(q^2)$ is slowly varying over momentum transfers comparable to the pion mass, the main variation only occurring for q of order of the nucleon mass. Although it is true that there are intermediate states of mass as low as $3m_\pi$, these do not come in strongly in the pseudovector coupling model. For, if each of the three pion momenta are of order m_π, the coupling is weak (as $f^2 = 0.08$). Strong effective couplings come only for higher values of q, and hence not close to the pole with three intermediate pions. Finally, if we consider the sum of all diagrams of the form

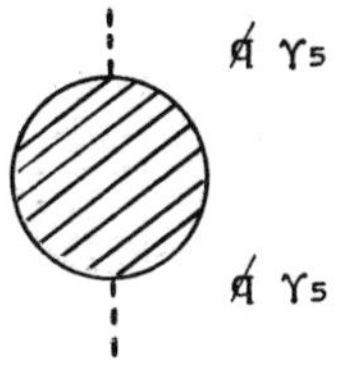

the answer is $q^2K(q^2)$. The blob stands for the sum of all intermediate states except a single pion.

Let us now go on to consider the renormalization of the pion exchange diagram. The simplest diagram giving rise to a nuclear force is

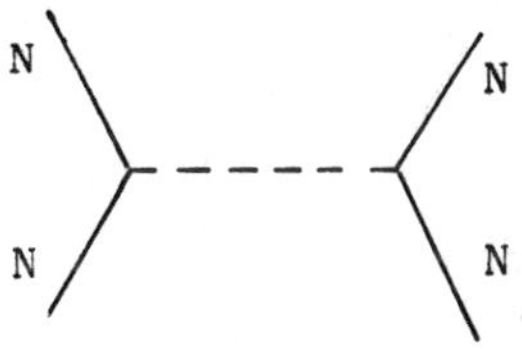

At each vertex the pion couples through $a_0\not{q}\gamma_5$, where q is the momentum transfer. There will be corrections to this exchange diagram of two types. First, each vertex will be modified by virtual pions, of which a typical diagram is

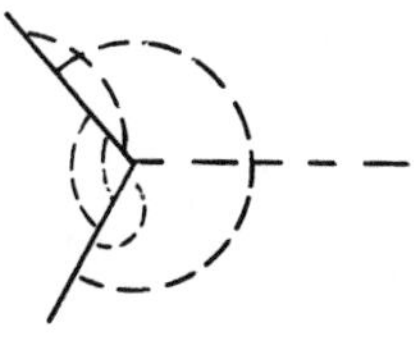

Secondly, the propagation of the pion will not be simply  ,
but will be

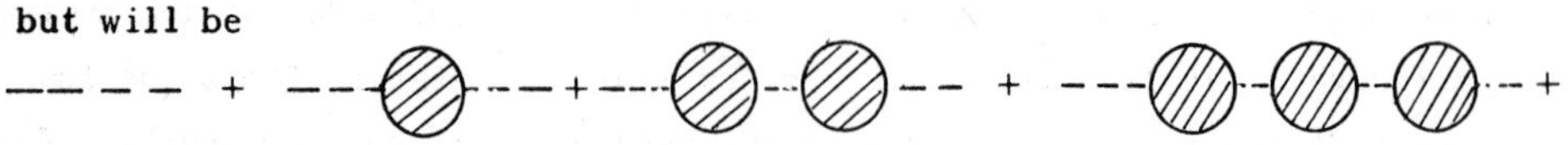

The result of including all these corrections will be the experimental pion-exchange contribution to the scattering amplitude, which is

$$a^2_{exp}\ \not{q}\gamma_5 \frac{1}{q^2 - m_\pi^2} \not{q}\gamma_5 \ .$$

Let us go through this more slowly for the case of pion-nucleon scattering. The single bare-pion exchange diagram gives rise to an amplitude

$$a_0^2\ \not{q}\gamma_5\ (1/q^2 - m_0^2)\not{q}\gamma_5 \ .$$

Suppose we consider still, a single bare-pion exchange but correct the vertices to all orders,

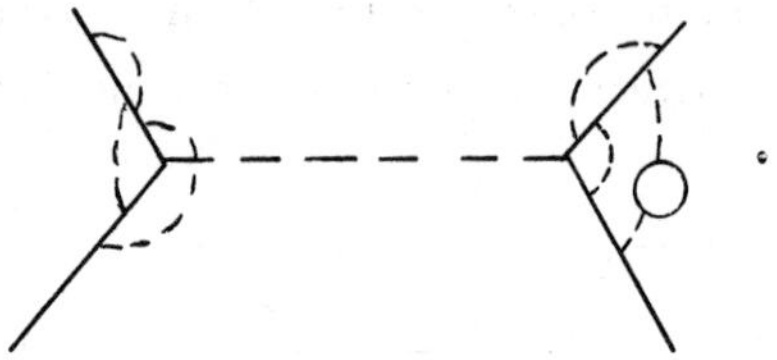

The mathematical contribution to the amplitude is

$$\left[\frac{a_0}{Z_A(q^2)}\right]^2 \not{q}\gamma_5(1/q^2 - m_0^2)\ \not{q}\gamma_5 \ ,$$

since, in the discussion of the axial vector beta decay we defined $[Z_A(q^2)]^{-1}$ to be the sum of all vertex corrections for axial vector coupling. Next, if we consider the sum of all diagrams with a single generalized nucleon loop breaking the pion exchange:

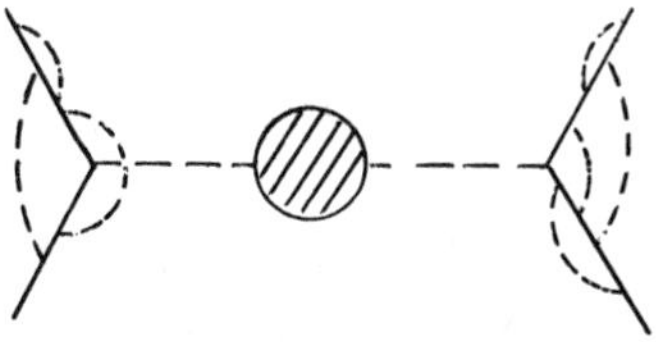

we get

$$\left[\frac{a_0}{Z_A(q^2)}\right]^2 \not{q}\gamma_5 \frac{1}{q^2 - \pi_0^2} \; a_0^2\, q^2 K(q^2) \frac{1}{q^2 - m_0^2} \not{q}\gamma_5 \; .$$

If we add another generalized nucleon loop to the pion propagator, we multiply the preceding amplitude by the factor

$$a_0^2\, q^2 K(q^2) \frac{1}{q^2 - m_0^2} \quad .$$

Evidently, if we add up such diagrams with all numbers of nucleon loops in the pion propagator, then we are just adding up a geometrical series and the final answer is

$$\left[\frac{a_0}{Z_A(q^2)}\right]^2 \not{q}\gamma_5 \frac{1}{q^2 - m_0^2 - a_0^2\, q^2 K(q^2)} \not{q}\gamma_5 \; .$$

We must now compare this result with the experimental pion-exchange contribution by noting that the amplitude must have a pole at $q^2 = m_\pi^2$, where m_π is the experimental pion mass. We see that

$$m_\pi^2 = m_0^2 + a_0^2 m_\pi^2 K(m_\pi^2) \quad \text{or} \quad \frac{m_\pi^2}{m_0^2} = \frac{1}{1 - a_0^2 K(m_\pi^2)} \quad .$$

Also by expanding the corrected propagator near $q^2 = m_\pi^2$, we find that

$$[q^2 - m_0^2 - a_0^2 K(q^2)] \approx [1 - a_0^2 K(m_\pi^2) - a_0^2 m_\pi^2 K'(m_\pi^2)] \cdot (q^2 - m_\pi^2)$$

so that the experimental pion-nucleon coupling constant is related to the bare pion-nucleon coupling by

$$a^2_{\exp} = \left[\frac{a_0}{Z_A(m_\pi^2)}\right]^2 \frac{1}{[1 - a_0^2\, K(m_\pi^2) - a_0^2\, m_\pi^2\, K'(m_\pi^2)]} \; .$$

The theoreticians like to call the renormalization factor, 1/[ ], for the pion Z_π.

So much for the discussion of the axial vector vertex and the pion propagator renormalization constants. We now turn to an evaluation of the pion decay rate in terms of the nuclear beta-decay axial vector coupling constant. To get all the renormalization constants straight, we will consider the pion decay under the assumption that the pion is produced off a nucleon. Thus, we shall consider the matrix element for a neutron to go into a proton, plus a lepton pair at a momentum transfer near the pion pole. Assuming that there is a direct pion-lepton weak coupling, the simplest diagram contributing to the nuclear beta decay which gives rise to a pole at the pion mass is

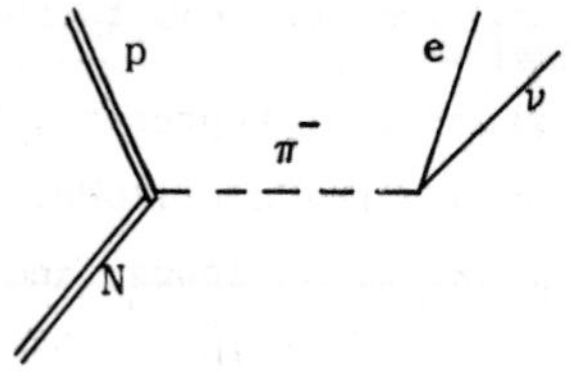

The direct nucleon-lepton term gives no pole so we leave it out. Another contribution of the same type is

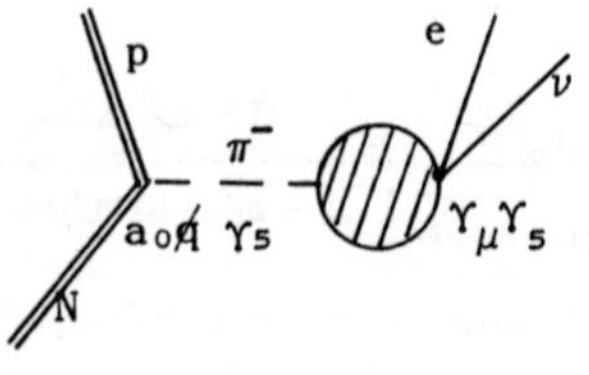

To these two diagrams we must add those diagrams with two bare-pion propagators

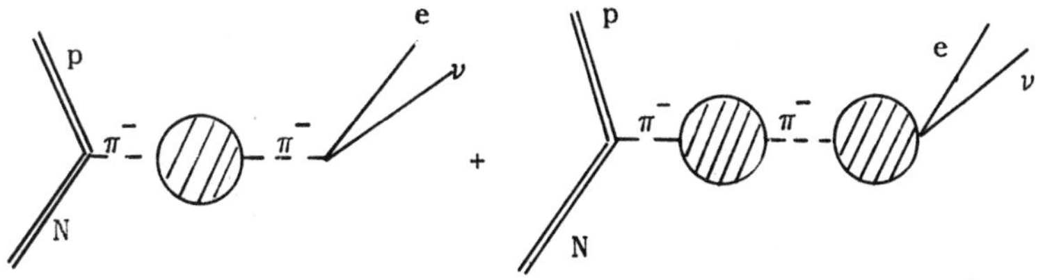

and three, and four and so on. Again the terms can be summed because they form geometric series. The result of all diagrams of this type is

$$\frac{a_0}{Z_A(q^2)} \not{A}\gamma_5 \frac{1}{q^2 - m_0^2 - a_0^2\, q^2 K(q^2)} \left[- \frac{G_{A(bare)}}{a_0}\, q_\alpha + a_0 q_\alpha K(q^2) G_{A(bare)} \right] (\bar{\psi}_e \gamma_\alpha a \psi_\nu) \,.$$

In the square bracket the coefficient $-G_{A(bare)}/a_0$ is the bare coupling of the pion to the lepton field, which we found earlier. The term $a_0 q_\alpha K(q^2) G_{A(bare)}$ represents the coupling of a bare pion to the generalized nucleon loop times the axial vector coupling of the nucleon loop to the lepton current.

Now this sum of diagrams must represent, near the pion pole, the dominant part of the nuclear beta-decay amplitude, which we can write down using the experimental coupling of pions to nucleons, and the experimental amplitude for a pion to decay into leptons. That is,

$$a_{exp} \frac{1}{g^2 - m_\pi^2} \sqrt{8\pi}\, F_\pi q_\alpha \bar{\psi}_e \gamma_\alpha a \psi_\nu \,.$$

Equating the two expressions near the pion pole, one finds

$$F_\pi = - \frac{G_{A(bare)}}{\sqrt{8\pi}\, a_{exp}\, Z_A(m_\pi^2)} \frac{1 - a_0^2 K(m_\pi^2)}{1 - a_0^2 \left[K(m_\pi^2) + m_\pi^2 K'(m_\pi^2) \right]} \,.$$

Recalling that the experimental nuclear beta-decay constant is $G_A = G_{A(\text{bare})}/Z_A(0)$ we see that we get the Goldberger-Treiman relation in terms of experimental coupling strength, except for a factor which is a ratio of renormalization functions

$$\frac{Z_A(0)}{Z_A(m_\pi^2)} \cdot \frac{1 - a_0^2\, K(m_\pi^2)}{1 - a_0^2\, [K(m_\pi^2) + m_\pi^2\, K'(m_\pi^2)]} \;.$$

Since the functions $Z_A(q^2)$ and $K(q^2)$ presumably vary appreciably only for q^2 of order m_N^2, the above ratio should be quite close to one. One expects, therefore, that the Goldberger-Treiman relationship should be quite good. Experimentally this relationship holds to eight per cent.

I shall now describe a more sophisticated way to get the same result. Our theory states that, in the limit that the pion mass goes to zero, if the lepton current is replaced by a pure gradient, the axial vector amplitude should then vanish. Let us now consider the beta decay of the nucleon. We would ordinarily write down the amplitude as the sum of two terms. One of them is the direct axial-vector coupling:

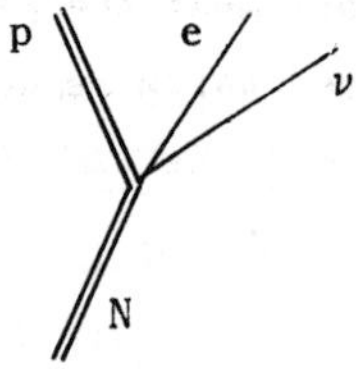

$$= G_A(\bar{p}\gamma_\alpha \gamma_5\, n)\,(\bar{e}\gamma_\alpha\, a_\nu) \;.$$

The other is the coupling through the pion:

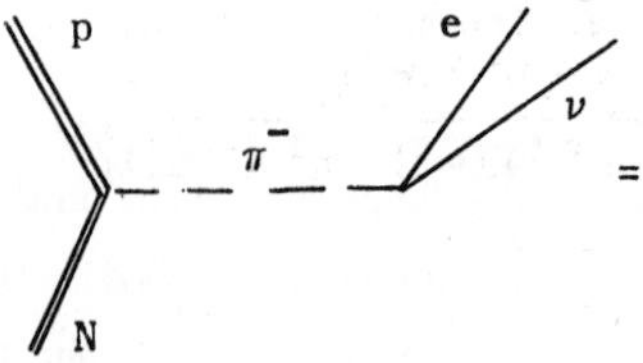

$$= a_{\exp}(\bar{p}\gamma_5 \not{q} n)\,\frac{1}{q^2 - m_\pi^2}\,\sqrt{8\pi}\; F_\pi q_\alpha \cdot (\bar{e}\gamma_\alpha a_\nu) \;.$$

In the limit $m_\pi \to 0$, the sum of these two must vanish when the lepton current $(\bar{e}\gamma_\alpha a\nu)$, is replaced by q_α, i.e.

$$G_A + \sqrt{8\pi}\; F_\pi\, a_{exp} = 0 \;.$$

This is the Goldberger-Treiman relation! The reason we apparently do not have a small correction is that we have skipped over a small point. If the pion mass were zero then the axial-vector coupling constant G_A, and the pion-nucleon coupling constant a_{exp}, would be different from their true values. It is this small change which is represented by the ratio of the renormalization constants that we encountered in the more detailed argument.

We can argue that the coupling strengths would not change materially in the gradient coupling theory if the pion mass went to zero. This is because pions with small momentum are effectively decoupled. Pions with momenta of the order m_π are coupled with a strength of only 0.08. Only when the pion momentum gets as large as a nucleon mass does the coupling tend to 15. When the pions have a high momentum, the fact that they have a mass is unimportant. Thus, the renormalization factors for the coupling due to pions will be the same, to an excellent approximation, when the pions have zero mass as when they have the physical mass. It is for this reason that I believe that the Goldberger-Treiman relation should be accurate.

In working with the field theory model described in the previous lecture we may notice a certain property of the axial vector current. The divergence of this current is proportional to the bare-pion field operator. In taking matrix elements, the axial vector current has to be renormalized in order to get G_A and the pion-field operator suffers a renormalization. These renormalization factors are not too different from unity. When this observation is analysed it results in the Goldberger-Treiman relation.

Recall that the matrix element of the axial current between two nucleons consisted of two terms. One was a $\gamma_\mu\gamma_5$ type coupling and another term, which arose via a virtual pion, was proportional to $q_\mu\gamma_5$. If we now compute the divergence of the axial vector current with $m_\pi^2 \neq 0$, we find that the contribution of the second term, the induced pseudoscalar term, goes to zero as $q^2 \to 0$. Consider now the matrix element of the pion-field operator between two nucleons. Since the source of the pion field is $ig/2M\ (\bar{n} \not{q} \gamma_5 p)$ and the source is equal to $(\Box^2 - m_0^2)\Phi$, we see that the matrix element of the pion-field operator is equal to

$$\left(\frac{i g_0}{2M}\right) \frac{(\bar{n} q \gamma_5 p)}{q^2 - m_0^2} .$$

Equating this expression with the matrix element of the divergence of the axial vector current we get again the Goldberger-Treiman relation.

Gell-Mann abstracted this result by assuming only that the divergence of the axial vector was proportional to the pion field $\nabla_\alpha J_\alpha^A = K\Phi$, without getting the constant of proportionality, K, from my specific theory. He then calculated the divergence of the nuclear-axial vector matrix element in terms of K, and the decay rate of the pion in terms of K. If one considers the ratio of these two amplitudes the factors of K drop out and one gets the Goldberger-Treiman relation.

More recently Gell-Mann has refined the argument by dropping all references to field operators, but I shall not give that argument.

Introduction to SU_3 — 3rd LECTURE

It is time, in our study of the weak interactions, to consider those decays which violate the conservation of hypercharge. Some understanding of these has been obtained with the help of SU_3 symmetry considerations and we therefore turn now to a short discussion of SU_3.

Let me begin by reviewing isotopic spin or SU_2. Suppose we have two particles with identical dynamical properties as far as a large group of interactions are concerned, e.g. the strong interactions, but which differ when another type of interaction, e.g. electromagnetic, is considered. Let them be a neutral particle $A \equiv A^0$, and a negatively charged particle $B \equiv B^-$, and let us assign to each of them an eigenvalue for the z component of isotopic spin: $+\frac{1}{2}$ for A, and $-\frac{1}{2}$ for B. The particles are assumed to have corresponding antiparticles $\bar{A}$ and $\bar{B}$, the quantum numbers of which are the opposite to those of the corresponding particle. By considering the states of two objects, one can generate states with isotopic spin 1 and 0, from these isodoublets. For example, if we consider new basis states A and B which are related to A′ and B′ by unitary transformations, then the state of an antiparticle and a particle, which is unchanged by the transformation, is $(\bar{A}A + \bar{B}B)/\sqrt{2}$. That state is therefore an isosinglet; i.e. it has $I = 0$. Under the unitary transformations, the three other orthonormal states $\bar{A}B$, $(\bar{A}A - \bar{B}B)/2$ and $\bar{B}A$, are transformed into linear combinations of each other, so that they form an isotopic triplet, i.e. $I = 1$. Let us call these three states by a new set of names so that we recall immediately that they form a triplet; in analogy with the Σ hyperons we use the symbol σ:

$$\sigma^- = -\bar{A}B, \quad \sigma^0 = -(\bar{A}A - \bar{B}B)/\sqrt{2}, \quad \sigma^+ = \bar{B}A$$

and in analogy with the Λ^0 hyperon we designate the isotopic singlet state by λ^0:

$$\lambda^0 = -(\bar{A}A + \bar{B}B)/\sqrt{2} \; .$$

Two basic objects allow us to construct all states which differ in their isotopic spin properties. However, in order to construct states which differ in another quantum number, say hypercharge, we have to introduce a third basic object. Thus, we add to our set of A and B a third particle $C \equiv C^-$, which has the same dynamical characteristics for a restricted set of interactions and which is negatively charged. We define its isotopic spin so that C forms an isotopic singlet. Under unitary transformations generated by isotopic- spin operators, C is not mixed with A and B. We define also a quantum number, e.g. hypercharge, which is -1 for C and 0 for A and B. With three basic objects it is interesting to see what happens when, in analogy to the procedure for isotopic transformations, we study the effects of unitary transformations on states composed of several of the three particles A, B, C, and the corresponding transformations on their antiparticles $\bar{A}$, $\bar{B}$ and $\bar{C}$.

If we concentrate on the states formed from a particle and an antiparticle, of which there are nine, we find that the state

$$\alpha = (\bar{A}A + \bar{B}B + \bar{C}C)/\sqrt{3}$$

is unchanged by such transformations and thus transforms as a singlet, whereas the other eight orthonormal states are transformed among themselves by a general change of the three basis states. The other eight, therefore, form an irreducible octet, which we display below:

Chart 1

$$-\underline{(\bar{A}C)} \qquad \underline{(\bar{B}C)}$$
$$\xi^- \qquad \xi^0$$

$$-\underline{(\bar{A}B)} \qquad \underline{1/\sqrt{2}\,(\bar{B}B - \bar{A}A)} \qquad \underline{(\bar{B}A)}$$
$$\sigma^- \qquad \sigma^0 \qquad \sigma^+$$

$$-\ \underline{1/\sqrt{6}\,[\bar{A}A + \bar{B}B - 2(\bar{C}C)]}$$
$$\lambda^0$$

$$\underline{(\bar{C}B)} \qquad \underline{(\bar{C}A)}$$
$$n \qquad p$$

The sign factors assigned to these states are chosen by a convention which is an extension of the Condon and Shortley specification. We have arranged the states so that a state gets transformed only into states in the same row, when the unitary transformations mix only A and B, that is, when we restrict ourselves to isospin transformations. The states are labled ξ^-, n, σ^+ etc. in analogue to the real particles Ξ^-, N, Σ^+ etc. as they have the same quantum numbers. If the SU_3 theory were perfect, then the particle states (or the corresponding particle states of other octets such as K^-, K^0, π^+, etc.) could be substituted for these small letters ξ^-, n, σ^+ in any expression written below without changing its transformation properties. Likewise antibaryons could be substituted with the corresponding quantum numbers, i.e. $-\bar{p}$ for ξ^-; $\bar{n}$ for ξ^0, $\bar{\lambda}$ for λ, $-\overline{\sigma^+}$ for σ^-, $\overline{\sigma^0}$ for σ^0, $-\overline{\sigma^-}$ for σ^+, $-\overline{\xi^-}$ for p, $\overline{\xi^0}$ for n. The above octet chart is written down immediately just by requiring that the states have the right quantum numbers. The coefficient $-2/\sqrt{6}$ for $\bar{C}C$ in λ is determined so that the λ state is orthogonal to the singlet.

Sum rules for mass splittings

We can generalize the scheme slightly at this point and thus obtain the first order mass sum rule. For this we assign masses to the C and $\bar{C}$ particles which are different from K/2, where we take K/2 to be the mass of A, $\bar{A}$, B and $\bar{B}$. The generalization consists in not identifying $\bar{A}$, $\bar{B}$ and $\bar{C}$ with the antiparticles of A, B and C, but just requiring that $\bar{A}$, $\bar{B}$ and $\bar{C}$ transform in the same way as the antiparticles. Thus, the mass of $\bar{C}$ can be different from that of C. We designate the mass of C by $K/2 + a - b$, and that of $\bar{C}$ by $K/2 + a + b$.

The other virtue of not necessarily identifying $\bar{A}$, $\bar{B}$ and $\bar{C}$ with the antiparticles of A, B and C is that then the ξ^- is not the antiparticle of p and so on. We will assume that the mass of the composite states is just equal to the sum of the masses of the component states. Carrying out this simple calculation we find the following table of masses:

$$p = K + b + a$$
$$\Xi = K - b + a$$
$$\Sigma = K$$
$$\Lambda = K + 2/3 \cdot 2a \ .$$

Eliminating a and b leads to a sum rule for the masses:

$$3M_\Lambda + M_\Sigma = 2M_N + 2M_\Xi \ .$$

Note that the b term breaks the mass symmetry for different strangeness, so that if we were constructing an octet of mesons using this scheme we would identify $\bar{A}$, $\bar{B}$ and $\bar{C}$ with the antiparticles of A, B and C, and thus set b = 0.

Incidentally, it is worth noting that because the masses are no longer equal, the mass operator connects the singlet state with that state of the octet which has I = 0 and Y = 0. It is thus not diagonal. If we diagonalize it we find new eigenvalues and new eigenvectors which are useful in the interpretation of ω and Φ, two of the vector mesons.

Octet operators

For the analysis of beta decay I would like to find the total isotopic-spin current in terms of my basic set of objects. In fact, with three basic objects I will get eight components of a generalized current instead of just the three that I get by considering isotopic-spin transformations.

The chart of the eight particles given on page 143 also permits us to discover a set of eight operators which transform like an octet. It is only necessary to read the A, $\bar{C}$ etc. as annhihilation of A, creation of C (or creation of $-\bar{A}$, destruction of $\bar{C}$) etc. Thus, the p-like operator (the operator which transforms like p) is $\bar{C}A$ or annihilate A, create C plus annihilate $\bar{C}$ create $-\bar{A}$. That is, the result of the p-like operator on any state is found by taking each term and rewriting it with each A replaced by C, and adding what one gets with each $\bar{C}$ replaced by $-\bar{A}$ (terms with neither A nor $\bar{C}$ in them are to be dropped). For example, the p-like operator on n = ($\bar{C}B$) converts it to $-\bar{A}B$ or σ^-. This we write as $+(\overline{\sigma^-} n)$. Again the p-like operator on p itself ($\bar{C}A$) converts it to ($\bar{C}C - \bar{A}A$) which is $\sqrt{1/2}\,\sigma^0 + \sqrt{3/2}\,\lambda$, which we write as $+\sqrt{1/2}\,(\overline{\sigma^0} p) + \sqrt{3/2}\,(\overline{\lambda^0} p)$. Proceeding in this way we find the effect of each operator on each member of the octet, with results given in the following chart:

Chart 2

$$p_{\text{operator}} = \frac{1}{\sqrt{12}}\left[-(\overline{\xi^-}\sigma^0) - (\overline{\sigma^0}p) - \sqrt{3}\,(\overline{\xi^-}\lambda) - \sqrt{3}\,(\bar{\lambda}p) - \sqrt{2}\,(\overline{\xi^0}\sigma^+) - \sqrt{2}\,(\overline{\sigma^-}n)\right]$$

$$n_{\text{operator}} = \frac{1}{\sqrt{12}}\left[-\sqrt{2}\,(\overline{\xi^-}\sigma^-) + \sqrt{2}\,(\overline{\sigma^+}p) + (\overline{\sigma^0}n) - (\overline{\xi^0}\sigma^0) + \sqrt{3}\,(\overline{\xi^0}\lambda) - \sqrt{3}\,(\bar{\lambda}n)\right]$$

$$\sigma^+_{\text{operator}} = \frac{1}{\sqrt{8}}\left[-(\bar{n}p) - (\overline{\xi^-}\xi^0) - \sqrt{2}\,(\overline{\sigma^0}\sigma^+) - \sqrt{2}\,(\overline{\sigma^-}\sigma^0)\right]$$

$$\sigma^0_{\text{operator}} = \frac{1}{\sqrt{12}}\left[(\overline{\xi^0}\xi^0) - (\overline{\xi^-}\xi^-) + (\bar{p}p) - (\bar{n}n) + 2\,(\overline{\sigma^+}\sigma^+) - 2(\overline{\sigma^-}\sigma^-)\right]$$

$$\sigma^-_{\text{operator}} = \frac{1}{\sqrt{6}}\left[(\bar{p}n) + (\overline{\xi^0}\xi^-) + \sqrt{2}\,(\overline{\sigma^0}\sigma^-) + \sqrt{2}\,(\overline{\sigma^+}\sigma^0)\right]$$

$$\lambda_{\text{operator}} = \frac{1}{2}\left[-\,(\overline{\xi^-}\xi^-) - (\overline{\xi^0}\xi^0) + (\bar{n}n) + (\bar{p}p)\right]$$

$$\xi^0_{\text{operator}} = \frac{1}{\sqrt{12}}\left[(\bar{n}\,\sigma^0) - (\overline{\sigma^0}\xi^0) - \sqrt{2}\,(\overline{\sigma^-}\xi^-) + \sqrt{2}\,(\bar{p}\,\sigma^+) + \sqrt{3}\,(\bar{\lambda}\xi^0) - \sqrt{3}\,(\bar{n}\lambda)\right]$$

$$\xi^-_{\text{operator}} = \frac{1}{\sqrt{12}}\left[(\overline{\sigma^0}\xi^-) + (\bar{p}\sigma^0) + \sqrt{2}\,(\overline{\sigma^+}\xi^0) + \sqrt{2}\,(\bar{n}\sigma^-) + \sqrt{3}\,(\bar{\lambda}\xi^-) + \sqrt{3}\,(\bar{p}\lambda)\right]$$

Note the operators σ_+, σ_0 and σ_- are the isotopic spin operators: $-I_-$, I_Z and I_+, respectively.

You will note from these tables that the σ^+ operator transforms like the lowering operator for isotopic spin and is thus the operator we would use for the non-strangeness changing beta-decay current, at least for the vector part. Similarly, to describe strangeness changing weak decays, the corresponding operator that we would use would be the operator corresponding to p, which, as you will note, automatically implies that $\Delta S = \Delta Q$.

Thus, SU_3 determines the relative coefficients in the beta decay for us. It turns out, however, that there is another octet of operators, which we shall display later, that may be used for the beta-decay currents. The use of these will introduce another parameter into the analysis of the weak decays, but will not change the isotopic and hypercharge selection rules that are apparent from the octet we have just derived.

The use of such currents to describe beta decay is just a guess and we shall try to check it out in later lectures. This, in fact, is Cabibbo's theory of weak decays.

We have called this set of eight operators an octet. In fact, it is an octet in the sense of SU_3 because if we make transformations among the three basic elements used to construct our scheme, the set of eight operators will transform into each other in exactly the same way that the set of eight composite particles transform into each other.

<u>Reduction of the direct product of two octets</u>

Combining two particles with octet transformation properties produces 64 possible states which, under the various operators listed above in Chart 2, are transformed into one another. From these 64, multiplets may be formed whose states transform only among themselves. These multiplets contain 1, 8, 8, 10, $\overline{10}$ and 27 members. Let the state of two particles be written as $p\lambda$, say, meaning the first is p, the second is λ in its transformation properties. (For example, the first may be an anti Ξ^-; the second, η^0.) The state λp means the first is λ, the second is p (in our example, the first is anti Λ, the second is K^+). We shall write, for short

$$(pn) = (pn - np)$$
$$[pn] = (pn + np) .$$

Since $(\bar{n}n) + (\bar{p}p) + (\overline{\xi^-}\xi^-) + (\xi^0\overline{\xi^0}) + (\overline{\sigma^+}\sigma^+) +$ etc. is evidently invariant, replacing each antiparticle by a particle of the same transformation properties, we get that $\xi^0 n - \xi^- p + n\xi^0 - \sigma^-\sigma^+$ etc. is invariant. Hence, our normalized singlet is

SINGLET

$$\{[\xi^- p] - [\xi^0 n] + [\sigma^+ \sigma^-] - \sigma^0\sigma^0 - \lambda\lambda\}/\sqrt{8}\,.$$

The forms for the p-like operator etc. in Chart 2 permit us, in the same way, to find an octet called the antisymmetric octet.

We denote the states by their quantum numbers $\{Y, I, I_z\}$ within the families.

ANTISYMMETRIC OCTET (8_A)

$\{1, \tfrac{1}{2}, \tfrac{1}{2}\} = \{(p\sigma^0) + \sqrt{2}\,(\sigma^+ n) + \sqrt{3}\,(p\lambda)\}/\sqrt{12}$

$\{1, \tfrac{1}{2}, -\tfrac{1}{2}\} = \{(\sigma^0 n) + \sqrt{2}\,(p\sigma^-) + \sqrt{3}\,(n\lambda)\}/\sqrt{12}$

$\{0, 1, 1\} = \{(p\xi^0) + \sqrt{2}\,(\sigma^+\sigma^0)\}/\sqrt{6}$

$\{0, 1, 0\} = \{(p\xi^-) + (n\xi^0) + 2\,(\sigma^+\sigma^-)\}/\sqrt{12}$

$\{0, 1, -1\} = \{(n\xi^-) + \sqrt{2}\,(\sigma^0\sigma^-)\}/\sqrt{6}$

$\{0, 0, 0\} = \{(n\xi^0) + (p\xi^-)\}/2$

$\{-1, \tfrac{1}{2}, \tfrac{1}{2}\} = \{(\xi^0\sigma^0) + \sqrt{2}\,(\sigma^+\xi^-) + \sqrt{3}\,(\lambda\xi^0)\}/\sqrt{12}$

$\{-1, \tfrac{1}{2}, -\tfrac{1}{2}\} = \{(\sigma^0\xi^-) + \sqrt{2}\,(\xi^0\sigma^-) + \sqrt{3}\,(\lambda\xi^-)\}/\sqrt{12}$

The other octet is composed of states which are symmetric under the exchange of the two particles.

SYMMETRIC OCTET (8_S)

$\{1,\tfrac{1}{2},\tfrac{1}{2}\} = \{\sqrt{3}\,[p\sigma^0] - [p\lambda] - \sqrt{6}\,[n\sigma^+]\}/\sqrt{20}$

$\{1,\tfrac{1}{2},-\tfrac{1}{2}\} = \{-\sqrt{3}\,[n\sigma^0] - [n\lambda] + \sqrt{6}\,[p\sigma^-]\}/\sqrt{20}$

$\{0,1,1\} = \{-\sqrt{3}\,[p\xi^0] + \sqrt{2}\,[\lambda\sigma^+]\}/\sqrt{10}$

$\{0,1,0\} = \{2\,[\lambda\sigma^0] - \sqrt{3}\,[p\xi^-] - \sqrt{3}\,[n\xi^0]\}/\sqrt{20}$

$\{0,1,-1\} = \{\sqrt{2}[\lambda\sigma^-] - \sqrt{3}\,[n\xi^-]\}/\sqrt{10}$

$\{0,0,0\} = \{[\sigma^0\sigma^0] - [\lambda\lambda] - 2\,[\sigma^+\sigma^-] + [p\xi^-] - [n\xi^0]\}/\sqrt{20}$

$\{-1,\tfrac{1}{2},\tfrac{1}{2}\} = \{-[\lambda\xi^0] - \sqrt{3}\,[\sigma^0\xi^0] + \sqrt{6}\,[\sigma^+\xi^-]\}/\sqrt{20}$

$\{-1,\tfrac{1}{2},-\tfrac{1}{2}\} = \{-[\lambda\xi^-] + \sqrt{3}\,[\sigma^0\xi^-] - \sqrt{6}\,[\sigma^-\xi^0]\}/\sqrt{20}$

The remaining twenty states which are antisymmetric under exchange of the two particles fall into two multiplets of ten states. These deciments contain an isotopic singlet, doublet, triplet and quartet, and the hypercharge of the isotopic multiplets differs by one unit in a progressive way. The two decimets are related by a reflection transformation called R, under which: $Y \to -Y$, $I \to I$, $I_z \to -I_z$ and $p \to \xi^-$, $n \to \xi^0$, $\sigma^- \to \sigma^+$, $\lambda \to \lambda$.

DECIMET (10)

$\{1,\tfrac{3}{2},\tfrac{3}{2}\} = (\sigma^+ p)/\sqrt{2}$

$\{1,\tfrac{3}{2},\tfrac{1}{2}\} = \{\sqrt{2}\,(\sigma^0 p) + (\sigma^+ n)\}/\sqrt{6}$

$\{1,\tfrac{3}{2},-\tfrac{1}{2}\} = \{\sqrt{2}\,(\sigma^0 n) + (\sigma^- p)\}/\sqrt{6}$

$\{1,\tfrac{3}{2},-\tfrac{3}{2}\} = (\sigma^- n)/\sqrt{2}$

$\{0,1,1\} \quad = \{(\sigma^+\sigma^0) + \sqrt{2}\ (\xi^0 p) + \sqrt{3}\ (\sigma^+\lambda)\}/\sqrt{12}$

$\{0,1,0\} \quad = \{(\sigma^+\sigma^-) + (\xi^- p) + (\xi^0 n) + \sqrt{3}\ (\sigma^0\lambda)\}/\sqrt{12}$

$\{0,1,-1\} \quad = \{(\sigma^0\sigma^-) + \sqrt{2}\ (\xi^- n) + \sqrt{3}\ (\sigma^-\lambda)\}/\sqrt{12}$

$\{-1,\tfrac{1}{2},\tfrac{1}{2}\} \quad = \{(\xi^0\sigma^0) + \sqrt{2}\ (\sigma^+\xi^-) + \sqrt{3}\ (\xi^0\lambda)\}/\sqrt{12}$

$\{-1,\tfrac{1}{2},-\tfrac{1}{2}\} \quad = \{(\sigma^0\xi^-) + \sqrt{2}\ (\xi^0\sigma^-) + \sqrt{3}\ (\xi^-\lambda)\}/\sqrt{12}$

$\{-2,0,0\} \quad = (\xi^0\xi^-)/\sqrt{2}$

<u>DECIMET</u> ($\overline{10}$)

$\{2,0,0\} \quad = (np)/\sqrt{2}$

$\{1,\tfrac{1}{2},\tfrac{1}{2}\} \quad = \{(\sigma^0 p) + \sqrt{2}\ (n\sigma^+) + \sqrt{3}\ (p\lambda)\}/\sqrt{12}$

$\{1,\tfrac{1}{2},-\tfrac{1}{2}\} \quad = \{(n\sigma^0) + \sqrt{2}\ (\sigma^- p) + \sqrt{3}\ (n\lambda)\}/\sqrt{12}$

$\{0,1,1\} \quad = \{(\sigma^0\sigma^+) + \sqrt{2}\ (p\xi^0) + \sqrt{3}\ (\sigma^+\lambda)\}/\sqrt{12}$

$\{0,1,0\} \quad = \{(\sigma^-\sigma^+) + (p\xi^-) + (n\xi^0) + \sqrt{3}\ (\sigma^0\lambda)\}/\sqrt{12}$

$\{0,1,-1\} \quad = \{(\sigma\ \sigma^0) + \sqrt{2}\ (n\xi^-) + \sqrt{3}\ (\sigma^-\lambda)\}/\sqrt{12}$

$\{-1,\tfrac{3}{2},\tfrac{1}{2}\} \quad = (\sigma^+\xi^0)/\sqrt{2}$

$\{-1,\tfrac{3}{2},\tfrac{1}{2}\} \quad = \{\sqrt{2}\ (\sigma^0\xi^0) + (\sigma^+\xi^-)\}/\sqrt{6}$

$\{-1,\tfrac{3}{2},-\tfrac{1}{2}\} \quad = \{\sqrt{2}\ (\sigma^0\xi^-) + (\sigma^-\xi^0)\}/\sqrt{6}$

$\{-1,\tfrac{3}{2},-\tfrac{3}{2}\} \quad = (\sigma^-\xi^-)/\sqrt{2}$

The remaining twenty-seven states form a multiplet which is symmetric under the interchange of the particles. It is composed of a triplet with Y = 2, a doublet and a quarter with Y = 1, a singlet, a triplet and a quintet with Y = 0, a doublet and a quarter with Y = -1, and a triplet with Y = -2.

(27)

$\{2,1,1\} = pp$

$\{2,1,0\} = [np]/\sqrt{2}$

$\{2,1,-1\} = nn$

$\{1,\tfrac{3}{2},\tfrac{3}{2}\} = [p\sigma^+]/\sqrt{2}$

$\{1,\tfrac{3}{2},\tfrac{1}{2}\} = \{\sqrt{2}\,[p\sigma^0] + [n\sigma^+]\}/\sqrt{6}$

$\{1,\tfrac{3}{2},-\tfrac{1}{2}\} = \{\sqrt{2}\,[n\sigma^0] + [p\sigma^-]\}/\sqrt{6}$

$\{1,\tfrac{3}{2},-\tfrac{3}{2}\} = [n\sigma^-]/\sqrt{2}$

$\{1,\tfrac{1}{2},\tfrac{1}{2}\} = \{[p\sigma^0] + 3\sqrt{3}\,[p\lambda] - \sqrt{2}\,[n\sigma^+]\}/\sqrt{60}$

$\{1,\tfrac{1}{2},-\tfrac{1}{2}\} = \{-[n\sigma^0] + 3\sqrt{3}\,[n\lambda] + \sqrt{2}\,[p\sigma^-]\}/\sqrt{60}$

$\{0,2,2\} = \sigma^+\sigma^+$

$\{0,2,1\} = [\sigma^+\sigma^0]/\sqrt{2}$

$\{0,2,0\} = \{[\sigma^+\sigma^-] + [\sigma^0\sigma^0]\}/\sqrt{6}$

$\{0,2,-1\} = [\sigma^0\sigma^-]/\sqrt{2}$

$\{0,2,-2\} = \sigma^-\sigma^-$

$$\{0,1,1\} = \{\sqrt{2}\ [p\xi^{0}] + \sqrt{3}\ [\sigma^{+}\lambda]\}/\sqrt{10}$$

$$\{0,1,0\} = \{[p\xi^{-}] + [m\xi^{o}] + \sqrt{3}\ [\sigma^{0}\lambda]\}/\sqrt{10}$$

$$\{0,1,-1\} = \{\sqrt{2}\ [n\xi^{-}] + \sqrt{3}\ [\sigma^{-}\lambda]\}/\sqrt{10}$$

$$\{0,0,0\} = \{3\ [p\xi^{-}] - 3\ [n\xi^{0}] - [\sigma^{+}\sigma^{-}] + \sigma^{0}\sigma^{0} + 9\ \lambda\lambda\}/\sqrt{120}$$

$$\{-1,\tfrac{3}{2},\tfrac{3}{2}\} = [\sigma^{+}\xi^{0}]/\sqrt{2}$$

$$\{-1,\tfrac{3}{2},\tfrac{1}{2}\} = \{\sqrt{2}\ [\sigma^{0}\xi^{0}] + [\sigma^{+}\xi^{-}]\}/\sqrt{6}$$

$$\{-1,\tfrac{3}{2},-\tfrac{1}{2}\} = \{\sqrt{2}\ [\sigma^{0}\xi^{-}] + [\sigma^{-}\xi^{0}]\}/\sqrt{6}$$

$$\{-1,\tfrac{3}{2},-\tfrac{3}{2}\} = [\sigma^{-}\xi^{-}]/\sqrt{2}$$

$$\{-1,\tfrac{1}{2},\tfrac{1}{2}\} = \{\sqrt{2}\ [\sigma^{+}\xi^{-}] - [\sigma^{0}\xi^{0}] + 3\sqrt{3}\ [\lambda\xi^{0}]\}/\sqrt{60}$$

$$\{-1,\tfrac{1}{2},-\tfrac{1}{2}\} = \{-\sqrt{2}\ [\sigma^{-}\xi^{0}] + [\sigma^{0}\xi^{-}] + 3\sqrt{3}\ [\lambda\xi^{-}]\}/\sqrt{60}$$

$$\{-2,1,1\} = \xi^{0}\xi^{0}$$

$$\{-2,1,0\} = [\xi^{0}\xi^{-}]/\sqrt{2}$$

$$\{-2,1,-1\} = \xi^{-}\xi^{-}$$

One way to deduce these multiplets is to take an extreme case, say pp, which has isotopic spin 1 and hypercharge +2, and operate on it with all the raising and lowering operators, which in fact are just the octet of operators that we found at first (Chart 2). Doing this, we would get the multiplet with 27 objects. Next, we can take a state with extreme quantum numbers which is orthogonal to the member of the 27 with the same quantum numbers. We then follow the same procedure of generating the complete multiplet by use of the raising and lowering operators. By iteration of this procedure we will generate all the multiplets.

Couplings of the baryons and mesons   4th LECTURE

Last time we described how one could construct states of two particles, each one of which was a member of an octet, so that the resultant states would be grouped into multiplets. We found a singlet state, two '8''s, a '10', a '$\overline{10}$' and a '27'. The two '8''s can be distinguished by means of a certain type of inversion transformation which we define in such a way that $p \leftrightarrow \xi^-$, $n \leftrightarrow \xi^0$, $\sigma^- \leftrightarrow \sigma^+$, $\sigma^0 \leftrightarrow \sigma^0$ and $\lambda \leftrightarrow \lambda$. Under this transformation, the first '8' we constructed was antisymmetric and the second '8' was symmetric.

One of the uses of the charts of the previous lecture is to construct couplings of the baryons and mesons which will be invariant under unitary spin transformations. Although this is not directly related to the weak interactions, I would like to pause a moment and discuss that application of the charts. From the construction of a unitary singlet from two '8''s, we know that the combination $-\pi^-\sigma^+ - \pi^+\sigma^- + \pi^0\pi^0 - K^+\xi^- - K^-p + K^0\xi^0 + \overline{K^0}n + \eta\lambda$ is an invariant. We stated before that you can construct certain combinations of two particles that transform like an octet. For example, if we substitute for σ^+, σ^-, σ^0 the antisymmetric σ^+, σ^-, σ^0 operators derived in the last lecture, then we get all the coupling coefficients of the pseudoscalar mesons to the nucleons. Let me write out part of this. To keep the normalization the same, the coupling constant will have to be $\sqrt{6}\,a$, where $a = g/2M$.

$$\sqrt{6}a\left\{\pi^-\left[\sqrt{1/6}(\bar{n}\gamma_5\not{q}p) + \sqrt{1/6}(\overline{\Xi^-}\gamma_5\not{q}\Xi^0) + \sqrt{1/3}(\overline{\Sigma^0}\gamma_5\not{q}\Sigma^+) + \right.\right.$$
$$\left. + \sqrt{1/3}\,\overline{\Sigma^-}\gamma_5\not{q}\Sigma^0)\right] + K^-\left[\sqrt{1/6}(\overline{\Xi^0}\gamma_5\not{q}\Sigma^+) + \right.$$
$$+ \sqrt{1/6}(\overline{\Sigma^-}\gamma_5\not{q}n) + 1/2(\overline{\Xi^-}\gamma_5\not{q}\Lambda) + 1/2(\bar{\Lambda}\gamma_5\not{q}p) +$$
$$\left.\left. + \frac{1}{2\sqrt{3}}(\overline{\Sigma^0}\gamma_5\not{q}p) + \frac{1}{2\sqrt{3}}(\overline{\Xi^-}\gamma_5\not{q}\Sigma^0)\right] + \ldots\right\} .$$

However, the coupling is not completely determined because one is also allowed to use the symmetric set of eight pairs of baryons. Since there are only two '8''s, there are thus only two constants which characterize the meson-baryon coupling. It is standard to call the coupling constant of the normalized antisymmetric octet of baryons to the mesons $\sqrt{6}\,a\,F$, and to call the coupling constant of the normalized symmetric octet of baryon pairs $\sqrt{10/3}\,a\,D$. The F and D are two parameters which must be discovered by comparison with experiment. There are rough indications from the study of Λ hyperfragments that the ratio D/F is positive and is of the order two or three.

SU_3 in the weak interactions

Returning to the weak interactions we find that we are faced with a slightly more difficult problem. We cannot make use of SU_3 symmetry to construct invariant weak couplings, because the weak Lagrangian must destroy conservation laws. More ingenuity is therefore required to construct the couplings governing the weak decays. As before, one can only try to guess the answer and see if experiment agrees with that guess. The most satisfactory guess that has been made to date is that of Cabibbo, which I shall now introduce in a way that seems most reasonable to me.

Let us consider first, the non-strangeness charging piece of the weak interaction current, because it is this piece that we think we know best of all. We expect from the conserved vector-current theorem that this part of the current should be the isotopic-spin current. The isotopic spin current is just the σ^{+}_{anti}, which is the antisymmetric-octet operator. Considering still the vector current, what would a logical extension of this idea be in order to cover strangeness changing decays? There is some evidence in leptonic decays that this part of the current must violate isotopic spin conservation in such a way that only a violation of a half unit is possible, $\Delta I = 1/2$. For example, in the decays $K \rightarrow \pi +$ leptons, the prediction of the $\Delta I = 1/2$ rule is

$$\frac{K_2^0 \rightarrow \pi + \text{leptons}}{K^+ \rightarrow \pi + \text{leptons}} = (2/1) \text{ prediction} = \frac{11{\cdot}1 \pm 1{\cdot}2}{6{\cdot}2 \pm 0{\cdot}9} \text{ experiment.}$$

There is other evidence for this rule but it is not very definitive. Nevertheless, the selection rule is the standard guess in the construction of the current. On the other hand, there is much better evidence for the selection rule $\Delta S = \Delta Q$. Assuming that the strangeness changing piece is also a member of an octet there is only one choice for the current, namely, the operator that transforms like the proton. From our charts you will note that the antisymmetric proton operator obeys both the $\Delta I = \frac{1}{2}$ and the $\Delta S = \Delta Q$ selection rules. We are led, thus, to propose that the vector current is $\sigma^{+}_{anti} + s p_{anti}$.

Experimentally the leptonic decays in which strangeness is violated are 20 times weaker than the non-strangeness changing decays. Therefore, the coefficient s, which measures the proportion of the strangeness-changing current must be definitely smaller than 1. The $K \to \pi e \nu$ is also somewhat smaller than might be expected. We will use this rate later to determine quite accurately the value of s.

Universality and the strangeness changing decays

How do we reconcile weakness of the strangeness-changing decays with the concept of universality. In our study of μ capture, nuclear beta-decay and muon decay, we found that np and the leptons were all coupled with the same strength within a few per cent. This observation, in fact, led to the idea that there was a universal coupling characterizing the weak interactions. However, today we know for example, that p couples much more weakly. Can we construct a theory of the coupling which retains the idea of universality? The answer is yes, and the way to do it was shown by Cabibbo. It is simply that we assume that the weak current is not the component σ^{+} nor the component p, but rather a skew component, but still normalized, i.e. we assume that the vector current is

$$\cos\Theta\, \sigma^{+V}_{anti} + \sin\Theta\, p^{V}_{anti} .$$

I have added the superscript V to designate the vector piece of the weak-interaction current. The idea then, is that the skew component is coupled to the leptons with the universal-coupling constant G_μ.

We turn now to the axial current. If there were no complications due to the strong interaction, the obvious choice for the axial current would be to use the same isotopic-coupling coefficients, and merely insert a γ_5. In other words, if we could deal with bare particles, the axial vector part of the current would be

$$\cos\Theta\ \sigma^{+A}_{anti} + \sin\Theta\ p^{A}_{anti}\ ,$$

where the A superscript is to indicate the Dirac matrix $\gamma_\mu\gamma_5$. But, of course, life is more complicated. If SU_3 were perfect, any component of the antisymmetric octet of operators would be conserved. Thus, the vector current would not be changed by renormalization. In fact, Gatto has shown that even to the first order in the mass shifts, the vector current is not renormalized. The axial vector current, however, is not conserved, even in the limit of exact SU_3 symmetry, so one must expect modifications due to renormalization. This means that the strength of the axial vector current will be changed and also that, starting from the antisymmetric octet for the axial vector current, we can get both the antisymmetric and the symmetric octets in the renormalized axial current. Thus, the renormalized axial vector current will take the form:

$$\sqrt{6}\ F_{BBW}\left[\cos\Theta\ \sigma^{+A}_{anti} + \sin\Theta\ p^{A}_{anti}\right] + \sqrt{10/3}\ D_{BBW}\left[\cos\Theta\ \sigma^{+A}_{symm} + \sin\Theta\ p^{A}_{symm}\right].$$

In the limit of SU_3 symmetry the angle Θ is independent of the particles which are coupled to the weak current, because renormalization cannot change the axis of the octet that is coupled with the weak decays. The renormalization coefficients, F and D are strongly dependent on the type of octets, i.e. pseudoscalar mesons, baryons and vector mesons.

Comparison of the Cabibbo theory with experiment

Let us turn now to a discussion of how well this proposal of Cabibbo agrees with experiment. The most important parameter of the theory is the angle Θ. One of the best ways to determine it is to consider the decay

$$K^+ \rightarrow \pi^0 + e^+ + \nu \ .$$

Two pseudoscalar mesons in a J = 1 state have a parity of (-), and therefore only the vector-weak current is involved in this decay. We have two vectors P_K and P_π, to make the current. The most general form of the matrix element is

$$(P_K + P_\pi) + \xi \ (P_K - P_\pi) \ .$$

In the limit of unitary symmetry the ξ term would be absent. Experimentally, a study of the spectrum shows it to be very small and therefore we will drop it. Putting in the coefficient $1/\sqrt{2}$ from the $K^-\pi^0$ term in the p-like current and the coupling strength $\sqrt{2}$ G, we get for the matrix element:

$$G \sin \Theta \ (P_K + P_\pi)_\alpha \ (\bar{\nu}\gamma_\alpha ae) \ .$$

Making the calculation of the rate and comparing with my data (which may not be the latest, most accurate) I find that $|\sin \Theta| = 0.23 \pm 0.015$ (Cabibbo, using different data in his paper, found $|\sin \Theta| = 0.260 \pm 0.015$).

Another way to determine the angle which Cabibbo also proposed, was to look at the ratio of K and π decays into leptons. Both of these decays proceed only through the axial vector current because the K and π are pseudoscalar mesons. The geometric structure of the matrix element is, as we have already discussed, $\sqrt{8\pi}\ F_\pi q_\alpha^\pi(\bar{\mu}\gamma_\alpha A\nu)$ and $\sqrt{8\pi}\ F_K q_\alpha^K(\bar{\mu}\gamma_\alpha a\nu)$.

There is only one octet that can be made from a single set of mesons. Hence, the Cabibbo theory would state that $F^K/F^\pi = \tan \Theta$.. Experimentally

$$F_\pi = \frac{5.95 \times 10^{-8}}{m_\pi} \quad \text{and} \quad F_K = \frac{5.55 \times 10^{-8}}{m_K} \ ,$$

so that tan Θ is very nearly equal to m_π/m_K. Numerically $|\sin\Theta|$ from the experiments is 0.26 ± 0.02, which agrees with the first determination. This provides the first check on the Cabibbo hypothesis. (Incidentally, in my later calculations I shall use $|\sin\Theta| = 0.245$, because then $\sin^2\Theta = 0.06$, a simple number for computational purposes.)

Another consequence of the Cabibbo theory is that the nuclear beta-decay vector coupling constant G_V, should differ from the muon beta-decay coupling G_μ. In fact, $G_V = G_\mu \cos\Theta$ in the Cabibbo theory. Since $\cos\Theta$ is about 0.97, we see that this theory very possibly resolves this difficulty in the theory of weak interactions!

Determination of the axial vector current F/D ratio

The next question is how well the Cabibbo theory fits with the leptonic decays of the hyperons. To study this let us make a table of the leptonic decay matrix elements, and use our charts of the F and D octets to construct the proportions of vector and axial vector currents in each decay.

Non-strangeness changing decays. These are to be multiplied by $\cos\Theta$.

Reactions	Vector	Axial
$n \to p + e + \nu$	1	$F + D$
$\Sigma^0 \to \Sigma^+ + e + \bar{\nu}$	$-\sqrt{2}$	$-\sqrt{2}\,F$
$\Sigma^- \to \Sigma^0 + e + \bar{\nu}$	$\sqrt{2}$	$\sqrt{2}\,F$
$\Sigma^- \to \Lambda + e + \bar{\nu}$	0	$\sqrt{2/3}\,D$
$\Sigma^+ \to \Lambda + e + \bar{\nu}$	0	$\sqrt{2/3}\,D$
$\Xi^- \to \Xi^0 + e + \bar{\nu}$	1	$(F - D)$

<u>Strangeness changing decays</u>. These are to be multiplied by sin Θ

Reactions	Vector	Axial
$\Sigma^0 \to p + e + \bar{\nu}$	$\frac{1}{\sqrt{2}}$	$\frac{1}{\sqrt{2}}(F - D)$
$\Lambda \to p + e + \bar{\nu}$	$\sqrt{3/2}$	$\sqrt{3/2}\ (F + 1/3\ D)$
$\Xi^- \to \Sigma^0 + e + \bar{\nu}$	$\sqrt{1/2}$	$\frac{1}{\sqrt{2}}(F + D)$
$\Xi^- \to \Lambda + e + \bar{\nu}$	$\sqrt{3/2}$	$\sqrt{3/2}\ (F - 1/3\ D)$
$\Xi^0 \to \Sigma^+ + e + \bar{\nu}$	1	$(F + D)$
$\Sigma^- \to n + e + \bar{\nu}$	1	$(F - D)$

The best relation we can use to partially determine F and D is the fact that for the decay of the neutron the axial vector coupling is 1.20 ± 0.04, relative to the vector coupling. Thus,

$$F + D = 1.20 \pm 0.04 .$$

Strangeness-changing decay rates can now be used to determine other relations between F and D. There is a standard rate for these decays predicted under the assumption that the weak current is just the matrix element of $\gamma_\alpha(1 + i\gamma_5)$. This rate is called the universal Fermi interaction (U.F.I.) rate. Neglecting small relativistic corrections, for any of these decays the rate should be $(V^2 + 3\ A^2/4)$ times the U.F.I. rate. The experimental branching ratios, together with the U.F.I. predictions, are given in the following table.

Decay	U.F.I.	Experimental branching ratios
$\Lambda \to p + e + \bar{\nu}$	1.5×10^{-2}	$0.81 \pm 0.10 \times 10^{-3}$
$\Sigma^- \to N + e + \bar{\nu}$	5.8×10^{-2}	$1.37 \pm 0.34 \times 10^{-2}$
$\Sigma^- \to \Lambda + e + \bar{\nu}$	1.0×10^{-4}	$0.07 \pm 0.03 \times 10^{-4}$
$\Sigma \to \Lambda + \bar{e} + \nu$	0.6×10^{-4}	$0.07 \pm 0.04 \times 10^{-4}$ (4 events).

From the rate of decay of the Λ, we find

$$F + \tfrac{1}{3}D = 0.68 \pm 0.07 .$$

There is evidence from the polarization of this leptonic decay that $F + \tfrac{1}{3} D > 0$. Using this relation, together with the first, we deduce

$$F = 0.40 \mp 0.10, \; D = 0.78 \pm 0.12 .$$

Cabibbo's original values were $F = 0.30$, $D = 0.95$. The small difference results from slightly different data and from the fact that Cabibbo used 1.26 instead of 1.20 for $-G_A/G_V$

With F and D thus determined, do the other leptonic decays agree with Cabibbo's theory? In many cases only a few events of a given decay have been observed so that the statistical errors and, even more important, the systematic errors in the determination of the rates, are very large. Of the remaining decays, for which experimental information is available, perhaps the reaction $\Sigma^- \rightarrow n + e + \bar{\nu}$ is known to the greatest accuracy. Converting the experimental rate for this reaction, one finds $|F - D| = 0.40 \pm 0.16$. You will note that this is certainly consistent with the value $F - D = -0.38 \pm 0.22$ which was predicted above. Another prediction is that the reaction $\Xi^- \rightarrow \Lambda + e + \bar{\nu}$ should have a branching ratio of $(0.50 \pm 0.05) \times 10^{-3}$. Experimentally, the branching ratio is two or three times 10^{-3}, but this is based on only a handful of events. The predictions on the $\Sigma \rightarrow \Lambda$ decays are also consistent with the crude experimental values.

The D to F ratio for the axial vector current is $2{\cdot}2 \pm 0{\cdot}8$. This is the same ratio as is claimed for the coupling of the pseudoscalar mesons to the baryons, which is thought to be about 2, 3 or 4. This value came originally from very crude theoretical analysis of the strong interactions and some study of the ΛN interaction in hyperfragments. I may remark here that an extension of the Goldberger-Treiman argument to the strangeness-changing current will result in the prediction that the D to F ratio for the strong interactions should be the same as it is for the axial vector weak baryon-baryon current.

Generalization of the Goldberger-Treiman Relation 5th LECTURE

One can explore the question of a supposed equality between the F/D ratios in the strong interactions and in the axial vector weak current by studying a generalization of the Goldberger-Treiman relation. There are several ways to obtain this generalization. One of them would proceed in analogy with my first derivation of the G-T relation for pions. To do this I would extend my model so that it had eight baryons and eight pseudoscalar mesons coupled to baryon pairs using the pseudovector $\not{q}\gamma_5$ coupling. I would then couple both the baryon pairs to the lepton current in such a way that if I neglected the meson masses a divergence added to the lepton current would have no effect. In complete analogy to the pionic case, I would have in lowest order the relation

$$F_{K(\text{unrenormalized})} = \frac{G^{\text{Bare}}_{A(n\Lambda)}}{\sqrt{8\pi}\, a_0(n\Lambda k)} .$$

Renormalization corrections would have to be made of course. It is clear that the structure of the renormalization in the K case would be the same as it is in the π case. That is,

$$F_K = \frac{G_{A(n\Lambda)}}{\sqrt{8\pi}\, a_{(n\Lambda K)}} \frac{Z_{A(n\Lambda K)}(0)}{Z_{A(n\Lambda K)}(m_K^2)} \frac{1 - a_{0(n\Lambda K)}^2 K_K(m_K^2)}{\left[1 - a_{0(n\Lambda K)}^2 K_K(m_K^2) + m_K^2 K_K'(m_K^2)\right]}$$

$$= F_{K(\text{unrenormalized})} \times \frac{1 - a_{0(n\Lambda K)}^2 K_K(m_K^2)}{\left[1 - a_{0(n\Lambda K)}^2 (K_K(m_K^2) + m_K^2 K_K'(m_K^2))\right]^{1/2}} .$$

One can then attempt to argue that the ratio of the renormalization factors is close to one. This will be far less convincing, however, in the case of the K because m_K^2 is far greater than m_π^2, and m_K^2 is much nearer to the next threshold for intermediate states than m_π^2 was. In the case of the pion, the distance from $q^2 = 0$ to the pole is m_π^2, whereas the next smallest energy denominator lies at a distance $9\ m_\pi^2$ from $q^2 = 0$. On the other hand, for the K, $q^2 = 0$ is $(500\ \text{MeV})^2$ away from the K pole and only about $(770\ \text{MeV})^2$ away from the $K\pi\pi$ intermediate state. Thus, in the π case we had a factor of 9 in our favour, but in the K case this factor is only about 2. On the other hand, with pseudovector coupling, as we explained before, low momentum pions (and kaons) are only weakly coupled since $f^2 = 0.08$ is small, so these "nearest pole terms" are not expected to be large. I suspect that the functions $Z(q^2)$ and $K(q^2)$ only begin their serious variation near q^2 equal to the nucleon mass squared.

Granting the validity of these arguments that lead to the Goldberger-Treiman relation, the following point can be made. In the limit of SU_3 symmetry $F_\pi \tan\Theta$ should equal F_K, at least if unrenormalized. But the renormalization factors of F exhibited in the second form of the above equation should also be nearly the same. This explains why we can get $\tan\Theta$ from comparison of $\pi\mu\nu$ and $K\mu\nu$ decay. This being the case, the first form of the equation shows that the experimental meson-baryon couplings should be proportional to the experimental axial vector beta-decay couplings. Another way of stating this (since it is assumed that both types of couplings transform as an octet) is that both octets must have the same character. Thus, assuming the Goldberger-Treiman relation, one finds that F/D for the weak axial vector current is the same as F/D for the meson-baryon coupling. Although there are indications that this may be true, there is as yet no sharp experimental test available to check this prediction.

Leptic Decays

Let me summarize what we know about the leptic decays. If there is no strangeness change, we have essentially a complete theory of all the interactions with two coupling constants, G_V and G_A. F_π is supplied via the Goldberger-Treiman relations. When we come to the strangeness-changing decays, we do not know whether we have a good theory or not until we gather more experimental data. We do have a theory, the Cabibbo theory, which is consistent with the data now available, but the sharpness of the tests is not very great. Cabibbo's theory involves two more parameters: sin Θ and the F/D ratio. If some day we can justify more adequately the Goldberger-Treiman relation, then the F/D ratio would come out of a strong interaction theory. The Cabibbo theory would then involve only the parameter Θ. All observed leptic decays then have theoretically predictable properties, with the exception of $K \rightarrow \pi + \pi + e + \nu$.

Non-leptic decays

The non-leptic decays also arise from the assumption of a current-current interaction. If we take the theoretical view that the current is the sum of pieces of the form

$$J = (\bar{\mu}\nu_{\mu}) + (\bar{e}\nu) + "\sigma^{+}" \cos\Theta + "p" \sin\Theta ,$$

then the quadratic terms in the expansion of $\bar{J} \cdot J$

$$\bar{\sigma}\sigma^{+} \cos^{2}\Theta + \bar{\xi}\, p \sin^{2}\Theta$$

give rise to non-strangeness changing, non-leptic, weak interactions. It is these terms which give rise to a parity non-conserving nuclear force, for which evidence has been acquired at Cal Tech by Boehm. Other than by experiments of this type, such terms are difficult to get at experimentally.

The cross-products in the expansion of $\bar{J} \cdot J$ are $[\bar{\sigma} p + \bar{\xi}\sigma^{+}] \sin\Theta \cos\Theta$. The term $\bar{\sigma} p$ accounts for those decays for which $\Delta S = +1$ and the term $\bar{\xi}\sigma^{+}$, the hermitian conjugate term, accounts for those decays for which $\Delta S = -1$. Since one is the adjoint of the other, we need consider only one of them.

We have a much more difficult task in making predictions for the non-leptic decays because the renormalizations are much more elaborate. In other words, we have a four-fermion coupling term which is much screwed about by renormalizations of the strong interactions. In the theory of the leptic decays much was predicted on the basis of the hypothesis that the weak current had certain transformation properties. For the non-leptonic decays, on the other hand, the form $\bar{J} \cdot J$ does not have well-defined transformation properties, with regard to unitary spin or even with regard to isotopic spin. Because the situation is not very clear, let us concentrate at first on the transformation properties of the currents.

The strangeness changing decays result from the coupling of an isotopic-spinor current with an isotopic-vector current. With respect to isospin, therefore, the interaction $\bar{J} \cdot J$ has a piece which transforms like isotopic spin $3/2$, as well as one of isotopic spin $1/2$. In the $\Delta S = |1|$ decays, therefore, our current-current interaction leads to the selection rules $\Delta I = 1/2$ or $\Delta I = 3/2$. The first thing that we must check is whether there is any evidence for $\Delta I = 5/2$ in these decays. If one looks at the data to check this, one is surprised and finds a terribly interesting fact. Almost all the data seem to be consistent with only $\Delta I = 1/2$ terms in the amplitude. Very small $\Delta I = 3/2$ amplitudes are required to fit the data, and no $\Delta I = 5/2$ is required at all. The fact that $\Delta I = 3/2$ was so small was totally unexpected and has no explanation theoretically on the basis of the current-current hypothesis.

Tests of the $\Delta I = 1/2$ rule

In the absence of being able to give a satisfactory theoretical justification for this rule, I will discuss the data which substantiate it. Consider first the disintegration of the Λ. There are two non-leptic channels open

$$\Lambda \to p + \pi^-, \ \Lambda \to n + \pi^0 \ .$$

On the basis of the $\Delta I = 1/2$ rule, since the isotopic spin of the Λ is zero, the charged pion decay amplitude should be $\sqrt{2}$ times the neutral-pion decay amplitude. Hence, the rates should be in the ratio 2 to 1. If there is a decay amplitude into the isospin $3/2$ state of the pion-nucleon system, measured by a coefficient a, then the ratio of the two rates should be $|(\sqrt{2} + a)/(1 - \sqrt{2}a)|^2$.

The experimental branching fraction for the decay into $n+\pi^0$ is 0.33 ± 0.02 of all non-leptic decays. The data, therefore, indicate complete agreement with the $\Delta I = \frac{1}{2}$ rule and show that $|a| < 0.05$. This excellent evidence for the $\Delta I = \frac{1}{2}$ rule is substantiated by the fact that the polarization properties for the neutral and charged modes are the same. The ratio of the s to p-wave amplitudes is measured by the anisotropy of the direction of the pion with respect to the spin of the Λ. The coefficient of this anisotropy term is called α, and if you check the measured values of α for the two modes, you will find that they agree within the experimental errors.

The next baryon to consider is the Σ. There are three non-leptic decays

$$1)\quad \Sigma^+ \rightarrow p + \pi^0$$

$$2)\quad \Sigma^+ \rightarrow n + \pi^+$$

$$3)\quad \Sigma^- \rightarrow n + \pi^- .$$

If we label the amplitudes for each process by A_1, A_2 and A_3 respectively, it turns out that the only prediction of the $\Delta I = \frac{1}{2}$ rule is

$$\sqrt{2}\, A_1 = A_2 + A_3 .$$

Now each amplitude A_i is a two-component vector, one component for the s wave and one component for the p wave. The rates are measured by the squares of the lengths of these vectors and are almost all the same. This means that the three vector amplitudes must form an isosceles right triangle with $\sqrt{2}\, A$ being the base of the triangle. Since the anisotropy coefficients for the second and third decays are almost zero, both amplitudes lie along the coordinate axes in an s, p-plane. Therefore, the first amplitude should lie at 45° to these axes. The anisotropy coefficient α, should therefore be 1 for the reaction. Experimentally, $\alpha = 0.73$. This fact is slightly annoying, but it is not sufficiently bad that we should consider it as evidence against the $\Delta I = \frac{1}{2}$ rule. This measurement is not a very good test of the $\Delta I = \frac{1}{2}$

rule because the experimental errors could be large. The experimental errors will have to be improved a great deal before one can consider the Σ decays to be evidence against the $\Delta I = \frac{1}{2}$ rule.

Another test of the $\Delta I = \frac{1}{2}$ rule comes from the study of $K \to \pi + \pi$. The decay rate for $K^+ \to \pi^+ + \pi^0$ is suppressed relative to $K_1^0 \to \pi + \pi$ by a factor 500. Two pions in a symmetric spatial state must have either I = 0 or I = 2. The wave function for $\pi^+ + \pi^0$, with the spin-parity assignment 0^+, must therefore be I = 2, whereas a neutral 0^+ state of two pions can have both I = 2 and I = 0. Since the K meson has $I = \frac{1}{2}$, the $\Delta I = \frac{1}{2}$ rule predicts that the decay $K^+ \to \pi^+ + \pi^0$ is severely suppressed. Also, the $\Delta I = \frac{1}{2}$ rule predicts that the branching ratio

$$\frac{K_1^0 \to \pi^+ + \pi^-}{K_1^0 \to \pi^0 + \pi^0} = 2/1 .$$

Experimentally, the branching fraction for neutral K_1^0 decays is either 0.26 ± 0.02 or 0.335 ± 0.014 depending on which experiment you choose to believe. From the observed rate of $K^+ \to \pi^+ + \pi^0$, we know the amplitude for decay of the K into the I = 2 state. If we take into account the possible interference of the I = 2 with the I = 0 amplitude in K decays, we find that the ratio $K_1^0 \to \pi^0 + \pi^0 / K_1^0 \to \pi + \pi$ need not be exactly 1/3 but may be somewhere between 0.28 and 0.38 (depending on the phase of the interference). Interference effects are thus quite large.

Finally, consider the decays of the K into three pions. Experimentally it is known that the Dalitz plot is almost flat, so that all three pions appear to be in S states. Thus, the spatial wave function is totally symmetric. By use of the generalized Pauli principle, the isotopic spin-wave function must also be totally symmetric. Therefore only I = 1 and I = 3 is possible. There is only one totally symmetric isospin wave function compatible with the $\Delta I = \frac{1}{2}$ rule, and that function has I = 1. The isotopic factors in the rates are given in the following table:

	Weight
$K_2^0 \to \pi^0 + \pi^0 + \pi^0$	3
$K_2^0 \to \pi^+ + \pi^- + \pi^0$	2
$K^+ \to \pi^+ + \pi^0 + \pi^0$	1
$K^+ \to \pi^+ + \pi^- + \pi^+$	4

The ratio of the first two, $3/2$, and the last two, $1/4$ are correct even if $\Delta I = 3/2$ is admitted (for only $\Delta I = 5/2$ can reach $I = 3$). But the relation of the K_2^0 rates to the K^+ rates depends explicitly on the $\Delta I = 1/2$ assumption. Since the available kinetic energy in these three pion decays is small, it is important to include also the change in phase space due to the fact that the charged pion is heavier than the neutral one. The data then, are in accord with predictions, but the tests are not yet very stringent. For example, the ratio of the last two rates given here as $1/4$ is changed to 0.325 by phase-space factors. Experimentally, the ratio is 0.30 ± 0.04. Phase space predicts the ratio of the first two should be 1.89 (instead of $3/2$); experimentally it is 1.6 ± 0.6.

Up to the present point there could have been a mixture of $\Delta I = 1/2$ and $\Delta I = 3/2$. If there were, then the K_2^0 rates would not be determined relative to the K^+ rates. If the $\Delta I = 1/2$ rule is assumed then all four rates are related in the proportion given by the weights in the above table. Another way of putting this is that from the known rate $K^+ \to \pi + \pi + \pi$, one can predict the rate for $K_2^0 \to \pi^+ + \pi^- + \pi^0$. This turns out to be $3.1 \pm 0.2 \times 10^6$/sec. There are two experiments giving $2.9 \pm 0.1 \times 10^6$/sec and $2.3 \pm 0.5 \times 10^6$/sec; both are thus consistent with the $\Delta I = 1/2$ hypothesis.

In summary, the evidence for the $\Delta I = 1/2$ rule is quite good. The $\Delta I = 3/2$ amplitudes are small, but not necessarily zero. There is no evidence for the $\Delta I = 5/2$ amplitude. The intriguing questions are:

a) whether the $\Delta I = \frac{1}{2}$ rule could be an exact symmetry of the weak couplings, and

b) if this is not so, how this rule can become so prominent dynamically.

Attempts to deduce the $\Delta I = \frac{1}{2}$ rule — 6th LECTURE

In this lecture we shall present some of the attempts that have been made to deduce the $\Delta I = \frac{1}{2}$ rule for the strangeness changing non-leptic decays. Let me emphasize that this mystery comes just from the isotopic spin properties of the $\bar{J} \cdot J$ form assumed for the weak interactions, and is neither generated nor solved by Cabibbo's choice for the weak interaction current. No answer is known for this mystery. Therefore, we can only list some of the speculations that have been raised and criticize them.

The first interesting question is, if we assume that the strangeness changing non-leptic interaction is of the form

$$(\overline{\sigma^+} p) \cos \Theta \sin \Theta$$

and calculate the amplitudes, then, are the $\Delta I = \frac{3}{2}$ amplitudes dynamically suppressed or are the $\Delta I = \frac{1}{2}$ amplitudes dynamically enhanced, or both? There is no doubt that in the $\overline{\sigma^+} p$ form both the $\Delta I = \frac{1}{2}$ and $\Delta I = \frac{3}{2}$ amplitudes are present with roughly equal weights. However, the strong interactions through renormalization effects will modify the relative weights of the $\Delta I = \frac{3}{2}$ and $\Delta I = \frac{1}{2}$ contributions. It could be that the mesonic corrections are of such a form that the effective strength for the $\Delta I = \frac{1}{2}$ matrix elements is enhanced relative to those for which $\Delta I = \frac{3}{2}$. In addition, we would also like to distinguish between the two cases $\Delta I = \frac{1}{2}$ enhanced, or $\Delta I = \frac{3}{2}$ suppressed. The problem would be very easily answered if we could calculate these renormalizations, but no reliable computation can be made. Therefore, we cannot answer the question in a unique and direct fashion.

Nevertheless, I would like to report on two little calculations which may or may not be significant for the question. The calculations do represent an attempt to find the order of magnitude of the effects. You may not wish to consider this line of flimsy reasoning; we are becoming very uncertain about this matter, nevertheless, I shall present it. Let us calculate the decay $\Lambda \to p + \pi^-$, presuming that the graph

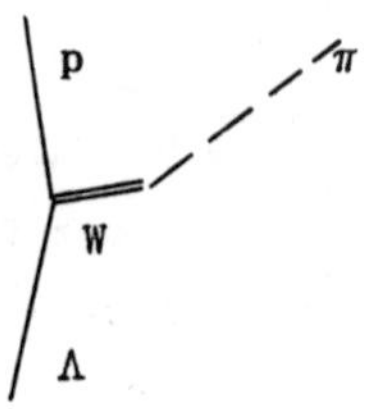

dominates the amplitude. Both vertices can be obtained from experiment. The Λpw vertex comes from the experimental determination of parameters in the Cabibbo theory of the leptic decays, whereas the Wπ vertex comes from the known decay rate of π^+. If one does this calculation, one finds both $\Delta I = 1/2$ and $\Delta I = 3/2$ terms of equal magnitude and one gets an estimate for the rate of 8×10^7/sec. The reason that one gets both $\Delta I = 1/2$ and $\Delta I = 3/2$ terms is that there is no corresponding diagram for the decay $\Lambda \to n + \pi^0$. We now make the assumption that this rate gives a good estimate of the strength of the $\Delta I = 3/2$ terms in the amplitudes. Now, if we compare this estimate with the actual rate of 2.4×10^9/sec, we see on the basis of this argument that the $\Delta I = 1/2$ amplitude must be considerably enhanced. However, this cannot be the whole story. The ratio of the two rates is one to thirty. That means the amplitude for the $\Delta I = 3/2$ is $1/\sqrt{30} = 0.18$, but we already know from the discussion of the experimental validity of the $\Delta I = 1/2$ rule that the $\Delta I = 3/2$ amplitude is less than 0.045 in magnitude. (There is a way out, perhaps, if the $\Delta I = 3/2$ amplitude violates CP. Then there would be no interference term, so that a $\Delta I = 3/2$ amplitude this large would not contradict the experimental branching ratio.) The result of this argument is that the $\Delta I = 1/2$ term is enhanced and the $\Delta I = 3/2$ term is cut down.

However, since the amplitudes from this calculation are off by a factor of five, one way or the other, it is difficult to pretend that this calculation means very much.

Another case in which we can make a similar calculation is the decay $K \rightarrow \pi + \pi$. Consider the following diagram

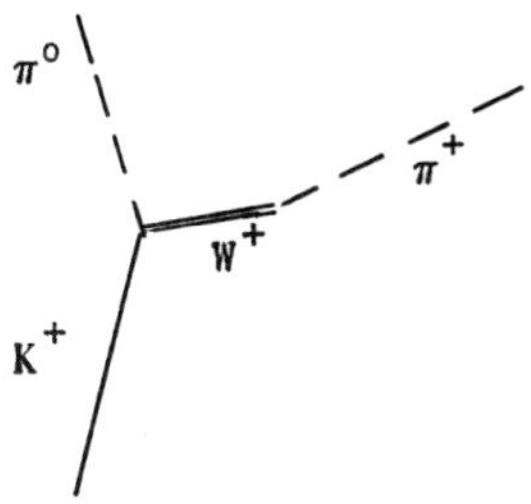

The $K^+\pi^0 W$ vertex can be calculated from the $K \rightarrow \pi +$ lepton-decay rate and, in a manner similar to the previous case, we find an estimate of 9×10^7/sec, whereas the experimental rate is 1.55×10^7/sec. Thus, the theoretical estimate must be cut down in reality. As explained previously, the K^+ amplitude comes only from the $\Delta I = 3/2$ terms, so that we have another hint that the $\Delta I = 3/2$ amplitudes are suppressed. Furthermore, the experimental rate for $K_1^0 \rightarrow \pi + \pi$ is considerably greater than what one could get from such an estimate. That seems to indicate that the $\Delta I = 1/2$ amplitude is considerably faster than one estimates from such calculations. Thus, it looks like there is some other type of diagram that must dynamically enhance the $\Delta I = 1/2$ amplitudes.

There are two fundamentally different ways in which people have tried to approach the $\Delta I = 1/2$ rule. The first proposal is that $\Delta I = 1/2$ is an exact rule. To make an exact $\Delta I = 1/2$ rule we have to augment the charged current-current interaction by adding neutral current terms for the strongly interacting particles. If we add a term of the form $(\bar{\sigma}\sigma n)$ with the right amplitude to the $\bar{J} \cdot J$ form, we then get a perfect $\Delta I = 1/2$ coupling. (We do not want to add neutral currents for the leptons because decays like $K \rightarrow \mu + \bar{e}$, $K \rightarrow \nu + \bar{\nu}$, and so on are not observed.) This theory results in two predictions. First, that the $\Delta I = \frac{1}{2}$ rule is exact and secondly, that some day a neutral weak-vector boson might be discovered. Thus, this theory predicts no more than the $\Delta I = \frac{1}{2}$ rule as far as the weak interactions are concerned.

Can the $\Delta I = \frac{1}{2}$ rule be perfect? Since the K^+ does in fact disintegrate into two pions, the $\Delta I = \frac{1}{2}$ rule seems to be violated. People have long speculated that the K^+ decay amplitude results from electromagnetic corrections. If the process is electromagnetic, the rate should be down by a factor $(e^2)^2 \sim 1/20000$, but the observed rate is suppressed relative to the K_1^0 rate by a factor of only 1/500. The question of how to jack up the electromagnetic correction has occupied the minds of many theorists but no one has yet published an explanation that is satisfactory. Thus, no clarity has resulted from the hypothesis that the weak interaction transforms exactly like $\Delta I = \frac{1}{2}$.

The second point of view commonly adopted is that renormalization effects are decidedly different for the $\Delta I = \frac{1}{2}$ and the $\Delta I = \frac{3}{2}$ amplitudes. Many people have tried to argue that there are certain diagrams which are enhanced considerably and which transform only like $\Delta I = \frac{1}{2}$. For example, consider the $\overline{\sigma}^{\mp}$ p cross-term $(\bar{p}\Lambda)(\bar{n}p)$. From such a term there is a diagram of the form

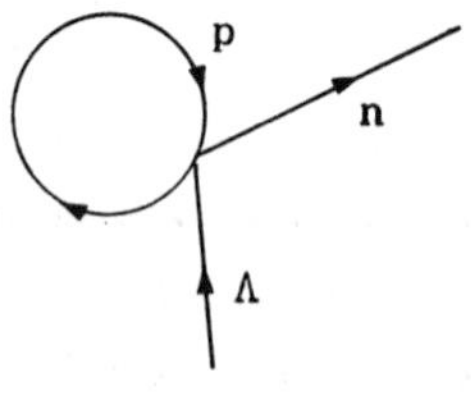

This type of diagram is not defined in perturbation theory, but it certainly may well be that such a term should be included in the correct expansion of the amplitude and it might be that it has a large coefficient. You will note that because the Λ goes directly into the neutron, this diagram gives only a

$\Delta I = \frac{1}{2}$ change. This explains why $\Delta I = \frac{1}{2}$ is so big. At the same time, this argument does not say $\Delta I = \frac{3}{2}$ decays are impossible, but allows such decays to proceed at a small rate with perhaps some renormalizations. However, since we really cannot compute anything, all that such a theory does is restate the experimental data in a different language. This theory thus predicts nothing new.

It seems that the same $\Delta I = \frac{1}{2}$ loop diagrams would result from Cabibbo's complete current. As an exercise you may write out all the terms in the $\overline{\sigma^{\mp}}\, p$ form that lead to cannibalistic loop diagrams and check to see that they all give $\Delta I = \frac{1}{2}$.

In the octet framework the proposition that $\Delta I = \frac{1}{2}$ terms dominate for strangeness changing non-leptonic interactions has been generalized by many people to the hypothesis that part of the weak Lagrangian transforms like an octet in the eightfold way. In particular the strangeness changing piece transforms like the "n" member of the octet. Since the $\bar{J} \cdot J$ form is the symmetric product of two octets and the only symmetric multiplets contained in the direct product are '1', '8' and '27', the hypothesis consists of completely suppressing '27'. (Terms which transform as '1' do not lead to strangeness changing decays, of course.) Are there any new rules from the assumption of an octet other than those associated with $\Delta I = \frac{1}{2}$? Most unfortunately there are no relations predicted among the reaction amplitudes that can be observed experimentally. Some predictions have been made, but these were based, in addition, on specific assumptions, e.g. there are no gradients in the coupling. This, however, is not in the same spirit as a prediction based only on symmetry principles.

Benjamin Lee derived the relation

$$-A(\Lambda \to p+\pi^-) + 2A(\Xi^- \to \Lambda + \pi^-) = 3A(\Sigma^+ \to p + \pi^0).$$

To derive this relation, however, he assumed R invariance in addition to SU_3. (R invariance is the symmetry based on the transformation $p \to \overline{\Xi^-}$, $n \to \overline{\Xi^0}$, $\Sigma^+ \to \Sigma^-$, and so on. This is simply reflection through the centre of the octet.)

However, because the Ξ's and nucleons have such different masses, R invariance is not in agreement with the facts of nature.

Cabibbo also concluded at one time that the $K_1^0 \to \pi + \pi$ was forbidden by the octet scheme, but this conclusion rested on the additional assumption that there were no gradients in the coupling. Since there is no reason why the matrix element should not involve gradients, the K_1^0 is not forbidden to decay into two pions.

It is rather interesting and disappointing that the assumption of definite SU_3 transformation properties for the non-leptic weak interactions has given us nothing. It seems that a qualitatively different idea is needed to clear up the puzzle of the non-leptic decays. I shall close these lectures with the hopeful speculation that some clever theorist may be able to tie together the fact that CP seems to be violated in weak interactions, and the fact that there are certain unexpected isotopic selection rules in the weak interactions.

Weak decay data summary

Muon Mass, 105.655 ± 0.01 MeV, and lifetime, $2.212 \pm 0.001 \times 10^{-6}$ sec, determine the weak decay constant to be

$$G = (1.0233 \pm 0.0004) \times 10^{-5} \, (\hbar c)^{1/2} \, M_p^{-2}$$

(M_p = proton mass).

Nuclear β decay $O^{14} \rightarrow N^{14}$ (corrected for electromagnetic effects) implies that the value of G for the vector part of the current is 0.980 ± 0.005 times G. Other β-decay experiments, including neutron decay asymmetry and lifetime of 1013 ± 29 seconds, suggest that the axial coupling is -1.26 times the vector coupling.

π^+ [Mass 139.59 ± 0.05; lifetime $(2.55 \pm 0.03) \times 10^{-8}$]. The branching ratio $\pi^+ \rightarrow e^+ + \nu / \pi^+ \rightarrow \mu^+ + \nu$ agrees with predictions of theory to $\pm 2\%$. The Goldberger-Treiman formula for amplitude $\pi^+ \rightarrow \mu^+ + \nu$ is too small by 8%.

K^+ [Mass 493.9 ± 0.2; lifetime $(1.224 \pm 0.013) \times 10^{-8}$ sec]. The branching is $64\% \pm 4\%$ into $\mu + \nu$; $(19 \pm 1)\%$ to $\pi^+ + \pi^0$; $5.7 \pm 0.3\%$ to $\pi^+ + \pi^+ + \pi^-$; $(1.7 \pm 0.2)\%$ to $\pi^+ + \pi^0 + \pi^0$; and $7.6 \pm 1.1\%$ to leptons and π^0. For decay into π + leptons, $K^+ \rightarrow \pi^0 + \mu^+ + \nu$ and $K^+ \rightarrow \pi^0 + e^+ + \nu$, total rate is $6.2 \pm 0.9 \times 10^8$ sec. If the amplitude is written $(p_K + p_\pi) + \xi(p_K - p_\pi)$, then the spectrum of μ indicates that ξ is not large. Ratio of muon to electron decay is: theoretical, $0.65 + 0.13\xi + 0.02\xi^2$; experimental, 0.70 ± 0.06. $K^+ \rightarrow \pi^+ + \pi^- + e^+ + \nu$ is $2.3 \pm 0.7 \times 10^{-5}$ of total disintegration.

K_1^0 [Mass 497.8 ± 0.6, lifetime $(1.00 \pm 0.04) \times 10^{-10}$ sec] goes into $\pi^0 + \pi^0$ or $\pi^+ + \pi^-$. Branching ratio to $\pi^0 + \pi^0$ by two experiments is $26 \pm 2\%$ or $33.5 \pm 1.4\%$.

$\underline{K_2^0}$ (Mass more than K_1^0 by about 0.8 $h/\tau(K_1)$; rate of decay $18 \pm 2 \times 10^6$ disintegration per sec.) For decay into leptons $\pi^{\mp} + \mu^{\pm} + \nu$ and $\pi^{\mp} + e^{\pm} + \nu$ rate is $11.1 \pm 1.2 \times 10^6$ sec^{-1}. For decay into 3π's ($\pi^0 + \pi^0 + \pi^0$ and $\pi^+ + \pi^- + \pi^0$) the rate into charged pions is, by one experiment, $2.9 \pm 0.7 \times 10^6$ sec^{-1} and by another is given as 0.171 ± 0.023 times the total rate into any charged products (therefore pions + leptons). There is some evidence for decay into two pions $\pi^+ + \pi^-$, thereby violating CP invariance at a branching ratio near 2×10^{-3}.

HYPERONS

Hyperon non-leptic decays

Particle	Mass MeV	Lifetime sec	Branching ratio	α	β	Υ
Λ	1115.36 ± 0.14	$2.51 \pm 0.09 \times 10^{-10}$	$N + \pi^0$ $1/3$ (to 2%)	$+ 0.56 \pm 0.20$		$+ 0.08 \pm 0.03$
			$P + \pi^-$ $2/3$	$+ 0.62 \pm 0.05$		$+ 0.78 \pm 0.04$
Σ^+	$1189 \cdot 40 \pm 0.20$	$0.76 \pm 0.06 \times 10^{-10}$	$N + \pi^+$ $51 \pm 4\%$	$- 0.03 \pm 0.08$		
			$P + \pi^0$ $49 \mp 4\%$	$- 0.78 \pm 0.08$		
Σ^-	$1197 \cdot 04 \pm 0.30$	$1.59 \pm 0.05 \times 10^{-10}$	$N + \pi^-$ 100%	$- 0.10 \pm 0.30$		
Ξ^-	$1318 \cdot 04 \pm 1.02$	$1.77 \pm 0.05 \times 10^{-10}$	$\Lambda + \pi^-$ 100%	$- 0.51 \pm 0.08$	$\pm (0.32 \pm 0.17)$	0.80 ± 0.08 (if spin $1/2$)
Ξ^0	1311 ± 8	2.4 to 3.9×10^{-10}	$\Lambda + \pi^0$			

$$\alpha = \frac{2 \text{ Re } S^*P}{|S|^2 + |P|^2} ; \quad \Upsilon = \frac{|S|^2 - |P|^2}{|S|^2 + |P|^2} ; \quad \beta = \frac{2 \text{ Im } S^*P}{|S|^2 + |P|^2} \cdot (\alpha^2 + \beta^2 + \Upsilon^2 = 1)$$

S,P amplitudes for S and P waves.

Hyperon leptic decays branching fraction

	UFI Theory	Experiment
$\Lambda \to p + e + \nu$	$1{\cdot}5 \times 10^{-2}$	$0.81 \pm 0.10 \times 10^{-3}$
$p + \mu + \nu$	0.2×10^{-2}	$\sim 1 \times 10^{-4}$
$\Xi \to \Lambda + e + \nu$	2.0×10^{-2}	$(2 \text{ or } 3) \times 10^{-3}$
$\Sigma^- \to N + e^- + \nu$	5.8×10^{-2}	$1.37 \pm 0.34 \times 10^{-3}$
$N + \mu^- + \nu$	2.6×10^{-2}	$0.66 \pm 0.14 \times 10^{-3}$
$\Sigma^- \to \Lambda + e^- + \nu$	1.0×10^{-4}	$0.07 \pm 0.03 \times 10^{-4}$
$\Sigma^+ \to \Lambda + e^+ + \nu$	0.6×10^{-4}	$0.07 \pm 0.04 \times 10^{-4}$

UFI means rate according to universal coupling constant G times V - A. If actual coupling in G times s(V - tA) then the rate is approximately $s^2/4\ (1 + 3t^2)$ times as much.

Asymmetry and spectrum of Λ decay indicate that t is approximately 1 for this decay.

VECTOR AND AXIAL CURRENTS UNDER FIRST ORDER SYMMETRY BREAKING

R. Gatto,
University of Florence.

In this lecture we shall discuss weak and electromagnetic currents in the eightfold way with first order symmetry breaking. We shall also see that under the following two general assumptions:

i) the vector currents and the electromagnetic current belong to the same unitary octet[1-3];

ii) the breaking of unitary symmetry is due to a term behaving like the eighth component of an octet[1];

the following result holds.

To first order in the symmetry-breaking interaction all the vector coupling constants are not renormalized. If applied to strangeness-violating leptonic decays of baryons and mesons, this result allows one to predict uniquely the vector coupling constants (i.e. the limits of the vector amplitudes for vanishing momentum transfers) up to first order in symmetry breaking.

The four $\Delta S = 0$ currents of the vector octet, namely j_1, j_2, j_3, and j_8, are clearly not renormalized at any order in the symmetry-breaking interaction to the accuracy of isotopic spin conservation. In fact, j_1, j_2, and j_3 are the local isotopic spin currents, and j_8 is the local hypercharge current. Their divergence is zero even after symmetry breaking and this implies their non-renormalization. For the components j_4, j_5, j_6, and j_7 a non-zero divergence supposedly comes in as soon as the full unitary symmetry is broken. In this sense the result we obtain, that to first order these currents are not renormalized for vanishing momentum transfer, appears to be shocking at first sight. An essential ingredient of the proof is the obvious consequence of the above assumption (i) that the electromagnetic current is formed out of the currents of the vector octet, implying that the current with which we are dealing has definite behaviour under charge conjugation. A definite C character of the currents (odd for vector and even for axial) implies their definite CP character (even for both vector and axial). The consequences one would derive for currents with non-definite behaviour under CP (with connected implications on time reversal) will be briefly surveyed in the last section.

I. THE CURRENT OCTETS

We consider:

an octet of vector currents j_ℓ $(\ell = 1,\ldots,8)$
an octet of axial currents j^5_ℓ $(\ell = 1,\ldots,8)$.

The electromagnetic current is

$$j_{em} = j_3 + \frac{1}{\sqrt{3}} j_8 .$$

The weak currents are:

$$j_{\pm} = \frac{1}{2}(j_1 \pm i\, j_2) \quad \text{vector current with } \Delta S = 0\,, \quad \Delta Q = \pm 1$$

$$s_{\pm} = \frac{1}{2}(j_4 \pm i\, j_5) \quad \text{vector current with } \Delta S = \pm 1, \quad \Delta Q = \pm 1$$

and

$$j^5_{\pm} = \frac{1}{2}(j^5_1 \pm i\, j^5_2) \quad \text{axial current with } \Delta S = 0\,, \quad \Delta Q = \pm 1$$

$$s^5_{\pm} = \frac{1}{2}(j^5_4 \pm i\, j^5_5) \quad \text{axial current with } \Delta S = \pm 1, \quad \Delta Q = \pm 1 .$$

II. FIRST CLASS AND SECOND CLASS AMPLITUDES

In the general expansions:

$$<B_f|j_\mu|B_i> = \left(\frac{m_i m_f}{E_i E_f}\right)^{1/2} \bar{u}_f(F_1\gamma_\mu + F_2\sigma_{\mu\nu}K_\nu + F_3K_\mu)u_i$$

$$<B_f|j_\mu^5|B_i> = \left(\frac{m_i m_f}{E_i E_f}\right)^{1/2} \bar{u}_f(G_1\gamma_\mu + G_2\sigma_{\mu\nu}K + G_3K_\mu)\gamma_5 u_i ,$$

where B_i and B_f denote initial and final baryon, we call:

the vector amplitudes proportional to γ_μ and $\sigma_{\mu\nu}K_\nu$ }
the axial amplitudes proportional to $\gamma_\mu\gamma_5$ and $K_\mu\gamma_5$ } first class amplitudes

the vector amplitude proportional to K_μ }
the axial amplitude proportional to $\sigma_{\mu\nu}K_\nu\gamma_5$ } second class amplitudes

III. CHARGE CONJUGATION ON AN OCTET

For an octet that goes into itself under charge conjugation we define, following Gell-Mann[4)], an octet charge conjugation quantum number C, which coincides with the charge conjugation number of the components 1, 3, 4, 6, and 8 (and is opposite to that of 2, 5, and 7).

Now: the charge conjugation properties of j_ℓ are fixed from the assumption that j_{em} is obtained from the octet. We must have, for j_ℓ, C = -1.

For the octet j_ℓ^5 we assume that C = +1, as for its dominant amplitude (for low momentum transfer) $\gamma_\mu\gamma_5$.

IV. FIRST ORDER SYMMETRY BREAKING

It is assumed here that the term which breaks the symmetry transforms like the eighth component of an octet. Let B and $\bar{B}$ represent the baryon and antibaryon octets, and let us make use of the matrices λ_i defined by

Gell-Mann[1]. The matrices λ_i are constructed in perfect analogy to the isotopic spin matrices τ_1, τ_2, τ_3. They can be chosen as follows:

$$\lambda_{1,2,3} = \begin{bmatrix} \tau_{1,2,3} & 0 \\ 0 & 0 \end{bmatrix} \qquad \lambda_4 = \begin{bmatrix} 0 & 0 & 1 \\ 0 & 0 & 0 \\ 1 & 0 & 0 \end{bmatrix} \qquad \lambda_5 = i \begin{bmatrix} 0 & 0 & -1 \\ 0 & 0 & 0 \\ 1 & 0 & 0 \end{bmatrix}$$

$$\lambda_6 = \begin{bmatrix} 0 & 0 & 0 \\ 0 & 0 & 1 \\ 0 & 1 & 0 \end{bmatrix} \qquad \lambda_7 = i \begin{bmatrix} 0 & 0 & 0 \\ 0 & 0 & -1 \\ 0 & 1 & 0 \end{bmatrix} \qquad \lambda_8 = \frac{1}{\sqrt{3}} \begin{bmatrix} 1 & 0 & 0 \\ 0 & 1 & 0 \\ 0 & 0 & -2 \end{bmatrix} .$$

The matrices $\frac{1}{2}\tau_i$ are Hermitian, traceless, and satisfy the same commutation rules as the generators of SU_2. Similarly the matrices $\frac{1}{2}\lambda_i$ are Hermitian, traceless, and satisfy the same commutation rules as the generators of SU_3, namely

$$[F_i, F_j] = i f_{ijk} F_k .$$

We can form the following traces linear in $\bar{B}$, B, λ_i (where i denotes the i-th component of the octet) and with λ_8 occurring at most linearly:

$$\mathrm{Tr}[\bar{B} B \lambda_i], \quad \mathrm{Tr}[\bar{B} \lambda_i B], \quad \mathrm{Tr}[\bar{B} B \lambda_i \lambda_8], \quad \mathrm{Tr}[\bar{B} \lambda_i \lambda_8 B], \quad \mathrm{Tr}[\bar{B} \lambda_i B \lambda_8],$$

$$\mathrm{Tr}[\bar{B} \lambda_8 B \lambda_i], \quad \mathrm{Tr}[\bar{B} B \lambda_8 \lambda_i], \quad \mathrm{Tr}[\bar{B} \lambda_8 \lambda_i B], \quad \mathrm{Tr}[\bar{B} B]\,\mathrm{Tr}[\lambda_i \lambda_8],$$

$$\mathrm{Tr}[\bar{B} \lambda_i]\,\mathrm{Tr}[B \lambda_8], \quad \mathrm{Tr}[\bar{B} \lambda_8]\,\mathrm{Tr}[B \lambda_i] .$$

However, they are not all independent. There is an identity valid for traceless 3×3 matrices that says that the sum of the traces of four elements equals the sum of the terms Tr[-] Tr[-]. This was expected in: $8 \times 8 \times 8 \times 8$, 1 is contained eight times. Thus we must have eight scalars, instead of the nine above, linear in λ_8. We can thus eliminate one trace. For example, let us eliminate $\mathrm{Tr}[\bar{B} \lambda_i B \lambda_8]$.

V. RESTRICTIONS FOLLOWING FROM CHARGE CONJUGATION

We now exploit the consequences of charge conjugation. The symmetry-breaking term commutes with the charge conjugation operator. The perturbed currents must thus retain the charge conjugation behaviour of their unitary symmetric limits. Charge conjugation on a spinor ψ leads to:

$$\psi^c = C\bar{\psi}^T$$

$$\bar{\psi}^c = -\psi^T C^{-1}$$

where

$$C\gamma_\mu^T C^{-1} = -\gamma_\mu$$

and

$$C^T = -C .$$

Similarly on B

$$B^c = C\bar{B}^T$$

$$\bar{B}^c = -B^T C^{-1} .$$

The transposition on B is obvious if you recall that

$$B = \begin{bmatrix} -\frac{2}{\sqrt{6}}\Lambda & p & n \\ -\Xi^- & \frac{1}{\sqrt{6}}\Lambda + \frac{1}{\sqrt{2}}\Sigma^0 & \Sigma^- \\ \Xi^0 & \Sigma^+ & \frac{1}{\sqrt{6}}\Lambda - \frac{1}{\sqrt{2}}\Sigma^0 \end{bmatrix}$$

whereas

$$\bar{B} = \begin{bmatrix} -\frac{2}{\sqrt{6}}\bar{\Lambda} & -\bar{\Xi}^- & \bar{\Xi}^0 \\ \bar{p} & \frac{1}{\sqrt{6}}\bar{\Lambda} + \frac{1}{\sqrt{2}}\bar{\Sigma}^0 & \bar{\Sigma}^+ \\ \bar{n} & \bar{\Sigma}^- & \frac{1}{\sqrt{6}}\bar{\Lambda} - \frac{1}{\sqrt{2}}\bar{\Sigma}^0 \end{bmatrix}$$

so that $\bar{B}B$ behaves as a neutral object. Let us now discuss the charge conjugation properties of the invariants. Let Γ indicate a Dirac covariant. We have

$$C^{-1}\,\Gamma C = \omega_\Gamma \Gamma^T ,$$

where $\omega_\Gamma = +1$ when $\Gamma = S,P,A$, and $\omega_\Gamma = -1$ for V,T. For the terms without λ_8, which survive in the unitary symmetric limit, we have

$$\mathrm{Tr}[\bar{B}^c \Gamma B^c \lambda_i] = -\,\omega_\Gamma \mathrm{Tr}[B^T \Gamma^T \bar{B}^T \lambda_i]$$

$$= \omega_\Gamma \epsilon_i\, \mathrm{Tr}[\bar{B}\Gamma B \lambda_i] ,$$

where $\epsilon_i = 1$ for i = 1,3,4,6,8, and $\epsilon_i = -1$ for i = 2,5,7. In fact, the λ's are hermitian. Therefore, $\lambda_i^T = \lambda_i^*$ and we just have to recall that they are all real except for i = 2,5,7.

Similarly

$$\mathrm{Tr}[\bar{B}^c \lambda_i \Gamma B^c] = +\,\omega_\Gamma \epsilon_i\, \mathrm{Tr}[\bar{B}\lambda_i \Gamma B].$$

Note that we have made use of the anticommutation relations of Dirac fields. We should also point out that the K_ν in the covariants is not affected by the transposition of the two spinors. It corresponds in configuration space to $\partial_+ = (\overleftarrow{\partial}/\partial x_\mu) + (\overrightarrow{\partial}/\partial x_\mu)$. Next we find

$$\mathrm{Tr}[\bar{B}^c \Gamma B^c \lambda_i \lambda_8] = +\,\omega_\Gamma \mathrm{Tr}[\lambda_8^T \lambda_i^T \bar{B}\Gamma B]$$

$$= \omega_\Gamma \epsilon_i\, \mathrm{Tr}[\bar{B}\Gamma B \lambda_8 \lambda_i]$$

$$\mathrm{Tr}[\bar{B}^c \lambda_i \lambda_8 \Gamma B^c] = \omega_\Gamma \epsilon_i\, \mathrm{Tr}[\bar{B}\lambda_8 \lambda_i \Gamma B]$$

$$\mathrm{Tr}[\bar{B}^c \lambda_i \Gamma B^c \lambda_8] = \omega_\Gamma \epsilon_i\, \mathrm{Tr}[\bar{B}\lambda_i \Gamma B \lambda_8]$$

$$\mathrm{Tr}[\bar{B}^c \lambda_8 \Gamma B^c \lambda_i] = \omega_\Gamma \epsilon_i\, \mathrm{Tr}[\bar{B}\Gamma \lambda_8 B \lambda_i]$$

$$\mathrm{Tr}[\bar{B}^c \Gamma B^c \lambda_8 \lambda_i] = \omega_\Gamma \epsilon_i \,\mathrm{Tr}[\bar{B} \Gamma B \lambda_i \lambda_8]$$

$$\mathrm{Tr}[\bar{B}^c \lambda_8 \lambda_i \Gamma B^c] = \omega_\Gamma \epsilon_i \,\mathrm{Tr}[\bar{B} \Gamma \lambda_i \lambda_8 B].$$

Next we have

$$\begin{aligned}
\mathrm{Tr}[\bar{B}^c \Gamma B^c]\,\mathrm{Tr}[\lambda_i \lambda_8] &= \omega_\Gamma 2\mathrm{Tr}[\bar{B} \Gamma B]\delta_{i8} \\
&= \omega_\Gamma \epsilon_i \,\mathrm{Tr}[\bar{B} \Gamma B]\,\mathrm{Tr}[\lambda_i \lambda_8] \\
\mathrm{Tr}[\bar{B}^c \lambda_i]\Gamma\,\mathrm{Tr}[B^c \lambda_8] &= \omega_\Gamma \,\mathrm{Tr}[\bar{B}^T \lambda_8]\Gamma\,\mathrm{Tr}[B^T \lambda_i] \\
&= \omega_\Gamma \epsilon_i \,\mathrm{Tr}[\bar{B} \lambda_8]\Gamma\mathrm{Tr}[B \lambda_i] \\
\mathrm{Tr}[\bar{B}^c \lambda_8]\Gamma\,\mathrm{Tr}[B^c \lambda_i] &= \omega_\Gamma \,\mathrm{Tr}[\bar{B}^T \lambda_i]\Gamma\,\mathrm{Tr}[B^T \lambda_8] \\
&= \omega_\Gamma \epsilon_i \,\mathrm{Tr}[\bar{B} \lambda_i]\Gamma\,\mathrm{Tr}[B \lambda_8]\,.
\end{aligned}$$

In conclusion, we see that the invariants $\mathrm{Tr}[\bar{B} B \lambda_i \lambda_8]$ and $\mathrm{Tr}[\bar{B} B \lambda_8 \lambda_i]$ under charge conjugation go into each other and take on a sign $\omega_\Gamma \epsilon_i$, and the same happems for the pair $\mathrm{Tr}[\bar{B} \lambda_i \lambda_8 B]$ and $\mathrm{Tr}[\bar{B} \lambda_8 \lambda_i B]$, and for the pair $\mathrm{Tr}[\bar{B} \lambda_i]\,\mathrm{Tr}[B \lambda_8]$ and $\mathrm{Tr}[\bar{B} \lambda_8]\,\mathrm{Tr}[B \lambda_i]$. All the remaining invariants go into themselves apart from the sign $\omega_\Gamma \epsilon_i$.

VI. FIRST CLASS COVARIANTS

We can now use all this knowledge to write down the expression for first class covariants, both vector and axial. For vector first class covariants $\omega_\Gamma = -1$ and we want the current octet to go into minus itself under charge conjugation. For axial first class covariants $\omega_\Gamma = +1$ but we want the current to go into itself under charge conjugation. Therefore, of the invariants all those that go into themselves are perfectly acceptable. Also the pairs of invariants that get interchanged are perfectly acceptable provided we take each of them with equal coefficient. We thus find for first class covariants (both vector and axial) the following general expansion:

$$a_0\, Tr[\bar{B}B\lambda_i] + b_0\, Tr[\bar{B}\lambda_i B] + a\, Tr[\bar{B}B\{\lambda_i,\lambda_8\}] + b\, Tr[\bar{B}\{\lambda_i,\lambda_8\}B]$$

$$+ d\, Tr[\bar{B}\lambda_8 B\lambda_i] + g\, Tr[\bar{B}B]\, Tr[\lambda_i\lambda_8] + h\left[Tr[\bar{B}\lambda_i]\, Tr[B\lambda_8] + Tr[\bar{B}\lambda_8]\, Tr[B\lambda_i]\right].$$

As we have already said, the term $Tr[\bar{B}\lambda_i B\lambda_8]$ has been eliminated.

VII. SECOND CLASS COVARIANTS

For the second class vector covariant $\omega_\Gamma = +1$ (the Dirac matrix Γ is 1) and we still want the current to go into minus itself under charge conjugation. For the second class axial covariant $\omega_\Gamma = -1$, but we want the current to go into itself under charge conjugation. In both cases all the invariants that go into themselves cannot be accepted. We are only left with the pairs that transform into each other provided we take them with opposite coefficients. We thus have for second class covariants the expansion

$$a'\, Tr\left[\bar{B}B[\lambda_i,\lambda_8]\right] + b'\, Tr\left[\bar{B}\,[\lambda_i,\lambda_8]B\right]$$

$$+ h'\left[Tr[\bar{B}\lambda_i]\, Tr[B\lambda_8] - Tr[\bar{B}\lambda_8]\, Tr[B\lambda_i]\right].$$

The above expression contains λ_8 linearly. It thus goes to zero when there is no symmetry breaking. We thus find that there are no second class amplitudes in the limit of full symmetry[5] (Wolfenstein's theorem).

VIII. FIRST CLASS AMPLITUDES FOR LEPTONIC DECAYS

From the expansion of Chapter VI we can immediately derive the following expressions for the first class amplitudes (vector or axial) with $\Delta S = 0$:

$$(n \to p) = b_0 + 2b$$

$$(\Sigma^- \to \Lambda) = \frac{1}{\sqrt{6}} (a_0 + b_0 + 2a + 2b + d + 6h)$$

$$(\Lambda \to \Sigma^+) = (\Sigma^- \to \Lambda) .$$

The last of these equations holds to any order under the assumptions we have made.

For the first class amplitudes (vector or axial) with $\Delta s = 1$ we similarly find:

$$(\Sigma^- \to n) = a_0 - a + d$$

$$(\Sigma_0 \to p) = \frac{1}{\sqrt{2}} (\Sigma^- \to n)$$

$$(\Lambda \to p) = \frac{1}{\sqrt{6}} (a_0 - 2b_0 - a + 2b + d + 6h)$$

$$(\Xi^- \to \Lambda) = \frac{1}{\sqrt{6}} (- 2a_0 + b_0 + 2a - b + 4d + 6h)$$

$$(\Xi^0 \to \Sigma^+) = b_0 - b$$

$$(\Xi^- \to \Sigma^0) = \frac{1}{\sqrt{2}} (\Xi^0 \to \Sigma^+).$$

The relations between $(\Sigma^- \to n)$ and $(\Sigma^0 \to p)$, and between $(\Xi^- \to \Sigma^0)$ and $(\Xi^0 \to \Sigma^+)$, only follow from the $\Delta T = \frac{1}{2}$ behaviour of the current (which is implicit in the supposed octet behaviour).

IX. SECOND CLASS AMPLITUDES FOR LEPTONIC DECAYS

From the expansion of Chapter VII we obtain for the second class amplitudes (vector or axial) with $\Delta S = 0$:

$$(n \to p) = 0$$

$$(\Sigma^- \to \Lambda) = - \sqrt{6}h' = - (\Lambda \to \Sigma^+).$$

For the second class amplitudes (vector or axial) for $\Delta S = 1$ leptonic decays we find:

$$(\Sigma^- \to n) = -3a'$$

$$(\Sigma^0 \to p) = \frac{1}{\sqrt{2}} (\Sigma^- \to n)$$

$$(\Lambda \to p) = \sqrt{\frac{3}{2}} (-a' + 2b' + 2h')$$

$$(\Xi^- \to \Lambda) = \sqrt{\frac{3}{2}} (2a' - b' - 2h')$$

$$(\Xi^0 \to \Sigma^+) = -3b'$$

$$(\Xi^- \to \Sigma^0) = \frac{1}{\sqrt{2}} (\Xi^0 \to \Sigma^+) .$$

Again, the second and last relation simply follow from $\Delta T = \frac{1}{2}$. For second class amplitudes we thus have:

i) in the unitary symmetric limit all second class amplitudes vanish (Wolfenstein's theorem);

ii) the known relation $(\Sigma^- \to \Lambda) = -(\Lambda \to \Sigma^+)$ for second class amplitudes [which holds at any order, see Weinberg[6]];

iii) the relation[7] $-\sqrt{6}[(\Lambda \to p) + (\Xi^- \to \Lambda)] = (\Sigma^- \to n) + (\Xi^0 \to \Sigma^+)$ among $\Delta S = 1$ second class amplitudes.

X. ELECTROMAGNETIC AMPLITUDES

First class electromagnetic amplitudes

We obtain

$$(p \to p) = -a_0 + 2b_0 + 4a + 4b - d + 3g$$

$$(n \to n) = -a_0 - b_0 + 4a - 2b - d + 3g$$

$$(\Sigma^+ \to \Sigma^+) = a_0 + 2b_0 - 2a + 4b - d + 3g$$

$$(\Sigma^- \to \Sigma^-) = 2a_0 - b_0 + 4a - 2b + 2d + 3g$$

$$(\Sigma^0 \to \Sigma^0) = \frac{1}{2}(\Sigma^+ \to \Sigma^+) + \frac{1}{2}(\Sigma^- \to \Sigma^-)$$

$$(\Lambda \to \Lambda) = -\frac{1}{2}a_0 - \frac{1}{2}b_0 + 3a + 3b + \frac{3}{2}d + 3g + 6h$$

$$(\Xi^- \to \Xi^-) = 2a_0 - b_0 + 4a - 4d + 3g$$

$$(\Xi^0 \to \Xi^0) = -a_0 - b_0 - 2a + 4b + 2d + 3g$$

$$(\Sigma^0 \to \Lambda) = \frac{1}{2\sqrt{3}}[(\Sigma^0 \to \Sigma^0) + 3(\Lambda \to \Lambda) - 2(\Xi^0 \to \Xi^0) - 2(n \to n)]$$

$$(\Lambda \to \Sigma^0) = (\Sigma^0 \to \Lambda).$$

Second class electromagnetic amplitudes

They are all zero except

$$(\Sigma^0 \to \Lambda) = -3\sqrt{3}h' = -(\Lambda \to \Sigma^0).$$

The relation between the form factors of the Σ's given above is a well-known consequence of charge independence and, of course, it holds to any order in the SU_3 breaking interaction. The other relation given above for the $(\Sigma^0 \to \Lambda)$ first class electromagnetic form factors is a direct consequence of the model and was pointed out first by Okubo. The relation reported above for second class $\Sigma^0 \to \Lambda$ amplitudes also holds to any order.

We have thus, in principle, seven independent first class amplitudes, one for each particle of the octet, $p, n, \Sigma^+, \Sigma^-, \Lambda, \Xi^-, \Xi^0$, excluding Σ^0 which can be expressed through the other Σ's. These amplitudes are expressed in terms of seven unknowns: a_0, b_0, a, b, d, g, h. These same parameters appear in the $\Delta S = 0$ and $\Delta S = 1$ transitions.

XI. A NON-RENORMALIZATION THEOREM FOR THE VECTOR CURRENT OCTET

We are now going to explore the limits of the amplitudes for vanishing momentum transfer. It is convenient to write down explicitly the form of the expansion of Chapter VI in the case of $j_{em} = j_3 + (1/\sqrt{3})\, j_8$. We make use of the equations

$$\{\lambda_i, \lambda_j\} = 2d_{ijk}\, \lambda_k$$

and

$$\mathrm{Tr}[\lambda_i \lambda_j] = 2\delta_{ij}$$

that our λ's satisfy. The values of d_{ijk} can be found in Gell-Mann's paper. We easily obtain the expansion

$$\left(a_0 + \frac{2}{\sqrt{3}}\, a\right) \mathrm{Tr}[\bar{B} B \lambda_3] + \left(b_0 + \frac{2}{\sqrt{3}}\, b\right) \mathrm{Tr}[\bar{B} \lambda_3 B] + \left(a_0 - \frac{2}{\sqrt{3}}\, a\right) \frac{1}{\sqrt{3}}\, \mathrm{Tr}[\bar{B} B \lambda_8]$$

$$+ \left(b_0 - \frac{2}{\sqrt{3}}\, b\right) \frac{1}{\sqrt{3}}\, \mathrm{Tr}[\bar{B} \lambda_8 B] + \frac{2}{\sqrt{3}} \left(\frac{2}{3}\, a + \frac{2}{3}\, b + g\right) \mathrm{Tr}[\bar{B} B]$$

$$+ c \left[\mathrm{Tr}[\bar{B} \lambda_3 B \lambda_8] - \mathrm{Tr}[\bar{B} \lambda_8 B \lambda_3]\right] + h \left[\mathrm{Tr}[\bar{B} \lambda_3]\, \mathrm{Tr}[B \lambda_8]\right.$$

$$\left. + \mathrm{Tr}[\bar{B} \lambda_8]\, \mathrm{Tr}[B \lambda_3] + \frac{2}{\sqrt{3}}\, \mathrm{Tr}[\bar{B} \lambda_8]\, \mathrm{Tr}[B \lambda_8]\right].$$

This current is non-renormalized. In the limit of vanishing momentum transfer it must reduce to

$$-\frac{1}{2}\left[\mathrm{Tr}[\bar{B} B \lambda_3] - \mathrm{Tr}[\bar{B} \lambda_3 B] + \frac{1}{\sqrt{3}}\, \mathrm{Tr}[\bar{B} B \lambda_8] - \frac{1}{\sqrt{3}}\, \mathrm{Tr}[\bar{B} \lambda_8 B]\right].$$

This is only possible provided that in that limit

$$a_0 = -\frac{1}{2},\ b_0 = \frac{1}{2} \ \text{ and } \ a = b = c = g = h = 0.$$

We thus have the following result [by Ademollo and Gatto[7]]: In the limit of zero momentum transfer the amplitudes $a_0, b_0, \ldots, h$ conserve their values of the unitary symmetric limit.

In other words: <u>to first order in the symmetry-breaking interactions all the vector coupling constants are not renormalized.</u> We recall the two main assumptions for the validity of the theorem:

i) the breaking of unitary symmetry is due to a term behaving like the eighth component of an octet;

ii) the vector currents and the electromagnetic current belong to the same unitary octet.

The most useful application of this result is to strangeness violating leptonic decays of baryons and mesons. The vector coupling constants are uniquely predicted including first order symmetry breaking.

More explicitly, with a coupling of the form

$$\frac{1}{\sqrt{2}} G \sin \vartheta [\bar{\psi}_f \gamma_\mu (f_V + f_A \gamma_5) \psi_i] [\bar{\psi}_\ell \gamma_\mu (1 + \gamma_5) \psi_\nu]$$

we have

$$f_V(\Sigma^- n) = -1$$

$$f_V(\Sigma^0 p) = -(2)^{-1/2}$$

$$f_V(\Lambda p) = -(3/2)^{1/2}$$

$$f_V(\Xi^- \Lambda) = (3/2)^{1/2}$$

$$f_V(\Xi^0 \Sigma^+) = 1$$

$$f_V(\Xi^- \Sigma^0) = (2)^{-1/2},$$

where $f_V(\Sigma^- n)$, for instance, is the vector coupling for $\Sigma^- \to n + \text{leptons}$.

Perhaps it may be useful to illustrate the result in a different way. We have seen in Chapter X that the seven electromagnetic amplitudes of $p, n, \Sigma^+, \Sigma^-, \Lambda, \Xi^-, \Xi^0$ are expressed linearly in terms of the seven parameters a_0, b_0, a, b, d, g, h. The system of linear equations is that of Chapter X. We do not know the electromagnetic amplitudes in general but we do know them for vanishing momentum transfer. For each of them the limiting value is exactly the electric charge of $p, n, \Sigma^+, \Sigma^-, \Lambda, \Xi^-$, and Ξ^0, respectively. In this limit we can thus solve the system and determine a_0, b_0, a, b, d, g, h uniquely, provided the determinant is different from zero. The 7×7 determinant is, in fact, different from zero as can be immediately checked. Without actually solving the system we can just argue that one possible solution must be that of the unitary symmetry limit. However, as there is only one solution, this must also be the solution away from the unitary symmetry limit. The vector coupling constants are therefore non-renormalized.

XII. BOSONS

All the results of the previous sections apply, of course, to bosons as well.

We can form the following traces:

$$\mathrm{Tr}[\Pi\Pi\lambda_i] = \mathrm{Tr}[\Pi\lambda_i\Pi]$$

$$\mathrm{Tr}[\Pi\Pi\lambda_i\lambda_8] = \mathrm{Tr}[\Pi\lambda_i\lambda_8\Pi]$$

$$\mathrm{Tr}[\Pi\lambda_i\Pi\lambda_8] = \mathrm{Tr}[\Pi\lambda_8\Pi\lambda_i]$$

$$\mathrm{Tr}[\Pi\Pi\lambda_8\lambda_i] = \mathrm{Tr}[\Pi\lambda_8\lambda_i\Pi]$$

$$\mathrm{Tr}[\Pi\Pi]\ \mathrm{Tr}[\lambda_i\lambda_8]$$

$$\mathrm{Tr}[\Pi\lambda_i]\mathrm{Tr}[\Pi\lambda_8] = \mathrm{Tr}[\Pi\lambda_8]\ \mathrm{Tr}[\Pi\lambda_i],$$

where Π is the boson tensor.

There is one first class covariant

$$\partial_- = \frac{\overleftarrow{\partial}}{\partial x_\mu} - \frac{\overrightarrow{\partial}}{\partial x_\mu}$$

(difference of the derivative on the right and that on the left) and a second class covariant:

$$\partial_+ = \frac{\partial}{\partial x_\mu} + \frac{\vec{\partial}}{\partial x_\mu} .$$

Let us now discuss the behaviour under charge conjugation of the different terms. Under charge conjugation

$$\Pi \rightarrow \Pi^T .$$

Let us take a typical term of first class

$$Tr[\Pi \partial_- \Pi \lambda_i \lambda_8] \rightarrow Tr[\Pi^T \partial_- \Pi^T \lambda_i \lambda_8] = Tr[\lambda_8^T \lambda_i^T \Pi \partial_-^T \Pi] = - \epsilon_i \; Tr[\Pi \partial_- \Pi \lambda_8 \lambda_i]$$

noting that formally

$$\partial_-^T = - \partial_-$$

while

$$\partial_+^T = \partial_+ .$$

In this way we get under charge conjugation

$$Tr[\Pi \partial_- \Pi \lambda_i] \rightarrow - \epsilon_i \; Tr[\Pi \partial_- \Pi \lambda_i]$$

$$Tr[\Pi \partial_- \Pi \lambda_i \lambda_8] \rightarrow - \epsilon_i \; Tr[\Pi \partial_- \Pi \lambda_8 \lambda_i]$$

$$Tr[\Pi \partial_- \lambda_i \Pi \lambda_8] \rightarrow - \epsilon_i \; Tr[\Pi \lambda_i \partial_- \Pi \lambda_8]$$

$$Tr[\Pi \partial_- \Pi \lambda_8 \lambda_i] \rightarrow - \epsilon_i \; Tr[\Pi \partial_- \Pi \lambda_i \lambda_8]$$

$$Tr[\Pi \Pi] \partial_- Tr[\lambda_i \lambda_8] \rightarrow - \epsilon_i \; Tr[\Pi \Pi] \partial_- Tr[\lambda_i \lambda_8]$$

$$Tr[\Pi \lambda_i] \partial_- Tr[\Pi \lambda_8] \rightarrow - \epsilon_i \; Tr[\Pi \lambda_8] \partial_- Tr[\Pi \lambda_i] .$$

For the second class covariants (∂_+ instead of ∂_-) the transformations are the same except that the minus sign does not occur.

Assuming now that the current has $C = -1$, we write for the first class covariant the expansion

$$a_0 \, Tr[\Pi \partial_- \Pi \lambda_i] + a \, Tr[\Pi \partial_- \Pi\{\lambda_i,\lambda_8\}] + c \, Tr[\Pi \partial_- \Pi] \, Tr[\lambda_i \lambda_8] + d \, Tr[\Pi \partial_- \lambda_i] \, Tr[\Pi \lambda_8]$$

where the constants $a_0,\ldots,d$, of course, have no relation to those for the baryon case.

Again, forming the electromagnetic current and requiring that for zero momentum transfer it reduces to the form

$$-\frac{1}{2} Tr\left[\Pi \partial_- \Pi \left(\lambda_3 + \frac{1}{\sqrt{3}} \lambda_8\right)\right],$$

we find that all the vector coupling constants must be non-renormalized.

For $K^0 \to \pi^- + e^+ + \nu$, writing the interaction as

$$\frac{1}{\sqrt{2}} G \sin\vartheta \, f(p+q)_\mu \, \bar{u}_e \gamma_\mu (1+\gamma_5) u_\nu,$$

we can thus predict $f = 1$ including first order symmetry breaking.

For second class covariants, if we want our current to have $C = -1$, we only have the possibility

$$Tr\left[\Pi \partial_+ \Pi[\lambda_i,\lambda_8]\right] = 2if_{i8k} \, Tr[\Pi \partial_+ \Pi \lambda_k].$$

In fact, under C each term in the commutator goes into the other and the expression changes sign (for the components 1,3,4,6,8). From this expression we see that, as is well known, there are no second class terms in the unitary symmetric limit, and also there are no second class terms in the $\Delta S = 0$ transitions (valid to any order).

XIII. CURRENTS WITH INDEFINITE CHARGE CONJUGATION

As we have already seen, in the full unitary limit one has Wolfenstein's theorem[5]: First class amplitudes (vector γ_μ and $\gamma_{\mu\nu}K_\nu$, axial $\gamma_\mu\gamma_5$ and $K_\mu\gamma_5$) must belong to current octets with CP = + 1; second class amplitudes (vector $K_\mu\gamma_5$) must belong to octets with CP = - 1; and vice versa.

However, as soon as we introduce symmetry breaking into the theory, first class terms may appear also from octets with CP = - 1[8]
(among them γ_μ and $\gamma_\mu\gamma_5$, which give contributions for zero momentum transfer and may thus be expected to be important in leptonic decay of baryons). However, these terms must satisfy stringent restrictions. Their general expansion is of the form

$$a'' \operatorname{Tr}\left[\bar{B}B[\lambda_i,\lambda_8]\right] + b'' \operatorname{Tr}\left[\bar{B}[\lambda_i,\lambda_8]B\right] + c''\left[\operatorname{Tr}[\bar{B}\lambda_i]\operatorname{Tr}[B\lambda_8] - \operatorname{Tr}[\bar{B}\lambda_8]\operatorname{Tr}[B\lambda_i]\right].$$

For the $\Delta S = 0$ transitions this expansion implies the absence of such second class terms in all $\Delta S = 0$ transitions except for the amplitude $(\Sigma^- \to \Lambda)$ which must be equal and opposite to $(\Sigma^+ \to \Lambda)$. In particular, the second class terms will be absent in β decay. This result holds to any order in the symmetry breaking and is due to Weinberg[6].

For the $\Delta S = \pm 1$ leptonic decays these second class terms from CP = - 1 octets can contribute to all decays provided these amplitudes satisfy the usual $\Delta T = \frac{1}{2}$ relations: $1/\sqrt{2}(\Sigma^- \to n) = (\Sigma^0 \to p)$ and $1/\sqrt{2}(\Xi^0 \to \Sigma^+) = (\Xi^- \to \Sigma^0)$; and furthermore the relation

$$-\sqrt{6}[(\Lambda \to p) + (\Xi^- \to \Lambda)] = (\Sigma^- \to n) + (\Xi^0 \to \Sigma^+).$$

REFERENCES

1) M. Gell-Mann, Phys.Rev. 125, 1067 (1961).

2) N. Cabibbo and R. Gatto, Nuovo Cimento 21, 872 (1961).

3) N. Cabibbo, Phys.Rev.Letters 10, 531 (1962).

4) M. Gell-Mann, Phys.Rev.Letters 12, 155 (1964).

5) L. Wolfenstein, Phys.Rev. 135, B1436 (1964).

6) S. Weinberg, Phys.Rev. 112 1375 (1958).

7) M. Ademollo and R. Gatto, Phys.Rev.Letters Vol. 13, No. 7, 264 (1964).

8) N. Cabibbo,Physics Letters 12, 137 (1964).

FRACTIONALLY CHARGED PARTICLES AND SU_6

G. Zweig*)
California Institute of Technology.

I. THE SAKATA MODEL AND ITS MODIFICATION

In this course we are going to assume that the many strongly interacting particles are composites of a few fundamental objects (units), much as the nuclei are complex constructions of the proton and neutron. Unfortunately, the fundamental objects have yet to be discovered experimentally**) so we have a wide spectrum of possibilities. To narrow the field and give our problem a more explicit formulation, we will insist on picking a theory which contains the minimum number of units consistent with the observed strongly interacting particles and known conservation laws.

We know there exist particles of different isospin I, different strangeness S, different baryon number B. What is the minimum number of units necessary to construct these objects? One can form all I spins from products of $I = \frac{1}{2}$ states. For example, from the I spin doublet (p_0, n_0) one can form the $I = 1$ spin states:

$$\begin{aligned} \pi^+ &= \bar{n}_0 p_0 \\ \pi^0 &= (\bar{p}_0 p_0 - \bar{n}_0 n_0)/\sqrt{2} \\ \pi^- &= \bar{p}_0 n_0 \ . \end{aligned} \tag{1}$$

Here p_0 and n_0 are objects similar to the proton and neutron in that they are not strange and have $I_z = +\frac{1}{2}$ and $-\frac{1}{2}$, respectively. In order to accommodate strange particles like the K, it is necessary to introduce fundamental fields that carry strangeness. If we want to keep the number

*) Work supported by a US National Academy of Sciences National Research Council Postdoctoral Fellowship.

**) In fact, it is likely that the fundamental objects do not correspond to physical particles; rather, the units may form a convenient set of symbols that are helpful in expressing certain symmetries of the strong interactions.

of fields to a minimum, we are lead to a strangeness carrying isospin singlet Λ_0. The K could then be:

$$K^+ = \bar{\Lambda}_0 p_0 \qquad \bar{K}^0 = \bar{n}_0 \Lambda_0$$
$$K^0 = \bar{\Lambda}_0 n_0 \qquad K^- = \bar{p}_0 \Lambda_0 \; . \tag{2}$$

It is clear that <u>at least three</u> units are necessary

For baryons like the Σ and Ξ, we could have

$$\begin{aligned}
\Sigma^+ &= \pi^+\Lambda_0 = \bar{n}_0 p_0 \Lambda_0 \\
\Sigma^0 &= \pi^0\Lambda_0 = (\bar{p}_0 p_0 - \bar{n}_0 n_0)\Lambda_0/\sqrt{2} \\
\Sigma^- &= \pi^-\Lambda_0 = \bar{p}_0 n_0 \Lambda_0 \\
\Xi^0 &= \bar{K}^0\Lambda_0 = \bar{n}_0 \Lambda_0 \Lambda_0 \\
\Xi^- &= K^-\Lambda_0 = \bar{p}_0 \Lambda_0 \Lambda_0 \; .
\end{aligned} \tag{3}$$

For p we could take

$$p = p_0 \text{ or, } p = \bar{\Lambda}_0 \Lambda_0 p_0 \text{, or } p = (\bar{p}_0 p_0 + \bar{n}_0 n_0) p_0/\sqrt{2} \; . \tag{4}$$

Although there is some ambiguity here as to which choice we should make, it is evident that we may form the proton from our units.

Note that three meson units would not work since it would be impossible to construct the baryons. However, three baryon units like ($p_0 = p$, $n_0 = n$, $\Lambda_0 = \Lambda$) are seemingly all right.

We might try using mesons for two units, and a baryon for the other. This possibility we discard, however, because later we will want to argue that in a certain sense all three units are indistinguishable. So simplicity, combined with the known complexity of particle physics, leads us to unique spin, isospin, and strangeness assignments for the units.

Do p_0, n_0, and Λ_0 correspond to any known particles? The most obvious answer is that they are to be identified with the proton, neutron and Λ. We then obtain what is called the Sakata model[1].

The Sakata model not only allows one to construct the known strongly interacting particles, it also suggests the existence of a certain symmetry. We know that the strong interactions are invariant under rotations in isotopic spin space. This group of transformations, called SU_2 , mixes up the neutron and proton, but leaves the structure of the strong interactions unchanged:

$$SU_2 : p \longleftrightarrow n .$$

In the Sakata model where the p,n, and Λ are treated on an equal footing, it is natural to require that the strong interactions be invariant under a group of transformations which mix p,n, and Λ. SU_2 is now too small, but SU_3 will do:

SU_3 :

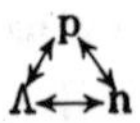

Although the strong interactions may be invariant under SU_3, it is clear that other interactions are not. The photon distinguishes the proton from the neutron and is presumably responsible for the p-n mass difference. There must be another mechanism, presently unknown, which is responsible for the Λ-nucleon mass splitting. If there were a particle coupled to strangeness much the same way as the photon is coupled to charge, then the Λ would be distinguished from the nucleon and the SU_3 symmetry would be appropriately broken*). The coupling constant involved would then be larger that the fine structure constant $e^2/\hbar c = 1/137$ in order to account for $\Lambda - N >> n - p$ **). On the other hand, this coupling should be considerably less than strong interaction couplings if SU_3 is to be a recognizable symmetry. This is just wild speculation, but does indicate the existence of simple theoretical mechanisms for breaking the symmetry.

*) Y. Ne'eman has suggested this possibility and explored some of its consequences[2]).

**) Here the particle symbol stands for the mass of that particle.

To sum up, the Sakata model provides a most economical formulism for the description of strongly interacting particles. It suggests that SU_3 might be a useful symmetry for the strong interactions, but it also indicates that this symmetry is violated.

Unfortunately, the Sakata model has difficulties. To see this we return to our description of mesons and baryons. There are $\bar{3}\times 3 = 9$ meson states formed for p,n,Λ and their antiparticles. (The bar over the 3 indicates that we are using 3 antiunits.) Under transformations contained in SU_3 eight of these states mix with one another. There is one state that remains unchanged. Therefore, the nine states may be naturally divided into sets (or irreducible representations) of 8 and 1. We write

$$\bar{3}\times 3 = 9 = 8+1.$$

This decomposition is quite gratifying for it provides an explanation for the observed grouping of mesons. For the baryons, however, we find

$$\bar{3}\times 3\times 3 = 3+3+\bar{6}+15.$$

The familiar sets of 8 and 10 used in baryon classification are not present and we are at an impasse. For this reason, Gell-Mann and Ne'eman suggested that it was not the Sakata model, but rather the symmetry group SU_3 that was of interest. If we forget about the Sakata model, we may postulate that the eight-dimensional representation should be used both for mesons and baryons.

However, there is another way out of the difficulty which also allows us to keep the desirable features of the Sakata model[3]. Suppose we build the baryons from a triplet of units using $3\times 3\times 3$ instead of $\bar{3}\times 3\times 3$. That is, the Ξ would be

$$\Xi \sim n_0\Lambda_0\Lambda_0 \ .$$

Then classification of baryons into sets of eight is possible since $3\times 3\times 3$ admits the decomposition

$$3\times 3\times 3 = 1+8+8+10.$$

Note that the ten-dimensional representation is also present, so that the decuplet which contains the Ω^- may also be considered as a composite of three units. The 27 representation and the $\overline{10}$ representation which occur naturally in the Gell-Mann-Ne'eman scheme and which do not seem to be used by nature for the baryons are absent.

The only difficulty now is that the baryons seems to have baryon number 3. We get around this by assigning baryon number $1/3$ to each unit.

Since the strongly interacting particles obey the relation $Q = c[I_z + (B+S)/2]$, we are led to using this relation for the units which comprise them. We then obtain charges $2/3$, $-1/3$, $-1/3$ for the p_0, n_0, Λ_0, respectively. These fractionally charged particles are called aces or quarks. Table 1 summarized their properties.

Table 1

Ace properties

	I	I_z	S	B	Y = B+S	Q	J
$a_1 = p_0$	$1/2$	$1/2$	0	$1/3$	$1/3$	$2/3$	$1/2$
$a_2 = n_0$	$1/2$	$-1/2$	0	$1/3$	$1/3$	$-1/3$	$1/2$
$a_3 = \Lambda_0$	0	0	-1	$1/3$	$-2/3$	$-1/3$	$1/2$

Note that mesons may be constructed from ace-antiace combinations, exactly as in the Sakata model. Only the eight- and one-dimensional representations appear. Other representations like the 10, $\overline{10}$, or 27, which are allowed in the Gell-Mann-Ne'eman model, are absent.

II. THE ACE MODEL

It is convenient to relabel p_0, n_0, and Λ_0 by a_1, a_2, a_3. Let us consider the group of unitary unimodular (SU_3) transformations and their effects on the aces or combination of aces. Under the action of an SU_3 transformation, the ace a_i becomes a_i'. We write

$$a_i \rightarrow a_i' = U_i^j a_j \text{ (summation over repeated indices)}, \tag{5}$$

where the unitarity of U means:

$$U_k^{\dagger i} U_i^j = \delta_k^j, \ (U_k^{\dagger i} \equiv (U_i^k)^*) \ , \tag{6}$$

while the unimodularity indicates that the determinant of the matrix U is 1. Note that the three aces transform into linear combinations of themselves, and that by appropriate choices of U's aces can be changed into one another†). This means that if we know of the existence of one ace, and if we know the world is SU_3 symmetric, then the other two aces must also exist. We say that the three aces form an irreducible representation of the group SU_3. The representation is labelled 3.

We denote antiaces by a^i, for example, $\bar{p}_0 = a^1$. The a^i transforms according to

$$a^i \rightarrow a^{i'} = (U^\dagger)_j^{\ i} a^j \ , \tag{7}$$

and form an irreducible representation of SU_3 called $\bar{3}$.

---

†) <u>Problem 1</u> - Verify this statement for the special case where we require

$$a_1 \rightarrow a_1' = a_2$$
$$a_2 \rightarrow a_2' = a_3$$
$$a_3 \rightarrow a_3' = a_1 \ .$$

Can any arbitrary permutation of the a_i's be induced by SU_3 transformations?

The pseudoscalar mesons are constructed from the nine ace-antiace combinations $a^i a_j$. It is easy to see that

$$\eta_1 \equiv \frac{1}{\sqrt{3}} a^k a_k = \frac{1}{\sqrt{3}} (\bar{p}_0 p_0 + \bar{n}_0 n_0 + \bar{\Lambda}_0 \Lambda_0) , \qquad (8)$$

changes into itself under any SU_3 transformation while the eight remaining states

$$P^i_j \equiv a^i a_j - \frac{1}{3} \delta^i_j a^k a_k , \qquad (9)$$

transform among themselves. If we know of the existence of one of these eight particle states, and if the world reflects SU_3 symmetry, then the other seven states must also exist. The singlet state η_1 need not exist, however, since SU_3 transformations do not connect it with the eight states P^i_j. We write $\bar{3} \times 3 = 8 + 1$.

It is a simple matter to check that P^i_j may be written in the form

$$P^i_j = \begin{pmatrix} \frac{\eta_8}{\sqrt{6}} + \frac{\pi^0}{\sqrt{2}} & \pi^+ & K^+ \\ \pi^- & \frac{\eta_8}{\sqrt{6}} - \frac{\pi^0}{\sqrt{2}} & K^0 \\ K^- & \overline{K^0} & -\frac{2\eta_8}{\sqrt{6}} \end{pmatrix} \qquad (10)$$

where

$$\eta_8 = (\bar{p}_0 p_0 + \bar{n}_0 n_0 - 2\bar{\Lambda}_0 \Lambda_0)/\sqrt{6} . \qquad (11)$$

The π and K states have been given in Eqs. (1) and (2)[+)]. Note that $\mathrm{Tr}\, P = P^i_i = 0$.

---

†) Problem 2 - Verify this form for P^i_j.

In the limit of SU_3 symmetry the p_o, n_o, and Λ_o are indistinguishable, and the eight pseudoscalar mesons must have equal masses. We express this by assigning the same mass to all the "deuces" $a^i a_j$ which form the octuplet. The principle breaking mechanism of the symmetry distinguishes Λ_o from p_o or n_o (N_o) and splits the meson masses. That is, $(\bar{p}_o p_o - \bar{n}_o n_o)\sqrt{2} = \pi^0$ has a mass equal to $\bar{p}_o n_o = \pi^-$ but not equal to $\bar{p}_o \Lambda_o = K^-$.

More exactly, we write for the meson mass terms in the SU_3 symmetric Hamiltonian

$$
\begin{aligned}
H^{(o)} &= H_8^{(o)} + H_1^{(o)} \\
H_8^{(o)} &= m\{1 - |\eta_1 > < \eta_1|\}^{*)} \qquad (12)\\
H_1^{(o)} &= M|\eta_1 > < \eta_1| \ .
\end{aligned}
$$

Here we have introduced $H_1^{(o)}$ to take care of the possible existence of a pseudoscalar meson singlet η_1. $H_8^{(o)}$ measures the octuplet masses, while $H_1^{(o)}$ gives the singlet mass. (Note $< \eta_1|H_8^{(o)}|\eta_1 > = 0$.) Let us rewrite these expressions in terms of deuces

$$
\begin{aligned}
H_8^{(o)} &= m\left\{\sum_{i,j} |a^i a_j> < a^i a_j| - \frac{1}{3}\ |a^k a_k> < a^\ell a_\ell|\right\}^{**)} \qquad (13)\\
H_1^{(o)} &= \frac{M}{3}\ |a^k a_k> < a^\ell a_\ell| \ .
\end{aligned}
$$

If the symmetry is broken, then the mass m associated with the deuce $a^i a_j$ will be a function of i and j; $m \to m^i_j$. Furthermore, $m^i_j = m^j_i$ since particles and antiparticles have the same mass. Now, the

---

*) When working with mesons we <u>assume</u> that mass squared is always to be used. To simplify the notation, however, we omit the squares on the masses.

**) Remember that closure gives $1 = \sum_{i,j} |a^i a_j> < a^i a_j|$ since the $a^i a_j$ form a complete set of states.

theory admits a natural phenomenological parameter of smallness, the dimensionless mass difference

$$(\Lambda_0 - n_0)/n_0 = \lambda. \tag{14}$$

clearly m^i_j is a function of λ. We will assume that this function is differentiable in λ and develop it in a power series.

$$m^i_j = m(\lambda\delta^i_3, \lambda\delta^3_j) = m(\lambda\delta^3_j, \lambda\delta^i_3) = m(0,0) + \lambda(\delta^i_3 + \delta^3_j)m' + O(\lambda^2). \tag{15}$$

m′ is the derivative of m evaluated at the origin*), while $O(\lambda^2)$ indicates that there are additional terms of the order of λ^2. Similarly,

$$M = M^i_j = M(\lambda\delta^i_3, \lambda\delta^3_j) = M(0,0) + \lambda(\delta^i_3 + \delta^3_j)M' + O(\lambda^2). \tag{16}$$

When SU_3 is broken (neglecting electromagnetism), we assume that the Hamiltonian has the form

$$H = \sum_{i,j} |a^i a_j> (m^i_j) < a^i a_j| - \frac{1}{3}\sum_k (m^k_k)^{1/2}$$

$$|a^k a_k> \sum_\ell (m^\ell_\ell)^{1/2} < a^\ell a_\ell| + \frac{1}{3}\sum (M^k_k)^{1/2} |a^k a_k> \tag{17}$$

$$\sum_\ell (M^\ell_\ell)^{1/2} < a^\ell a_\ell| .$$

---

*) More explicitly

$$m' = \frac{\partial}{\partial x} m(x,y)\Big|_{\substack{x=0\\y=0}}$$

Since $m(x,y) = m(y,x)$, we also have

$$m' = \frac{\partial}{\partial y} m(x,y)\Big|_{\substack{x=0\\y=0}}$$

We now expand the m's and M's to obtain*)

$$
\left\langle \left| \frac{H-m}{m} \right| \right\rangle = \begin{array}{c|cccc} & \langle \eta_1 | & \langle \eta_8 | & \langle K | & \langle \pi | \\ \hline |\eta_1\rangle & \frac{M}{m} - 1 + \frac{2}{3}A & -\frac{\sqrt{2}}{3}(A+a) & 0 & 0 \\ |\eta_8\rangle & -\frac{\sqrt{2}}{3}(A+a) & \frac{4}{3}a & 0 & 0 \\ |K\rangle & 0 & 0 & a & 0 \\ |\pi\rangle & 0 & 0 & 0 & 0 \end{array} + O(\lambda^2) \tag{18}
$$

where $a = \lambda(m'/m)$, $A = \lambda(M'/m)$.

If $M >> m$, then η_1 and η_8 mix to a negligible extent and we find

$$\eta_1 = M + \frac{2}{3} Am + O(\lambda^2,\ \eta_1 - \eta_8 \text{ mixing, and errors in the model})^{**)} \tag{19}$$

$$K = \frac{3\eta_8 + \pi}{4} + O(\lambda^2,\ \eta_1 - \eta_8 \text{ mixing, and errors in the model}). \tag{20}$$

$$(495 \text{ MeV})^2 \simeq (515 \text{ MeV})^2$$

The disagreement with experiment in this relation may be attributed to terms of the order λ^2, to the existence of a ninth pseudoscalar meson η_1, or to the inaccuracy of the model.

A general mass formula containing both η_1 and η_8 does not exist***).

---

*) It is interesting to note that if one neglects terms in λ^2, H transforms like the 33 component of a second rank tensor.

**) Here the particle symbol stands for the $(\text{mass})^2$ of that particle.

***) If we try the more restrictive but somewhat ad hoc assumption that

$$H = \sum_{i,j} m_j^i \, |a^i a_j\rangle \langle a^i a_j| - \frac{1}{3} m |a^k a_k\rangle \langle a^\ell a_\ell| + \frac{1}{3} M |a^k a_k\rangle \langle a^\ell a_\ell|$$

we obtain $(\varphi - \pi)(\omega - \pi) = 4/3\,(K - \pi)(\varphi + \omega - 2K)$. Here ω and φ are the energy eigenstate mixtures of η_1 and η_8. Schwinger has also found this formula[4].

There is another way of finding Eq. (20). Neglecting η_1 we write

$$H_8^{(o)} = m \text{ Tr } \bar{P}P = m \bar{P}^i_j P^j_i = m \{\bar{\pi}^+ \pi^+ + \ldots + \bar{\eta}_8 \eta_8\}^{\dagger)} , \qquad (21)$$

if SU_3 is exact. The matrix $\bar{P}$ is just the transpose of P with a bar over the particles. SU_3 is broken by distinguishing Λ_0 from p_0 and n_0 (the index 3 from 1 and 2). Hence

$$H_8 = m \bar{P}^i_j P^j_i + m_1 \bar{P}^3_j P^j_3 + m_2 P^i_3 P^3_i + m_3 P^3_3 P^3_3 , \qquad (22)$$

where equality of particle and antiparticle masses implies $m_1 = m_2$. The terms in m_1 and m_2 may be viewed as corrections to the SU_3 symmetric term in m. The term in m_3 is a correction to the terms in m_1 and m_2 and therefore is neglected in first approximation (it corresponds to terms in λ^2). We then write

$$H_8 = m \text{ Tr } \bar{P}P + m_1 \text{ Tr } \bar{P}(I_3 P + P I_3)^{\dagger\dagger)}, \qquad (23)$$

where

$$I_3 = \begin{pmatrix} 0 & 0 & 0 \\ 0 & 0 & 0 \\ 0 & 0 & 1 \end{pmatrix}$$

Note that this form is identical to the more familiar expression

$$H_8 = m' \text{ Tr } \bar{P}P + m_1' \text{ Tr } \bar{P}(\lambda_8 P + P\lambda_8) , \qquad (24)$$

and leads directly to Eq. (20). It is also equivalent to postulating that H_8 transforms like the 33 component of a tensor.

---

†) Problem 3 - Check this equation.

††) Problem 4 - Derive the mass formula from this expression.

Finally, there is a pictorial method for obtaining the mass formula in first order (where we neglect the possible existence of η_1). We denote

$$p_0 \text{ by } \bullet \, , \quad \bar{p}_0 \text{ by } 0$$

$$n_0 \text{ by } \blacktriangle \, , \quad \bar{n}_0 \text{ by } \triangle$$

$$\Lambda_0 \text{ by } \blacksquare \, , \quad \bar{\Lambda}_0 \text{ by } \square \, .$$

The meson amplitudes are then

$$\overset{\displaystyle 0}{\underset{\displaystyle \blacktriangle}{|}} \qquad \frac{1}{\sqrt{2}}\left(\overset{\displaystyle 0}{\underset{\displaystyle \bullet}{|}} - \overset{\displaystyle \triangle}{\underset{\displaystyle \blacktriangle}{|}} \right) \qquad \overset{\displaystyle \triangle}{\underset{\displaystyle \bullet}{|}}$$
$$\;\;\pi^- \qquad\qquad\qquad \pi^0 \qquad\qquad\qquad\qquad \pi^+$$

$$\overset{\displaystyle \square}{\underset{\displaystyle \blacktriangle}{|}} \qquad\qquad \overset{\displaystyle \square}{\underset{\displaystyle \bullet}{|}}$$
$$K^0 \qquad\qquad\qquad K^+$$

$$\overset{\displaystyle 0}{\underset{\displaystyle \blacksquare}{|}} \qquad\qquad \overset{\displaystyle \triangle}{\underset{\displaystyle \blacksquare}{|}}$$
$$K^- \qquad\qquad\qquad \bar{K}^0$$

$$\frac{1}{\sqrt{6}}\left(\overset{\displaystyle 0}{\underset{\displaystyle \bullet}{|}} + \overset{\displaystyle \triangle}{\underset{\displaystyle \blacktriangle}{|}} - 2\,\overset{\displaystyle \square}{\underset{\displaystyle \blacksquare}{|}} \right)$$

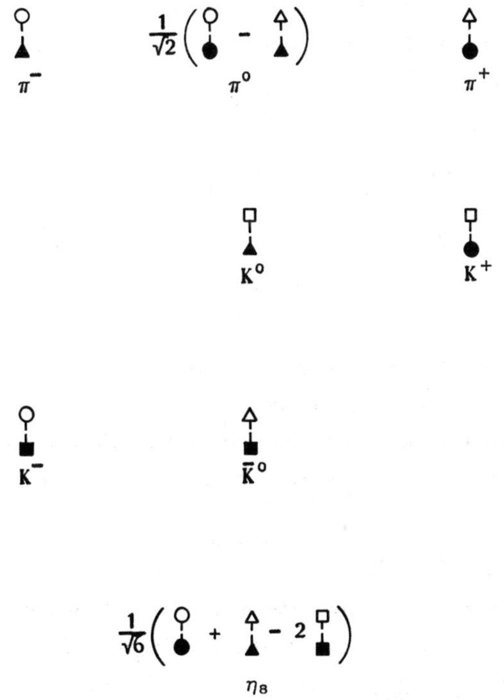

We may crudely reword our treatment of the masses of the mesons by saying that the mass of a meson is an average of the masses of the deuces which comprise it. If we distinguish the Λ_0 from p_0, n_0 but regard p_0 and n_0 as equivalent, we have:

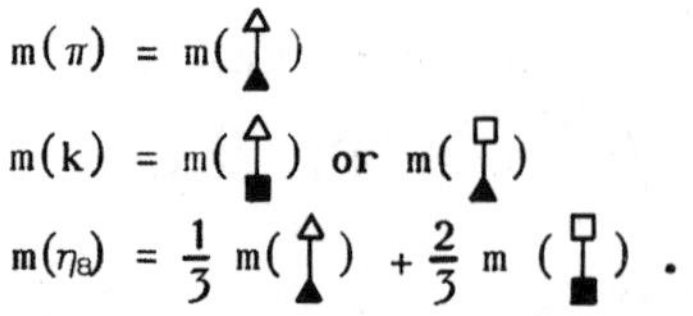

$$m(\pi) = m(\updownarrow)$$

$$m(k) = m(\updownarrow) \text{ or } m(\updownarrow) \tag{25}$$

$$m(\eta_8) = \frac{1}{3} m(\updownarrow) + \frac{2}{3} m(\updownarrow) .$$

Here $m(x)$ stands for the mass of x. The mass of a deuce $a^i a_j$ is assumed to be a_j

$$m(a^i a_j) = m(a^i) + m(a_j) - E_j^i , \tag{26}$$

where E_j^i is the $a^i a_j$ binding energy. E_j^i will be a function of $\lambda = (\Lambda_0 - n_0)/n_0$

$$E_j^i = E(\lambda \delta_3^i, \lambda \delta_j^3) = E(0,0) + \lambda(\delta_3^i + \delta_j^3) E' + O(\lambda^2) . \tag{27}$$

Hence,

$$m(a^i a_j) = 2m(n_0) + (\delta_3^i + \delta_j^3) \lambda (n_0 + E') + \cdots \tag{28}$$

This equation says that a deuce which contains a Λ_0 or $\bar{\Lambda}_0$ (square) has an extra mass of $\Lambda_0 - n_0 + \lambda E'$ as compared to a deuce containing n_0 or $\bar{n}_0$ (triangle). To obtain a first order mass formula one must only average the number of squares and triangles in the meson states, i.e.

$$K = \frac{3\eta_8 + \pi}{4} .$$

We are now ready to introduce effects caused by the distinguishability of p_0 and n_0. The natural parameter of smallness is $\alpha = e^2/\hbar c$ or equivalently $\nu = (n_0 - p_0)/n_0$. Neglecting the $\Lambda_0 - N_0$ splitting we write

$$m_j^i = \mu(-\nu \delta_1^i, -\nu \delta_j^1) = \mu(0,0) - \nu(\delta_1^i + \delta_j^1) \mu' + O(\nu^2), \tag{29}$$

and proceed as in the case where SU_3 was broken through the introduction of the parameter λ. We obtain

$$H_8 = \mu \bar{P}^i_j P^j_i + \mu_1(\bar{P}^1_j P^j_1 + \bar{P}^i_1 P^1_i) = \mu \operatorname{Tr} \bar{P}P + \mu_1 \operatorname{Tr} \bar{P}(I_1 P + PI_1), \quad (30)$$

where

$$I_1 = \begin{pmatrix} 1 & 0 & 0 \\ 0 & 0 & 0 \\ 0 & 0 & 0 \end{pmatrix} \quad (31)$$

Note that we have effectively distinguished the charge $2/3$ p_0 from the charge $-1/3$ n_0 and Λ_0. If we now add the $\Lambda_0 - N_0$ split by including a term $m_1 \operatorname{Tr} \bar{P}(I_3P + PI_3)$ to H_8 we find two relations:

1) $\pi^+ = \pi^0$ or equivalently

$$|(\pi^+ - \pi^0)/(K^0 - K^+)| << |^{*)} \quad (32)$$
$$(1/3) .$$

There are clearly effects that are not taken into account by the model which effectively contribute to H_8 a term of the form $\mu_2 \bar{P}^1_1 P^1_1$. Nevertheless, the model seems to include the main symmetry-breaking structure.

2)

$$\frac{K^0 + K^-}{2} = \frac{3\eta_8 + \pi}{4} + O(\lambda^2,\ \eta_8 - \eta_1 \text{ mixing, and inaccuracies in the model}). \quad (33)$$

We may summarize the octuplet pseudoscalar mass structure so far obtained by the symmetrical relation

$$H = m_0 + m_1 Y_0^2 + m_2 Q_0^2,$$

---

*) Remember that the symbol for a meson stands for the mass squared of that meson.

where $Y_0^2 = \frac{1}{4} Y^2 - I(I+1)$, $Q_0^2 = \frac{1}{4} Q^2 - U(U+1)$, and U is the U spin of the particles[5]. This indicates the similarity in the way in which SU_3 is broken by the principle symmetry-breaking mechanism and the electromagnetic interactions.

We may try to go a step further by assuming $m(x,y) = \mu(x,y)$*) [see Eqs. (15) and (29)] so that the difference between the two symmetry-breaking mechanisms is attributed to the difference between λ and ν. In this admittedly crude attempt we find

$$H = m_0 + m_1\{- \lambda Y_0^2 + \nu Q_0^2\} . \tag{34}$$

This furnishes an estimate of

$$\frac{\nu}{\lambda} = \frac{n_0 - p_0}{\Lambda_0 - n_0} = \frac{K^0 - K^+}{K - \pi} = 0.017 . \tag{35}$$

It is a curious fact that the treatment of the vector mesons does not completely parallel the description of the pseudoscalar mesons given above. Whereas there is little or no $\eta_8 - \eta_1$ mixing (the η_1 might not even exist), there is a large amount of singlet-octet mixing in the vector meson case. Consequently, it proves convenient to work with linear combinations of ω_8 and ω_1 (the octuplet and singlet I = 0 vector meson states). Let

$$\begin{aligned} \omega &= \sqrt{\frac{2}{3}}\,\omega_1 + \sqrt{\frac{1}{3}}\,\omega_8 = (\bar{p}_0 p_0 + \bar{n}_0 n_0)/\sqrt{2} \\ \varphi &= \sqrt{\frac{1}{3}}\,\omega_1 - \sqrt{\frac{2}{3}}\,\omega_8 = \bar{\Lambda}_0 \Lambda_0 . \end{aligned} \tag{36}$$

(Intuitively, it is clear that ω and φ might be useful states to work with after the symmetry is broken. Symmetry breaking means Λ_0 is distinguished from p_0 and n_0. ω and φ are the distinguishable parts of ω_8 and ω_1.) ω and φ will stand for the physically observed I = 0 vector mesons.

---

*) Such a relation would hold, for example, if the $\Lambda_0 - n_0$ split were due to a zero mass $J^P = 1^-$ particle coupled to strangeness.

We define the Hamiltonian of the vector meson states exactly as in Eq. (17) except that m and M now refer to vector meson masses. Expanding m and M, as in Eqs. (15) and (16), we find the vector meson analogue of Eq. (18), expressed this time in terms of ω and φ:

$$\langle|\frac{H-m}{m}|\rangle = \begin{array}{c} \\ |\varphi\rangle \\ |\omega\rangle \\ |K^*\rangle \\ |\rho\rangle \end{array} \begin{array}{cccc} \langle\varphi| & \langle\omega| & \langle K^*| & \langle\rho|\ ^{\dagger)} \\ \frac{1}{3}(\frac{M}{m}-1)+\frac{2}{3}(A+2a) & \frac{\sqrt{2}}{3}(\frac{M}{m}-1)+\frac{\sqrt{2}}{3}(A-a) & 0 & 0 \\ \frac{\sqrt{2}}{3}(\frac{M}{m}-1)+\frac{\sqrt{2}}{3}(A-a) & \frac{2}{3}(\frac{M}{m}-1) & & \\ 0 & 0 & a & 0 \\ 0 & 0 & 0 & 0 \end{array} \tag{37}$$

In general, there is no relation between the φ, ω, K^*, and ρ masses. Later in the course, however, we will consider a symmetry (called ace spin) higher than SU_3 which will tell us that the octuplet and singlet <u>vector</u> (but not pseudoscalar) mesons must be treated on an equal footing, i.e. $m^i_j = M^i_j$, which implies m = M, a = A. Then

$$\langle|\frac{H-m}{m}|\rangle = \begin{array}{c} \\ |\varphi\rangle \\ |\omega\rangle \\ |K^*\rangle \\ |\rho\rangle \end{array} \begin{array}{cccc} \langle\varphi| & \langle\omega| & \langle K^*| & \langle\rho| \\ 2a & 0 & 0 & 0 \\ 0 & 0 & 0 & 0 \\ 0 & 0 & a & 0 \\ 0 & 0 & 0 & 0 \end{array} \tag{38}$$

or,

$$\omega = \rho \qquad\qquad \varphi = 2K^* - \rho \tag{39}$$

$$(784)^2 \quad (753)^2 \qquad\qquad (1019)^2 \quad (1007)^2$$

---

†) <u>Problem 5</u> - Derive this form for $\langle|\frac{H-m}{m}|\rangle$.

We are able to do better than this. When the ace spin symmetry is broken, $m^i_j = M^i_j$ no longer holds. However, we would expect

$$\left| \frac{M}{m} - 1 \right| >> \left| A - a \right| = \lambda \left| \frac{M'}{m} - \frac{m'}{m} \right| , \tag{40}$$

since $(M/m) - 1$ and $(M'/m) - (m'/m)$ are expected to be of the same order. Then

$$\left\langle \left| \frac{H - m}{m} \right| \right\rangle = \begin{array}{c} \\ |\varphi\rangle \\ |\omega\rangle \\ |K^*\rangle \\ |\rho\rangle \end{array} \begin{array}{cccc} \langle\varphi| & \langle\omega| & \langle K^*| & \langle\rho| \\ \end{array} \begin{pmatrix} \frac{1}{3}(\frac{M}{m} - 1) + 2a & \frac{\sqrt{2}}{3}(\frac{M}{m} - 1) & 0 & 0 \\ \frac{\sqrt{2}}{3}(\frac{M}{m} - 1) & \frac{2}{3}(\frac{M}{m} - 1) & 0 & 0 \\ 0 & 0 & a & 0 \\ 0 & 0 & 0 & 0 \end{pmatrix} \tag{41}$$

which implies

$$(\omega - \rho)(\varphi - \rho) = \frac{4}{3} (K^* - \rho)(\varphi + \omega - 2K^*) . \tag{42}$$

The fact that $\omega \approx \rho$, $\varphi \approx 2K^* - \rho$ works so well implies that ace spin symmetry breaking proceeds mainly through the mechanism which distinguishes Λ_0 from p_0, n_0, and not through the mechanism which splits the octuplet from the singlet, i.e. $|(M/m - 1) << a$. Because of this circumstance we may neglect the off-diagonal terms in Eq. (41) and immediately obtain a simplified version of Eq. (42):

$$(\omega - \rho)/2 = \varphi + \rho - 2K^* , \tag{43}$$

which is correct to the known accuracy of the masses.

There is another equivalent procedure for finding Eqs. (39) and (43) which we shall now give. Ace spin symmetry will tell us that the vector meson octuplet and singlet are to be treated on an equal footing. Consequently, it is not convenient to subtract the singlet

$1/\sqrt{3}\, a^k a_k$ from $a^i a_j$ when forming the vector meson counterpart of P^i_j Eq. (9). Instead, we work with $a^i a_j \equiv G^i_j$ directly. In terms of φ and ω we have

$$G^i_j = \begin{pmatrix} \frac{\omega}{\sqrt{2}} + \frac{\rho}{\sqrt{2}} & \rho^+ & K^{*+} \\ \rho^- & \frac{\omega}{\sqrt{2}} - \frac{\rho}{\sqrt{2}} & K^{*o} \\ K^{*-} & \bar{K}^{*0} & \varphi \end{pmatrix} \text{ †)} \tag{44}$$

Note $\mathrm{Tr}\, G = \sqrt{2}\omega + \varphi = \sqrt{3}\,\omega_1 = \bar{p}_0 p_0 + \bar{n}_0 n_0 + \bar{\Lambda}_0 \Lambda_0$ as should be. When SU_3 is exact we have

$$H^{(0)} = m\ \mathrm{Tr}\ \bar{G}G\ . \tag{45}$$

Here, we have not included the SU_3 symmetric term $\mathrm{Tr}\ \bar{G}\ \mathrm{Tr}\ G$, since this would split the octuplet and singlet masses. If SU_3 is broken by distinguishing Λ_0 from p_0, n_0

$$H = m\ \mathrm{Tr}\ \bar{G}G + m_1\ \mathrm{Tr}\ \bar{G}(I_3G + GI_3), \tag{46}$$

which implies $\omega = \rho$, $\varphi = 2K^* - \rho$. Finally, we split the octuplet and singlet masses:

$$H = m\ \mathrm{Tr}\ \bar{G}G + m_1\ \mathrm{Tr}\ \bar{G}(I_3G + GI_3) + m_2\ \mathrm{Tr}\ \bar{G}\ \mathrm{Tr}\ G. \tag{47}$$

This yields

$$(\omega - \rho)/2 = \varphi + \rho - 2K^*\ . \text{ ††)} \tag{48}$$

---

†) Problem 6 - Check this expression for G^i_j .

††) Problem 7 - Find this mass formula using Eq. (47).

There is an amusing pictorial way of working with the vector
mesons when we treat the octuplet and singlet as being degenerate. We
represent the states as:

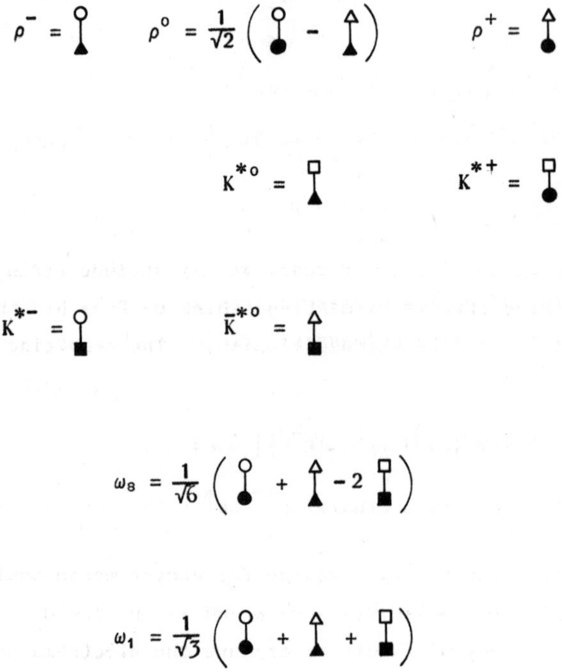

$$\rho^- = \text{(symbol)} \qquad \rho^0 = \frac{1}{\sqrt{2}}\left(\text{(symbol)} - \text{(symbol)}\right) \qquad \rho^+ = \text{(symbol)}$$

$$K^{*0} = \text{(symbol)} \qquad K^{*+} = \text{(symbol)}$$

$$K^{*-} = \text{(symbol)} \qquad \bar{K}^{*0} = \text{(symbol)} \tag{49}$$

$$\omega_8 = \frac{1}{\sqrt{6}}\left(\text{(symbol)} + \text{(symbol)} - 2\,\text{(symbol)}\right)$$

$$\omega_1 = \frac{1}{\sqrt{3}}\left(\text{(symbol)} + \text{(symbol)} + \text{(symbol)}\right)$$

When SU_3 is broken, ω_8 and ω_1 mix to give the energy eigenstates ω and φ.
It is clear that the mixing must be such that (symbol) becomes separate for (symbol), i.e.

$$\omega = \frac{1}{\sqrt{2}}\left(\text{(symbol)} + \text{(symbol)}\right)$$

$$\varphi = \text{(symbol)} \tag{36'}$$

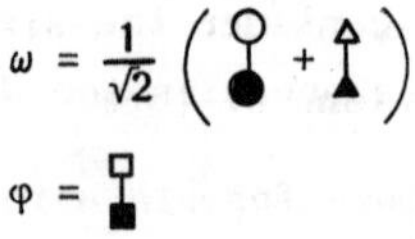

To obtain mass formulae we write

$$
\begin{aligned}
m(\rho) &= m\left(\begin{smallmatrix}\triangle\\ |\\ \blacktriangle\end{smallmatrix}\right) \\
m(\omega) &= m\left(\begin{smallmatrix}\triangle\\ |\\ \blacktriangle\end{smallmatrix}\right) \\
m(K^*) &= m\left(\begin{smallmatrix}\triangle\\ |\\ \blacksquare\end{smallmatrix}\right) \quad \text{or } m\left(\begin{smallmatrix}\square\\ |\\ \blacktriangle\end{smallmatrix}\right) \\
m(\varphi) &= m\left(\begin{smallmatrix}\square\\ |\\ \blacksquare\end{smallmatrix}\right)
\end{aligned}
\tag{50}
$$

Then we count triangles and squares to obtain

$$
\begin{aligned}
\rho &= \omega \\
\varphi &= 2K^* - \rho
\end{aligned}
\tag{39'}
$$

As in the pseudoscalar meson case, we may include certain electromagnetic symmetry-breaking effects by distinguishing p_0 from n_0, thereby adding a term $\mu_1 \mathrm{Tr}\, \bar{G}(I_1 G + G I_1)$ to the Hamiltonian. The resulting relations are

$$
\begin{aligned}
&\left|(\rho^+ - \rho^0)/(K^{*0} - K^{*+})\right| \ll 1 \\
&(\omega - \rho)/2 = \varphi + \rho - K^{*-} - K^{*0} \;.
\end{aligned}
\tag{51}
$$

We might try to go a step further by assuming the vector meson analogue of Eq. (35). Then $\nu/\lambda = (K^{*0} - K^{*+})/(K^* - \rho)$ which is predicted to be 0.017). Unfortunately, it may be very difficult to measure the electromagnetic mass differences of the vector mesons since their widths are so large.

So far, we have worked with ace-antiace pairs. What happens when we deal with the product of two aces? We get nine states $a_i a_j$, where it is advantageous to consider the six symmetric (S_{ij}) and three antisymmetric (A_{ij}) combinations of them.

Irreducible representation	Symmetry type	Number of states
$S_{ij} = a_i a_j + a_j a_i$	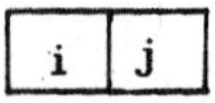	$\frac{1}{2}n(n+1) = 6$
$A_{ij} = a_i a_j - a_j a_i$	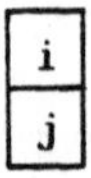	$\frac{1}{2}n(n-1) = 3$

$i,j = 1,2,3 \quad n = 3$

Notice that the order of the aces is important, otherwise $A_{ij} \equiv 0$. The decomposition of the deuces $a_i a_j$ into objects of definite symmetry is interesting because the symmetry properties of a tensor are invariant under SU_3. For example,

$$\begin{aligned} S_{ij} \to S'_{ij} &= U_i^a U_j^b S_{ab} \\ &= U_i^a U_j^b S_{ba} \\ &= U_j^b U_i^a S_{ba} \\ &= S'_{ji} \; . \end{aligned} \tag{52}$$

Similarly, $A'_{ij} = - A'_{ji}$. Hence, the states A_{ij} and S_{ij} do not mix under the action of SU_3. We indicate this by $3 \times 3 = 6 + \bar{3}$. (Forget about the bar over the three.) Consequently, we can imagine an SU_3 symmetric world with particles belonging to 6 but not to $\bar{3}$, or vice-versa.

Whereas the deuces $a^i a_j$ had $B = 0$, the deuces $a_i a_j$ have $B = 2/3$. However, both $a^i a_j$ and $a_i a_j$ are mesons (have integral spin)! †)

†) Problem 8 - Write out the particle states belonging to S_{ij} and A_{ij}. What are their quantum numbers?

We obtain the baryons from either $a_\ell S_{ij}$ (3×6) or $a_\ell A_{ij}$ $(3\times \bar{3})$. The irreducible representations or baryon groupings are found by constructing objects of definite symmetry type. We construct

Irreducible representation	Symmetry type	Number of states
$a_\ell S_{ij} + a_i S_{j\ell} + a_j S_{\ell i}$	$\begin{array}{\|c\|c\|c\|}\hline \ell & i & j \\ \hline\end{array}$	$\frac{1}{6}\, n(n+1)(n+2) = 10$
$a_\ell S_{ij} - a_i S_{\ell j}$	$\begin{array}{\|c\|c\|}\hline i & j \\ \hline \ell \\ \cline{1-1}\end{array}$	$\frac{1}{3}\, n(n^2 - 1) = 8$
$a_\ell A_{ij} + a_i A_{\ell j}$	$\begin{array}{\|c\|c\|}\hline i & \ell \\ \hline j \\ \cline{1-1}\end{array}$	$\frac{1}{3}\, n(n^2 - 1) = 8$
$a_\ell A_{ij} - a_i A_{\ell j} + a_j A_{\ell i}$	$\begin{array}{\|c\|}\hline \ell \\ \hline i \\ \hline j \\ \hline\end{array}$	$\frac{1}{6}\, n(n-1)(n-2) = 1$.

If we think of the baryons as formed from the S_{ij} mesons and the aces, then we would expect baryon sets of 8 and 10. Aces combined with the A_{ij} mesons give clusters of 8 and 1. It is not presently clear which 8 corresponds to the observed baryon octuplet. Later we will have more to say about this question. For most calculations either assignment will do.

Let us list the decuplet states:

$$\Delta^{++} = p_0 p_0 p_0 = T_{111}$$

$$\Delta^{+} = \frac{1}{\sqrt{3}}\,(p_0 p_0 n_0 + p_0 n_0 p_0 + n_0 p_0 p_0) \equiv \frac{1}{\sqrt{3}}\,(T_{112} + T_{121} + T_{211})$$

$$\Delta^{0} = \frac{1}{\sqrt{3}}\,(T_{221} + T_{212} + T_{122})$$

$$\Delta^{-} = T_{222} \tag{53}$$

$$\Sigma^{*+} = \frac{1}{\sqrt{3}}\,(T_{113} + T_{131} + T_{311})$$

$$\Sigma^{*0} = \frac{1}{\sqrt{6}}\left(T_{123} + T_{231} + T_{312} + T_{132} + T_{321} + T_{213}\right)$$

$$\Sigma^{*-} = \frac{1}{\sqrt{3}}\left(T_{223} + T_{232} + T_{322}\right)$$

$$\Xi^{*0} = \frac{1}{\sqrt{3}}\left(T_{133} + T_{313} + T_{331}\right)$$

$$\Xi^{*-} = \frac{1}{\sqrt{3}}\left(T_{233} + T_{323} + T_{332}\right)$$

$$\Omega^{-} = T_{333}$$

where $T_{ijk} = a_i a_j a_k$.

Note that these 10 states are totally symmetric.

The baryon octet formed from $a_\ell A_{ij} + a_i A_{\ell j}$ comes out to be

$$\begin{aligned}
p &= \frac{1}{\sqrt{2}}\left(T_{112} - T_{121}\right) & n &= \frac{1}{\sqrt{2}}\left(T_{212} - T_{221}\right) \\
\Lambda &= \frac{1}{\sqrt{12}}\left(T_{123} - T_{213} + T_{231} - T_{132} + 2T_{321} - 2T_{312}\right) & \Sigma^{+} &= \frac{1}{\sqrt{2}}\left(T_{131} - T_{113}\right) \\
\Sigma^{0} &= \frac{1}{2}\left(T_{123} + T_{213} - T_{132} - T_{231}\right) & \Sigma^{-} &= \frac{1}{\sqrt{2}}\left(T_{223} - T_{232}\right) \\
\Xi^{0} &= \frac{1}{\sqrt{2}}\left(T_{331} - T_{313}\right) & \Xi^{-} &= \frac{1}{\sqrt{2}}\left(T_{323} - T_{332}\right)
\end{aligned} \tag{54}$$

Baryon mass formulae may be easily obtained by the pictorial technique. For example, neglecting electromagnetism, we would write for the decuplet

$$m(\Delta) = m\left(\ \right) \qquad m(\Sigma^*) = m\left(\ \right) \qquad m(\Xi^*) = m\left(\ \right) \qquad m(\Omega) = m\left(\ \right) \tag{55}$$

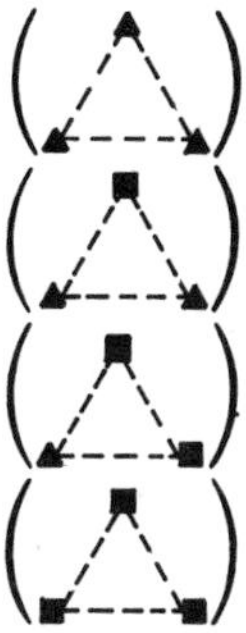

In the limit of SU_3 symmetry the squares and triangles are indistinguishable and all decuplet baryons have the same mass. If we distinguish the Λ_0 from the N_0 and say that the masses of the squares and triangles are no longer identical, we find the equal mass spacing relation

$$\Omega - \Xi^* = \Xi^* - \Sigma^* = \Sigma^* - \Delta \,. \tag{56}$$

More explicitly, we may determine relations among the baryon masses by assigning a mass m_{ijk} to the "trey" $a_i a_j a_k$. In analogy to the meson case we write

$$m_{ijk} = m(\lambda\delta_i^3 \,,\ \lambda\delta_j^3,\ \lambda\delta_k^3) \approx m(0,0,0) + \lambda(m_1'\delta_i^3 + m_2'\delta_j^3 + m_3'\delta_k^3) + O(\lambda^2).$$

Here (57)

$$m_1' \equiv \frac{\partial}{\partial x} m(x,y,z)\Big|_{x=0,y=0,z=0},\quad m_2' \equiv \frac{\partial}{\partial y} m(x,y,z)\Big|_{0,0,0},\quad m_3' \equiv \frac{\partial}{\partial z} m(x,y,z)\Big|_{0,0,0}$$

We proceed exactly as with the mesons to obtain for an isolated (unmixed) octet or decuplet the Gell-Mann - Okubo mass formula

$$H \approx H(3) \equiv m_0 + m_1 Y + m_2 Y_0^2 + O(\lambda^2, \text{ possible representation mixing effects, inaccuracies in the model}), \tag{58}$$

$$Y_0^2 = \frac{1}{4} Y^2 - I(I+1) \; . \tag{59}$$

For the decuplet, $I = \frac{1}{2}Y + 1$ so this relation becomes

$$H \approx H(3) = m_0 + m_1 Y + \text{ error terms.} \tag{60}$$

When n_0 and p_0 are distinguished, we expand

$$\begin{aligned} m_{ijk} &= m(\lambda\delta_i^3, \lambda\delta_j^3, \lambda\delta_k^3, -\nu\delta_i^1, -\nu\delta_j^1, -\nu\delta_k^1) \approx m(0,0,0,0,0,0) \\ &+ \lambda(m_1'\delta_i^3 + m_2'\delta_j^3 + m_3'\delta_k^3) - \nu(\mu_1'\delta_i^1 + \mu_2'\delta_j^1 + \mu_3'\delta_k^1) \end{aligned} \tag{61}$$

and find

$$H \approx H(3,1) \equiv m_0 + m_1 Y + m_2 Y_0^2 - \mu_1 Q + \mu_2 Q_0^2 + O(\lambda^2, \text{ possible representation mixing effects, } \Sigma^0 - \Lambda^0 \text{ mixing inaccuracies in the model}). \tag{62}$$

$$Q_0^2 = \frac{1}{4} Q^2 - U(U+1) \; . \tag{63}$$

(We have the symmetry $Y \leftrightarrow -Q$, $I \leftrightarrow U$.) For the decuplet this reduces to

$$H(3,1) = m_0 + m_1 Y - \mu_1 Q + \text{error terms} \; , \tag{64}$$

since $I = \frac{1}{2} Y + 1$ and $U = -\frac{1}{2} Q + 1$. There is equal spacing in charge and hypercharge.

We may try the assumption that the electromagnetic and principle symmetry breaking interactions differ in their symmetry breaking only through the parameters λ and $\nu (m_i' = \mu_i')$. Then,

$$H \approx H'(3,1) \equiv m_0 + m_1(\lambda Y + \nu Q) + m_2\{\lambda Y_0^2 - \nu Q_0^2\} \; , \tag{65}$$

which reduces for the decuplet to

$$H \approx H'(3,1) = m_0 + m_1(\lambda Y + \nu Q) \; . \tag{66}$$

We find the octuplet relations

$$[(\Xi^- + \Xi^0)/2 + (p+n)/2]/2 = (3\Lambda + \Sigma^0)/4$$
$$(1127) \qquad\qquad (1134)$$

$$\Xi^- - \Xi^0 = \Sigma^- - \Sigma^+ - (n-p)^{*)} \tag{67}$$
$$(6 \pm 1.3) \quad (7.0 \pm 0.5)$$

$$\Sigma^0 = (\Sigma^+ + \Sigma^-)/2$$
$$(1192.25 \pm 0.23) \quad (1193.2 \pm 0.4)$$

from Eq. (62).

Equation (65) gives in addition

$$\frac{\Sigma^- - \Sigma^+}{\Xi - N} = \frac{-2\nu m_1}{-2\lambda m_1} = \frac{\nu}{\lambda} = \frac{7.6}{380} = 0.020 \ , \tag{68}$$

$$\frac{(\Xi^- - \Xi^0) - (n-p)}{3/2(\Sigma - \Lambda)} = \frac{3\nu m_2}{3\lambda m_2} = \frac{\nu}{\lambda} = \frac{5.0}{117} = 0.043 \tag{69}$$

as compared to $\nu/\lambda = (K^0 - K^+)/(K - \pi) = 0.017$ [Eq. (35)]. The quantitative agreement here [Eq. (69)] is not good, although certain qualitative features of the baryon mass spectrum are explained (e.g. the more negative the particle in any baryon isospin multiplet, the heavier the mass).

If we include terms of order λ^2 but neglect electromagnetism, we find

$$H \approx H(33) \equiv H(3) + m_3 Y^2 + m_4 Y Y_0^2 + m_5 Y_0^4 \ . \tag{70}$$

There is no relation for the octuplet, but for the decuplet this reduces to

$$H = m_0 + m_1 Y + m_2 Y^2 \ , \tag{71}$$

---

*) This relation was first derived by Coleman and Glashow[6].

and yields

$$\Omega - \Delta = 3(\Xi^* - \Sigma^*).^{\dagger)} \tag{72}$$

If we now break the symmetry by distinguishing p_0 from n_0 and include terms of order ν, then

$$H \approx H(33,1) \quad H(33) + \mu_1 Q + \mu_2 Q_0^2 . \tag{73}$$

We may, if we wish, go back and treat the electromagnetic breaking of the symmetry more exactly. We know how to do this since we understand the electromagnetic interactions. Instead of H(3,1), it is better to use

$$H \approx H(3,11) \equiv H(3,1) + \mu_3 Q^2 + \mu_4 Q Q_0^2 + \mu_5 Q_0^4 . \tag{74}$$

The electromagnetic mass differences are now correctly given up to order α in the absence of the principle mass-splitting interactions.

Also of interest might be

$$H(33,11) \equiv H(3,11) + m_3 Y^2 + m_4 Y Y_0^2 + m_5 Y_0^4 \tag{75}$$

H(3,13), H(3,113), H(33,13), H(33,113), H(33,133), H(33,1133),*) etc.

In summary, we shall list the various mass formulae and indicate where they breakdown:

__Octuplet__

$$\frac{1}{2}\left\{ \frac{n+p}{2} + \frac{\Xi^- + \Xi^0}{2} \right\} = \frac{3\Lambda + \Sigma^0}{4} + 0(33)$$

$$\Xi^- - \Xi^0 = \Sigma^- - \Sigma^+ - (n-p) + 0(31)$$

$$\Sigma^0 = \frac{\Sigma^+ + \Sigma^-}{2} + 0(11) \tag{76}$$

$$\frac{\nu}{\lambda} = \frac{\Sigma^- - \Sigma^+}{\Xi - N}, \quad \frac{\nu}{\lambda} = \frac{(\Xi^- - \Xi^0) - (n-p)}{3/2(\Sigma - \Lambda)}$$

---

†) __Problem 9__ - Derive Eq. (72) by expanding m_{ijk} to second order in λ. This formula was first obtained by Okubo.

*) The notation indicates that H(33,1133) is the Hamiltonian up to terms of order λ^2 and $\nu^2\lambda^2$; that is, it contains terms of order λ, ν, ν^2, and $\nu^2\lambda$.

Decuplet

$$
\begin{aligned}
\Xi^{*-} - \Sigma^{*-} &= \Sigma^{*-} - \Delta^{-} + 0(33) \\
&= \Omega^{-} - \Xi^{*-} + 0(33) \\
\Xi^{*0} - \Sigma^{*0} &= \Sigma^{*0} - \Delta^{0} + 0(33) \\
3(\Xi^{*-} - \Sigma^{*-}) &= \Omega^{-} - \Delta^{-} + 0(333) \\
\Sigma^{*-} - \Sigma^{*0} &= \Delta^{-} - \Delta^{0} + 0(31) \\
&= \Xi^{*-} - \Xi^{*0} + 0(31) \\
\Sigma^{*0} - \Sigma^{*+} &= \Delta^{0} - \Delta^{+} + 0(31) \\
\Delta^{o} - \Delta^{+} &= \Delta^{+} - \Delta^{++} + 0(11) \\
&= \Delta^{-} - \Delta^{0} + 0(11) \\
\Sigma^{*-} - \Sigma^{*0} &= \Sigma^{*0} - \Sigma^{*+} + 0(11) \\
3(\Delta^{0} - \Delta^{+}) &= \Delta^{-} - \Delta^{++} + 0(111) \\
\Sigma^{*-} - \Sigma^{*0} &= \frac{1}{2}\left\{(\Xi^{*-} - \Xi^{*0}) + (\Delta^{-} - \Delta^{0})\right\} + 0(331) \\
\Sigma^{*0} - \frac{(\Sigma^{*+} + \Sigma^{*-})}{2} &= \Delta^{0} - \frac{(\Delta^{+} + \Delta^{-})}{2} + 0(311) \\
\frac{\nu}{\lambda} &= (\Delta^{+} - \Delta^{++})/(\Omega - \Xi^{*}) \; .
\end{aligned}
\qquad (77)
$$

III. A SYMMETRY HIGHER THAN SU_3

In order to attempt an explanation of certain curious features that are present in our formulism (e.g. the existence of a vector meson singlet nearly degenerate with the octuplet) we introduce a new symmetry. The trick is to exploit an additional ace property, spin. We have, in a sense, six aces, all of which are equivalent. They are

$$p_0\uparrow,\ p_0\downarrow,\ n_0\uparrow,\ n_0\downarrow,\ \Lambda_0\uparrow,\ \Lambda_0\downarrow = A_k \ (k = 1,\ldots,6). \qquad (78)$$

The arrow indicates whether the ace spin is up or down. We transform $p_0\uparrow$ into $\Lambda_0\downarrow$ by rotating the ace p_0 into Λ_0 in SU_3 space and by rotating the spin $\uparrow$ into $\downarrow$ in SU_2 space. Postulating that the world is invariant under this ace-spin symmetry would mean, for example, that a bound state of aces would remain bound with the same binding energy even if we were to change the strangeness, isospin, and spin orientation of the aces with an SU_6 transformation*). We would assume that whatever it is that causes the binding does not primarily depend upon these quantities.

Under SU_3 transformations:

A_1 A_3 A_5 mix among themselves

A_2 A_4 A_6 " " "

Under spacial notations:

A_1 A_2 mix among themselves

A_3 A_4 " " "

A_5 A_6 " " "

The group SU_6 which we will consider will mix all six of these objects. Postulating invariance under this group will lead to greater restrictions than postulating SU_3 or SU_2 separately.

We may also consider oriented antiaces:

$$\begin{array}{lll} A^1 = \bar{p}_0 \bar{\uparrow} & A^3 = \bar{n}_0 \bar{\uparrow} & A^5 = \bar{\Lambda}_0 \bar{\uparrow} \\ A^2 = \bar{p}_0 \bar{\downarrow} & A^4 = \bar{n}_0 \bar{\downarrow} & A^6 = \bar{\Lambda}_0 \bar{\downarrow} . \end{array} \tag{79}$$

The mesons are formed from oriented ace-antiace pairs $\bar{6}\times 6$ or $\bar{6}\times\bar{6}\times 6\times 6$. We treat the simplest case first. $\bar{6}\times 6$ is composed of the 36 states A^iA_j. Under SU_6, 35 of these objects transform among themselves, while one remains invariant.

---

*) Gürsey and Radicati have independently indicated that SU_6 might be a useful symmetry[7].

$$A^iA_j = (A^iA_j - \frac{1}{6}\,\delta^i_j\,A^kA_k) + \frac{1}{6}\,\delta^i_j\,A^kA_k \tag{80}$$

$$\bar{6}\times 6 = 36 = 35 + 1\ .$$

The type of mesons that are contained in $\bar{6}\times 6$ is easily ascertained. The SU_3 content is clearly $\bar{3}\times 3 = 1+8$. The angular momentum or SU_2 content is $\frac{1}{2}\times\frac{1}{2} = 0+1$. The SU_6 objects are then (8,1), (8,0), (1,1), (1,0) (the first entry gives the SU_3 representation, the second the spin. Note that there are a total of 36 states.) The irreducible representations 35 and 1 must therefore contain

$$\begin{aligned} 35:&\ \{(8,1),\ (8,0),\ (1,1)\} \\ 1:&\ \{(1,0)\}\ . \end{aligned} \tag{81}$$

If we take the parity of these states to be negative*), we have a pseudoscalar meson octet with a vector meson octet plus singlet, all degenerate in the SU_6 limit. There may be an isolated pseudoscalar meson singlet.

A matrix representation for the meson states is sometimes useful. Let

$$M^i_j = A^iA_j \tag{82}$$

$$M^i_j = \begin{pmatrix} \bar{p}_0p_0(\bar{\uparrow}\uparrow) & \bar{p}_0p_0(\bar{\downarrow}\uparrow) & \cdots \\ \bar{p}_0p_0(\bar{\uparrow}\downarrow) & \bar{p}_0p_0(\bar{\downarrow}\downarrow) & \cdots \\ \vdots & \vdots & \end{pmatrix} \tag{83}$$

---

*) If we think of a meson as a bound ace and antiace in an s state, then the parity of the meson is automatically negative since fermions and antifermions have opposite intrinsic parity. However, this type of reasoning is dangerous since it depends on the dynamics of the ace-anti-ace pair and is consequently not a result that may be abstracted into the language of SU_6.

$$= \begin{pmatrix} \bar{p}_0 p_0 & \bar{n}_0 p_0 & \bar{\Lambda}_0 p_0 \\ \bar{p}_0 n_0 & \bar{n}_0 n_0 & \bar{\Lambda}_0 n_0 \\ \bar{p}_0 \Lambda_0 & \bar{n}_0 \Lambda_0 & \bar{\Lambda}_0 \Lambda_0 \end{pmatrix} \times \begin{pmatrix} \bar{\uparrow}\uparrow & \bar{\downarrow}\uparrow \\ \bar{\uparrow}\downarrow & \bar{\downarrow}\downarrow \end{pmatrix} \tag{84}$$

$$= \begin{pmatrix} \frac{\eta_8}{\sqrt{6}} + \frac{\pi}{\sqrt{2}} + \frac{\eta_1}{\sqrt{3}} & \pi^+ & K^+ \\ \pi^- & \frac{\eta_8}{\sqrt{6}} - \frac{\pi}{\sqrt{2}} + \frac{\eta_1}{\sqrt{3}} & K^0 \\ K^- & \bar{K}^0 & -\frac{2}{\sqrt{6}}\eta_8 + \frac{\eta_1}{\sqrt{3}} \end{pmatrix} \times \begin{pmatrix} \bar{\uparrow}\uparrow & \bar{\downarrow}\uparrow \\ \bar{\uparrow}\downarrow & \bar{\downarrow}\downarrow \end{pmatrix} \tag{85}$$

$$\equiv D \times S.$$

Here we view the objects π, K, η_8, η_1 as mesons devoid of spin. For example, the ρ^0 would be represented by

$$(\rho_1^0,\ \rho_0^0,\ \rho_{-1}^0) = \rho_{S_z}^0, \tag{86}$$

$$\begin{aligned} \rho_1^0 &= \pi^0\ \bar{\downarrow}\uparrow & S_z &= +1 \\ \rho_0^0 &= \pi^0(\bar{\uparrow}\uparrow - \bar{\downarrow}\downarrow)/\sqrt{2} & S_z &= 0 \\ \rho_{-1}^0 &= \pi^0\ \bar{\uparrow}\downarrow & S_z &= -1\ . \end{aligned} \tag{87}$$

The index S_z gives the spin projection along the z axis. The π^0 meson would be

$$\pi_0^0 = \pi^0(\bar{\uparrow}\uparrow + \bar{\downarrow}\downarrow)/\sqrt{2} \qquad S_z = 0\ . \tag{88}$$

If we take the trace of M we find

$$M_i^i = D_k^k\, S_j^j = (\bar{p}_0 p_0 + \bar{n}_0 n_0 + \bar{\Lambda}_0 \Lambda_0)\ (\bar{\uparrow}\uparrow + \bar{\downarrow}\downarrow). \tag{89}$$

Except for normalization, this represents a spin-zero state with I = 0, S = 0, i.e. a pseudoscalar meson singlet. This object remains invariant under SU_6 transformations and should be subtracted from M if we are to form irreducible representations of SU_6. Consequently, we define a matrix N by:

$$N^i_j = M^i_j - \frac{1}{6}\,\delta^i_j\, M^k_k = A^i A_j - \frac{1}{6}\,\delta^i_j\, A^k A_k \;. \tag{90}$$

Note that Tr N = 0. N is the SU_6 counterpart of the traceless matrix P defined in Eq. (9). The 35 objects contained in the matrix N form an irreducible representation of SU_6 and may be written as the sum of three matrices:

$$N = N_1 + N_0 + N_{-1}. \tag{91}$$

Here, the objects in N_i all have $S_z = i$. One may readily verify that

$$\begin{aligned} N_1 &= G_1 \times \frac{1}{2}\,(\sigma_x + i\sigma_y) = G_1 \times \sigma_+ \\ N_0 &= \frac{1}{\sqrt{2}}\,\{P_0 \times I + G_0 \times \sigma_z\} \\ N_{-1} &= G_{-1} \times \frac{1}{2}\,(\sigma_x - i\sigma_y) = G_{-1} \times \sigma \;. \end{aligned} \tag{92}$$

Here, σ_i are the Pauli spin matrices and I is the identity matrix;

$$\begin{aligned} G_1 &= G\,\bar{\downarrow}\uparrow \\ G_0 &= G(\bar{\uparrow}\uparrow - \bar{\downarrow}\downarrow)/\sqrt{2} \\ G_{-1} &= G\,\bar{\uparrow}\downarrow \\ P_0 &= P(\bar{\uparrow}\uparrow + \bar{\downarrow}\downarrow)/\sqrt{2} \end{aligned} \tag{93}$$

and the matrices G and P are given by Eqs. (10) and (44).[†)]

We may rewrite our expression for N in terms of vector mesons polarized along the x,y, and z direction. An object ϵ polarized along the x axis is represented by ϵ_x where

---

†) <u>Problem 10</u> - Derive Eqs. (92).

$$\epsilon_x = (\bar{\uparrow}\bar{\downarrow})\frac{1}{\sqrt{2}}\sigma_x\begin{pmatrix}\uparrow\\ \downarrow\end{pmatrix} = (\bar{\uparrow}\bar{\downarrow})\frac{1}{\sqrt{2}}\begin{pmatrix}0 & 1\\ 1 & 0\end{pmatrix}\begin{pmatrix}\uparrow\\ \downarrow\end{pmatrix} = \frac{1}{\sqrt{2}}(\bar{\uparrow}\downarrow + \bar{\downarrow}\uparrow). \quad (94)$$

Similarly,

$$\epsilon_y = (\bar{\uparrow}\bar{\downarrow})\frac{1}{\sqrt{2}}\sigma_y\begin{pmatrix}\uparrow\\ \downarrow\end{pmatrix} = \frac{-i}{\sqrt{2}}(\bar{\uparrow}\downarrow - \bar{\downarrow}\uparrow)$$

$$\epsilon_z = (\bar{\uparrow}\bar{\downarrow})\frac{1}{\sqrt{2}}\sigma_z\begin{pmatrix}\uparrow\\ \downarrow\end{pmatrix} = \frac{1}{\sqrt{2}}(\bar{\uparrow}\uparrow - \bar{\downarrow}\downarrow) .$$

Then,

$$\begin{aligned} N &= \frac{1}{\sqrt{2}}(G_x \times \sigma_x + G_y \times \sigma_y + G_z \times \sigma_z + P_0 \times I) \;^{\dagger)} \\ &= \frac{1}{\sqrt{2}}\left(\sum_{i=x,y,z} G_i \times \sigma_i + P_0 \times I\right) \end{aligned} \quad (95)$$

Up to this point we have been working in the meson rest frame. The virtue of Eq. (95) is that it allows one to write down an expression for N which is manifestly Lorentz invariant

$$N = \frac{1}{\sqrt{2}}\left(- G\,\epsilon_\mu + P_0\,\frac{p_\mu}{m}\right) \times \sigma_\mu \,. \quad (96)$$

Here, ϵ_μ is the vector meson polarization four-vector, p_μ the pseudo-scalar meson four-momentum, $\sigma_0 = I$, and m is the SU_6 symmetric meson mass. Note that Eq. (96) reduces to Eq. (95) if we go to the meson rest frame. From the relativistically invariant form it is clear that under Lorentz transformations nothing terrible happens, like a ρ turning into a K^*.

When SU_3 is exact,

$$H^{(0)} = m\,\mathrm{Tr}\,\bar{N}N = m\{\mathrm{Tr}\,\bar{P}_0 P_0 + \sum_i \mathrm{Tr}\,\bar{G}_i G_i\} \,, \quad (97)$$

---

†) Problem 11 - Derive this expression for N.

where we have gone back to working in the meson rest system. (In obtaining this result remember that Tr $A \times B$ = Tr A Tr B and Tr $\sigma_i \sigma_j = 0$ unless $i = j$.) This indicates that all 35 meson states have the same mass. SU_6 symmetry is broken in four different ways

i) The S = 0 and S = 1 spin states are split. The Hamiltonian may then be written in the form

$$H^{(1)} = H^{(0)} + m_1 \text{ Tr } \bar{N} I \times \vec{S}^2 N$$
$$= H^{(0)} + 2m_1 \sum_i \text{Tr } \bar{G}_i G_i \; .$$

$\vec{S}^2$ is the operator which measures the spin of the mesons. Note that $H^{(1)}$ is still invariant under SU_3 and SU_2.

ii) SU_3 is broken by the unknown mechanism responsible for the $\Lambda_0 - N_0$ mass split

$$H^{(2)} = H^{(1)} + m_2 \text{ Tr } \bar{N}(I_3 \times IN + NI_3 \times I) \qquad (98)$$

$$= H^{(1)} + m_2 \{ \text{Tr } \bar{P}(I_3 P_0 + P_0 I_3) + \sum_i \text{Tr } \bar{G}_i (I_3 G_i + G_i I_3) \} . ^{\dagger)} \qquad (99)$$

iii) The octuplet singlet vector meson degeneracy is lifted. This is the SU_3 analogy of splitting the S = 0 and S = 1 states

$$H^{(3)} = H^{(2)} + m_3 \text{ Tr } \bar{N} \vec{r}^2 \times IN$$
$$= H^{(2)} + m_3' \left\{ \text{Tr } \bar{P}_0 P_0 + \sum_i \text{Tr } \bar{G}_i G_i \right\} + m_3'' \sum_i \text{Tr } \bar{G}_i \text{ Tr } G_i \; . \qquad (100)$$

Here $\vec{r}^2$ is the operator which measures the SU_3 representation that contains the mesons.

---

†) Problem 12 - Derive Eq. (99) from Eq. (98).

$H^{(2)}$ gives the relations

$$K = (3\eta + \pi)/4, \quad \omega = \rho, \quad K^* = (\varphi + \rho)/2, \tag{101}$$

$$K - \pi = K^* - \rho.$$

$$(0.22\ \text{MeV}^2) \quad (0.22\ \text{MeV}^2)$$

$H^{(3)}$ allows

$$K = (3\eta + \pi)/4, \quad (\omega - \rho)(\varphi - \rho) = \tfrac{4}{3}(K^* - \rho)(\varphi + \omega - 2K^*) \text{ or} \tag{102}$$

$$(\omega - \rho)/2 \approx \varphi + \rho - 2K^*, \quad K - \pi = K^* - \rho.$$

The fact that m_3 is rather small is curious.

iv) SU_3 is broken by electromagnetism.

$$H = H^{(4)} = H^{(3)} + m_4 \operatorname{Tr} \bar{N}(I_1 \times IN + NI_1 \times I) + m_5 \operatorname{Tr} \bar{N}I_1 \times INI_1 \times I$$

$$H^{(4)} = H^{(3)} + m_4\left\{\operatorname{Tr} \bar{P}_0(I_1P_0 + P_0I_1) + \sum_i \bar{G}_i(I_1G_i + G_iI_1)\right\} \tag{103}$$

$$+ m_5\left\{\operatorname{Tr} \bar{P}_0I_1P_0I_1 + \sum_i \operatorname{Tr} \bar{G}_iI_1G_iI_1\right\}.$$

We than would have $\pi^+ - \pi^- = \rho^+ - \rho^0$ (neglecting $\omega - \rho$ mixing)

$$K^0 - K^+ = K^{0*} - K^{+*}.$$

Previously, we indicated that $m_5 \ll m_4$, or

$$(\pi^+ - \pi^0)/(K^0 - K^+) \ll 1.$$

So far, we have discussed only spin 0 and spin 1 mesons. The f^0($\sim$ 1220 MeV) is thought to have spin 2. Where does it fit in? The simplest explanation is that it corresponds to $\bar{A}A$ in a p state. Alternatively, it may be contained in $\bar{A}\bar{A}AA$. We find:

$$\bar{6}\times\bar{6}\times 6\times 6 = 1296 = 2\times\{1\} + 4\times\{35\} + \{189\} + \{280\} + \{280\} + \{405\}$$

$$= 2\times\{(1,0)\} + 4\times\{(8,1),(8,0),(1,1)\} +$$

$$\{(27,0),(10,1),(\overline{10},1),(8,2),2\times(8,1),(8,0),(1,2),(1,0)\} +$$

$$\{(27,1),(10,2),(10,1),(10,0),(\overline{10},0),(8,2),2\times(8,1),(8,0),(1,1)\} +$$

$$\{(27,1),(\overline{10},2),(\overline{10},1),(10,0),(\overline{10},0),(8,2),2\times(8,1),(8,0),(1,1)\} +$$

$$\{(27,2),(27,1),(27,0),(10,1),(\overline{10},1),(8,2),2\times(8,1),(8,0),(1,2),(1,0)\}.$$

The smallest representation contained in $\bar{A}\bar{A}AA$ which could accommodate the f^0 would consist of 81 mesons (not counting their spin projections).

Let us construct the baryons. We start with the 36 states A_iA_j. Once again we must form tensors of a definite symmetry type if we are to obtain the irreducible representations of SU_6. We have

Irreducible representation	Symmetry type	Number of states
$S_{ij} = A_iA_j + A_jA_i$	[i | j] (one row)	$\frac{1}{2}n(n+1) = 21$
$A_{ij} = A_iA_j - A_jA_i$	[i / j] (one column)	$\frac{1}{2}n(n-1) = 15$

(104)

We are considering $\{(3,\frac{1}{2})\}\times\{(3,\frac{1}{2})\}$.
The SU_3 content is given by $3\times 3 = 6 + \bar{3}$.
The SU_2(spin) content is given by $\frac{1}{2}\times\frac{1}{2} = 0 + 1$.
The SU_6 objects must therefore be $(6,1),(6,0),(\bar{3},1),(\bar{3},0)$. These may be clustered together in only one manner if we are to obtain sets of 21 and 15 states. We have

$$S_{ij} \text{ contains } \{(6,1),(\bar{3},0)\} \qquad (105)$$
$$A_{ij} \quad '' \quad \{(6,0),(\bar{3},1)\}.$$

The baryons are obtained from either $A_\ell S_{ij}$ or $A_\ell A_{ij}$. The irreducible representations are given by

Irreducible representation	Symmetry type	Number of states
$A_\ell S_{ij} + A_i S_{j\ell} + A_j S_{\ell i}$	$\begin{array}{\|c\|c\|c\|}\hline \ell & i & j \\ \hline\end{array}$	$\frac{1}{6}n(n+1)(n+2) = 56$
$A_\ell S_{ij} - A_i S_{\ell j}$	$\begin{array}{\|c\|c\|}\hline i & j \\ \hline \ell & \\ \hline\end{array}$	$\frac{1}{3}n(n^2-1) = 70$
$A_\ell A_{ij} + A_i A_{\ell j}$	$\begin{array}{\|c\|c\|}\hline i & \ell \\ \hline j & \\ \hline\end{array}$	$\frac{1}{3}n(n^2-1) = 70$
$A_\ell A_{ij} - A_i A_{\ell j} + A_j A_{\ell i}$	$\begin{array}{\|c\|}\hline \ell \\ \hline i \\ \hline j \\ \hline\end{array}$	$\frac{1}{6}n(n-1)(n-2) = 20$

(106)

First we consider the case where the baryons are composites of the mesons (deuces) A_{ij} and the aces A_ℓ. We have

$$\begin{aligned}
A_\ell \times A_{ij} &= \{(3,\tfrac{1}{2})\} \times \{(6,0),(\bar{3},1)\} \\
&= (3\times 6, \tfrac{1}{2}\times 0),(3\times\bar{3},\tfrac{1}{2}\times 1) \\
&= (10+8,\tfrac{1}{2}),(8+1,\tfrac{3}{2}+\tfrac{1}{2}) \qquad (107)\\
&= (10,\tfrac{1}{2}),(8,\tfrac{1}{2}),(8,\tfrac{3}{2}),(8\tfrac{1}{2}),(1,\tfrac{3}{2}),(1,\tfrac{1}{2}) \\
&= \{(8,\tfrac{1}{2}),(1,\tfrac{3}{2})\} + \{(10,\tfrac{1}{2}),(8,\tfrac{3}{2}),(8,\tfrac{1}{2}),(1,\tfrac{1}{2})\} \\
&= \quad 20 \quad + \quad 70
\end{aligned}$$

Composites of S_{ij} and A_ℓ are

$$\begin{aligned}
A_\ell \times S_{ij} &= \{(3,\tfrac{1}{2})\} \times \{(6,1),(\bar{3},0)\} \\
&= \{(10,\tfrac{3}{2}),8,\tfrac{1}{2})\} + \{(10,\tfrac{1}{2}),(8,\tfrac{3}{2}),(8,\tfrac{1}{2}),(1,\tfrac{1}{2})\} \qquad (108)\\
&= \quad 56 \quad + \quad 70
\end{aligned}$$

The classification of the existing $J^P = \frac{1}{2}^+$ octuplet and $\frac{3}{2}^+$ decuplet is ambigious. One simple possibility would be to use the 56 states $(10, \frac{3}{2})$, $(8, \frac{1}{2})$. We shall now adopt this viewpoint and explore a few of its consequences*).

In the limit of SU_6 symmetry, all 56 states have the same mass, i.e. the octuplet and decuplet are degenerate. We assume the following pattern for the breaking of SU_6(it is identical to the one used for the meson case):

i) The $S = \frac{1}{2}$ and $S = \frac{3}{2}$ spin states are split.

$$H = H^{(1)} = m + m_1 \; S(S+1) \; . \tag{109}$$

Note that $H^{(1)}$ is invariant under SU_3 and SU_2, but not SU_6.

ii) SU_3 is broken by the $\Lambda_0 - N_0$ split. In first order we have

$$H = H^{(2)} = H^{(1)} + m_2 Y + m_3 Y_0^2$$
$$Y_0^2 = \frac{1}{4} Y^2 - I(I+1) \; . \tag{110}$$

This formula holds for <u>both</u> the octuplet and decuplet. In addition, to the baryon mass formulae already listed, we find

$$\underset{(125)}{\Xi - \Sigma} = \underset{(140)}{\Xi^* - \Sigma^*} \; . \tag{111}$$

iii) SU_3 is broken by electromagnetism (the $p_0 - n_0$ split).

---

*) This assignment may have difficulties in that it requires the space part of the three-ace wavefunction representing the baryons to be totally antisymmetric (the SU_6 part is totally symmetric). One might not expect this to be the lowest energy state. Another alternative would put the eight baryons together with a $\frac{3}{2}^+$ singlet (the 1405?) in the 20-dimensional representation. Since this representation is totally antisymmetric, the space part of the baryon wavefunction must be totally symmetric in the three aces. The existence of the $\frac{3}{2}^+$ decuplet would then require the existence of a second $\frac{1}{2}^+$ octet. However, this type of reasoning is dangerous since it depends on the dynamics of the ace-antiace pair and is consequently not a result that may be abstracted into the language of SU_6.

$$H = H^{(3)} = H^{(2)} + \mu_2 Q + \mu_3 Q_0^2 + \mu_4 Q Q_0^2 + \mu_5 Q_0^4$$

$$Q_0^2 = \frac{1}{4} Q^2 - U(U+1) .$$

In addition to the relations previously derived, we have

$$n - p = \Sigma^{*0} - \Sigma^{*+} . \text{ †)} \tag{112}$$

Unfortunately, we will not be able to consider the coupling of particles in any detail. We will, however, list a few results.

i) $\varphi \to \rho\pi$: Vector-vector-pseudoscalar meson couplings are given by $g \operatorname{Tr} \bar{G}(GP + PG)$ in the approximation where we treat the vector meson octuplet and singlet as being degenerate. Since this expression does not contain a $\varphi \to \rho\pi$ coupling, the decay mode is forbidden ††). We may obtain an order of magnitude estimate by splitting the singlet from the octuplet. We find

$$\begin{aligned}(\varphi \to \rho\pi, \text{ all charge states}) &= \beta^2 \times 160 \text{ MeV} \\ &= 0(1 \text{ MeV}) \qquad (110') \\ &\leq 1.0 \pm 0.6 \text{ MeV (exp.)}.\end{aligned}$$

Here, $\beta = (\omega - \rho)/\sqrt{2}(\varphi - \omega)$ *). The interaction responsible for the splitting of the $\omega\rho$ masses also induces the decay $\varphi \to \rho\pi$. The factor of 160 MeV comes from assuming that $\omega \to \rho\pi \to \pi\pi\pi$ dominates $\omega \to 3\pi$. The calculation does not contain symmetry breaking effects coming from $\operatorname{Tr} GP \operatorname{Tr} G\lambda_8$.

ii) Decay widths of the decuplet states. The strong interaction decays

---

†) Problem 13 - Derive mass rules (111) and (112) using the forms given for the mass terms in the Hamiltonian.

††) Problem 14 - Verify that $g \operatorname{Tr} \bar{G}(GP + PG)$ does not induce $\varphi \to \rho\pi$.

*) Remember that for mesons, the particle symbol stands for the $(\text{mass})^2$ of that particle.

of the decuplet states are:

$$\begin{array}{lll} \Delta \to N\pi & \Gamma_{exp} = 125 & \\ \Sigma^* \nearrow \Lambda\pi & \Gamma_{exp} = 53 & \\ \quad\searrow \Sigma\pi & \Gamma_{exp} = 0 \pm 2 & \\ \Xi^* \to \Xi\pi & \Gamma_{exp} = 7 \, . & \end{array} \tag{111'}$$

When SU_3 is exact there is one coupling G which governs the decay rate of all four modes. To check the validity of SU_3, we have taken the experimental values for the widths and calculated G from each one of the modes. In this way we obtain four values $G(\Delta N\pi)$, $G(\Sigma^*\Lambda\pi)$, $G(\Sigma^*\Sigma\pi)$, $G(\Xi^*\Xi\pi)$ for G. If SU_3 were exact, these values would all be identical.

We find using the Rarita-Schwinger formalism for spin $3/2$ particles,

$$\begin{aligned} G(\Delta N\pi) &= 1 \\ G(\Sigma^*\Lambda\pi) &= 1.1 \\ G(\Sigma^*\Sigma\pi) &= 0 \pm 0.5 \\ G(\Xi^*\Xi\pi) &= 0.6 \, . \end{aligned} \tag{112'}$$

The G's have the dimension of an inverse mass. We have normalized to $G(\Delta N\pi) = 1$.

The agreement is poor. However, if we take symmetry-breaking effects into account we find the coupling constant sum rule*):

$$\underset{(\sim 0.8)}{\frac{G(\Delta^{++}p\pi) + G(\Xi^{*-}\Xi^{0}\pi^{-})}{2}} = \underset{(\sim 0.8)}{\frac{3G(\Sigma^{*+}\Lambda\pi^{+}) + G(\Sigma^{*+}\Sigma^{+}\pi^{0})}{4}} \, . \tag{113}$$

The errors on the width measurements are large so it is difficult to

---

*) This relation has also been derived by Gupta and Singh[8].

judge the significance of this result. It is important to note that the coupling constant sum rule is also a mass sum rule in each of the three indices, i.e.

$$\frac{\Delta + \Xi^*}{2} = \frac{3\Sigma^* + \Sigma^*}{4}$$

$$\frac{N + \Xi}{2} = \frac{3\Lambda + \Sigma}{4} \qquad (114)$$

$$2\pi = 2\pi \, .$$

This implies that form factor effects (due to the fact that the mass of particles in an SU_3 representation are not the same) cancel in first order symmetry breaking. Alternatively, it helps remove the ambiguity associated with the fact that the G's have the dimensions of an inverse mass.

iii) By distinguishing the p_0 from the n_0 (first order in ν; or equivalently saying that $H_{\text{interaction}}$ transforms like the 11 component of a tensor), we may find electromagnetic coupling constant sum rules for the decuplet decays. Without discussing the feasibility of measuring these quantities we list:

Inter-isospin multiplet relations

a) $G(\Xi^{*-}\Xi^{0}\pi^{-}) - G(\Xi^{*0}\Xi^{0}\pi^{0}) = G(\Xi^{*-}\Xi^{-}\pi^{0}) - G(\Xi^{*0}\Xi^{-}\pi^{+})$ (115)

b) $\dfrac{G(\Sigma^{*+}\Lambda\pi^{+}) + G(\Sigma^{*-}\Lambda\pi^{-})}{2} = G(\Sigma^{*0}\Lambda\pi^{0})$ (116)

c) $G(\Sigma^{*+}\Sigma^{+}\pi^{0}) + G(\Sigma^{*-}\Sigma^{-}\pi^{0}) = G(\Sigma^{*0}\Sigma^{+}\pi^{-}) + G(\Sigma^{*0}\Sigma^{-}\pi^{+})$ (117)

d) $G(\Sigma^{*+}\Sigma^{+}\pi^{0}) + G(\Sigma^{*-}\Sigma^{-}\pi^{0}) = G(\Sigma^{*+}\Sigma^{0}\pi^{+}) + G(\Sigma^{*-}\Sigma^{0}\pi^{-})$ (118)

e) $2\sqrt{2}\, g(\Sigma^{*0}\Sigma^{0}\pi^{0}) = 2\{G(\Sigma^{*-}\Sigma^{-}\pi^{0}) - G(\Sigma^{*-}\Sigma^{0}\pi^{-})\}$
$\qquad + G(\Sigma^{*0}\Sigma^{+}\pi^{-}) - G(\Sigma^{*0}\Sigma^{-}\pi^{+})$. (119)

($\Sigma^{*0} \rightarrow \Sigma^{0} + \pi^{0}$ is forbidden if electromagnetic interactions are neglected. If we take the amplitude for $\Delta^{++} \rightarrow p + \pi^{+}$ to be $\sqrt{3}$, then $g(\Sigma^{*0}\Sigma^{0}\pi^{0})$ gives the amplitude for $\Sigma^{*0} \to \Sigma^{0} + \pi^{0}$.)

$$\text{f)} \quad \frac{G(\Delta^{++}p\pi^{+}) + (\Delta^{0}p\pi^{-})}{2} = G(\Delta^{+}p\pi^{0}) \qquad (120)$$

$$\text{g)} \quad \frac{G(\Delta^{+}n\pi^{+}) + G(\Delta^{-}n\pi^{-})}{2} = G(\Delta^{0}n\pi^{0}) \qquad (121)$$

$$\text{h)} \quad G(\Delta^{+}p\pi^{0}) + G(\Delta^{0}n\pi^{0}) = G(\Delta^{++}p\pi^{+}) + G(\Delta^{-}n\pi^{-}) \ . \qquad (122)$$

These are the coupling analogies of the mass relations

$$\frac{\Sigma^{-} + \Sigma^{+}}{2} = \Sigma^{0} \text{ and } \frac{\Sigma^{*-} + \Sigma^{*+}}{2} = \Sigma^{*0}.$$

<u>Trans-isospin multiplet relations</u>

$$\text{i)} \quad G(\Xi^{*0}\Xi^{-}\pi^{+}) - G(\Xi^{*-}\Xi^{-}\pi^{0}) = G(\Sigma^{*0}\Sigma^{-}\pi^{+}) - G(\Sigma^{*-}\Sigma^{-}\pi^{0}) \qquad (123)$$

$$\text{j)} \quad G(\Xi^{*-}\Xi^{0}\pi^{-}) - G(\Xi^{*-}\Xi^{-}\pi^{0}) + G(\Delta^{0}p\pi^{-}) - G(\Delta^{-}n\pi^{-}) = G(\Sigma^{*o}\Sigma^{+}\pi^{-}) - G(\Sigma^{*-}\Sigma^{-}\pi^{o}) \qquad (124)$$

$$\text{k)} \quad 3\{G(\Sigma^{*+}\Lambda\pi^{+}) - G(\Sigma^{*-}\Lambda\pi^{-})\} = G(\Sigma^{*+}\Sigma^{0}\pi^{+}) - G(\Sigma^{*-}\Sigma^{0}\pi^{-}) + 4\{G(\Delta^{0}n\pi^{0}) - G(\Delta^{-}n\pi^{-})\} \ . \qquad (125)$$

It is important to note that each one of these coupling constant sum rules is also a mass sum rule in each of the three indices. This helps remove form factor effects due to variations of mass within an isospin multiplet*).

*) A trans-isospin multiplet sum rule which does not satisfy a mass relation in its indices is

$$G(\Sigma^{*0}\Sigma^{+}\pi^{-}) - G(\Sigma^{*-}\Sigma^{0}\pi^{-}) = G(\Delta^{0}p\pi^{-}) - G(\Delta^{-}n\pi^{-}). \qquad (126)$$

REFERENCES

1) S. Sakata, Progr.Theoret.Phys. 16, 686 (1956).

2) Y. Ne'eman, Phys.Rev. 134, B 1355 (1964).

3) M. Gell-Mann, Phys.Letters 8, 214 (1964).
G. Zweig, CERN Report TH 401, Jan. 1964; and TH 412, Feb. 1964

4) J. Schwinger, Phys.Rev. 135, B 816 (1964).

5) S. Meshkov, C.A. Levinson and H.J. Lipkin, Phys.Rev.Letters 10, 361 (1963).

6) S. Coleman and S.L. Glashow, Phys.Rev.Letters 6, 423 (1961).

7) F. Gürsey and L.A. Radicati, Phys.Rev.Letters 13, 173 (1964).

8) V. Gupta and V. Singh, Phys.Rev, 135, B 1442 (1964).

SU_4

P. Tarjanne,

The Research Institute for Theoretical
Physics at the University of Helsinki

There are several reasons for taking up the study of the group SU_4 which in particle physics means especially the investigation of the properties of its representations.

i) The first reason is that the success of SU_3, combined with the fact that the experimentalists have continued their bump-hunting game, leads one to expand SU_3. The experimentalists have been most successful in their study of bosons, and as a result we have today lots of more or less well-established boson resonances in the region 300 - 1,600 MeV. The latest compilations list some 30 isotopic multiplets of which perhaps a dozen are universally accepted. Therefore, it seems worth while, in order to explain this multitude of mass spectrum fine structure, to look for some larger groups that would contain SU_3 as a subgroup, and would contain large multiplets capable of containing, say, all the known or suggested vector mesons in one multiplet. The group SU_4 suggests itself as an obvious candidate for such a super-symmetry.

ii) In the current literature one finds models based on SU_4 [1], SU_6 [2], and general SU_n [3]. Familiarity with SU_4 gives one some further insight into the general properties of these groups.

iii) It is easy to incorporate a baryon-lepton symmetry in the framework of SU_4 if we assign the four leptons $(e^-, \mu^-, \nu_e, \nu_\mu)$ into the four-dimensional fundamental representation of SU_4. It is also possible to generalize Cabibbo's theory of weak interactions [4] by requiring that the weak currents transform like components of the adjoint (15-dimensional) representation of SU_4.

iv) The most important reason to take up the study of SU_4 is, of course, that so many people do SU_3 work and there is probably not too much easy group theory that remains to be done. In order to ensure full employment, one has to find something slightly more complicated.

I. REPRESENTATIONS OF SU_4

(and assignment of particles to the representations)

Let us first review the starting points of the three different SU_3 models proposed so far:

1. Sakata model[5]

Fundamental three-dimensional representation: $\psi(p,n,\Lambda)$

Pseudoscalar mesons (M) and vector mesons (V) $\subset \psi\bar{\psi} = 3 \otimes \bar{3} = 8 + 1$

Baryons (B) and $\frac{3}{2}^+$-isobars (B*) $\subset \psi\psi\bar{\psi} = 3 \otimes 3 \otimes \bar{3} = 15 + \bar{6} + 3 + 3$

Remark: This model is not realized in nature.

2. Ace model[6]

Fundamental three-dimensional representation: $\psi(p_0, n_0, \Lambda_0)$

$$M,V \subset \psi\bar{\psi} = 3 \otimes \bar{3} = 8 + 1$$
$$B,B^* \subset \psi\psi\psi = 3 \otimes 3 \otimes 3 = 10 + 8 + 8 + 1$$

Personal remark: Unaesthetic (fractional Q and B).

3. Eightfold way[7]

Eight-dimensional baryon representation: $B(N,\Lambda,\Sigma,\Xi)$

$$M,V \subset B\bar{B} = 8 \otimes \bar{8} = 27 + 10 + \overline{10} + 8 + 8 + 1$$
$$B^* \subset BM = 8 \otimes 8 = 27 + 10 + \overline{10} + 8 + 8 + 1$$

Remark: Chooses eight without justification.

I wish to propose the following SU_4 model:

$$M,V \subset \psi\bar{\psi} = 4 \otimes \bar{4} = 15 + 1$$
$$B \subset \psi\psi\bar{\psi} = 4 \otimes 4 \otimes \bar{4} = 36 + \overline{20} + 4 + 4$$
$$B^* \subset BM = \overline{20} \otimes 15 = \overline{140} + 60 + 36 + \overline{20} + \overline{20} + \overline{20}' + 4.$$

Mesons

The structure of the 15-dimensional representation is shown in Fig. 1, which is obtained by starting from the illustration of the fundamental ψ by a regular tetrahedron in weight space, whose three axes are labelled by I_z, Y and the new additive quantum number Z, supercharge (also called charm, hyper-strangeness, oddness, etc.). In Fig. 1b we split up the SU_4 representation into SU_3 multiplets perpendicular to the Z-axis in order to facilitate the drawing of the diagrams.

Vector mesons: The particles assigned to the 15 states are the following: $\rho,\omega,\Phi,K^*,\kappa(725)$ and an additional new predicted super-charged isospin singlet vector meson λ with its antiparticle. One notes that ω and Φ belong to the same representation which explains the degeneracy of their unmixed states as required by the generally used mass formulae[8)].

Pseudoscalar mesons: Only the SU_3 octuplet (π,K,η) is well established, but also the $\eta\pi\pi(960)$ resonance would fit in well as the analogous state of the Φ.

Baryons

We have to use dynamical arguments in order to assign the baryons to the $\overline{20}$ (Fig. 2) instead of the 36, both of which contain a suitable SU_3 octuplet. The simplest kind of force calculation is the static Born approximation of Chew and Low that has been used to prove that in SU_3 there is a strong attraction in the decuplet state of the BM system for a suitable value of the F/D mixing parameter[9)]. This means essentially that we have to generalize the SU_2 operator $\vec{\tau}_1 \cdot \vec{\tau}_2$ to SU_4, which can be done by first calculating the eigenvalues of the first Casimir operator: a bilinear form of the infinitesimal generators.

The result of this calculation is that we find attraction in $\overline{20}$ but repulsion in 36 and 4 for the appropriate spin states $(p_{1/2})$ in the $4 \otimes 15$ scattering.

$\frac{3}{2}^+$ isobars

In baryon meson scattering there are two states, $\overline{140}$ and $\overline{20}'$ (N.B. 20 and 20′, Fig. 3, are inequivalent representations) that contain suitable SU_3 decuplets. The force calculations are complicated because of a new "F/D" mixing parameter.†)

II. MASS FORMULAE

There are several ways to approach the problem of non-degeneracy of the particles belonging to the same multiplet. One way is to classify the splitting modes according to their transformation properties under the group in question, i.e. we think of the Hamiltonian as being composed out of two parts, one SU_4 symmetric and one that transforms like some component (with $I_z = Y = Z = 0$) of some SU_4 representation.

Example 1: SU_2, splitting of ρ

$$\rho\bar{\rho}(I_z = 0) \quad \begin{cases} T = 2 : (\rho^+\rho^+ + \rho^-\rho^- - 2\rho^0\rho^0)/\sqrt{6} \\ T = 1 : (\rho^+\rho^+ - \rho^-\rho^-)/\sqrt{2} \\ T = 0 : (\rho^+\rho^+ + \rho^0\rho^0 + \rho^-\rho^-)/\sqrt{3} \end{cases}$$

We can illustrate this complete set of states by writing the $\rho^+\rho^-\rho^0$ mass matrix in the form:

---

†) Problem - Please show that for a range of values of this parameter the strongest attraction occurs in the $\overline{20}'$.

$$M = m_0 \begin{pmatrix} 1 & 0 & 0 \\ 0 & 1 & 0 \\ 0 & 0 & 1 \end{pmatrix} + m_1 \begin{pmatrix} 1 & 0 & 0 \\ 0 & -1 & 0 \\ 0 & 0 & 0 \end{pmatrix} + m_2 \begin{pmatrix} 1 & 0 & 0 \\ 0 & 1 & 0 \\ 0 & 0 & -2 \end{pmatrix}$$

$T = 0$ corresponds to degeneracy, $m = m_0$;

$T = 1$ is antisymmetric and charge conjugation thus requires $m_1 = 0$;

$T = 2$ leads to the only actual and allowed splitting mode.

Example 2: SU_3, splitting of octuplets

Let us assume isospin invariance so that we consider only $T = 0$ states. In the reduction $8 \otimes \bar{8}$ these occur in the symmetric representations 1, 8^S and 27, and in the antisymmetric representation 8^A. The singlet corresponds again to degeneracy, whereas 8^S and 8^A lead to the Gell-Mann - Okubo mass formulae. For bosons the coefficient of 8^A vanishes. No splitting of the type 27 is observed in nature, probably due to its dynamical instability.

In SU_4 the situation is more complicated, but we can start out by making the assumption of a hierarchical scheme of SU_n symmetries, which means that SU_4 is mainly broken in a way leaving SU_3 unbroken[10]. Now SU_3 can be incorporated in SU_4 in different ways, but the natural thing to assume is that SU_4 is broken along the supercharge axis so that SU_3 perpendicular to supercharge is conserved. We thus study the SU_3 singlets with $I_z = Y = Z = T = 0$, in the reductions:

$$15 \otimes \overline{15} = 84^S + 45^A + \overline{45}^A + 20''^S + 15^A + 15^S + 1^S \quad \text{for mesons;}$$

$$20 \otimes \overline{20} = 175 + 84 + 45 + \overline{45} + 20'' + 15 + 15 + 1 \quad \text{for baryons;}$$

$$20' \otimes \overline{20'} = 300 + 84 + 15 + 1 \quad \text{for isobars.}$$

There are, for the isobars (which are the simplest to study), three possible splitting modes, but the one analogous to Gell-Mann - Okubo splitting is the only one that can lead to a situation where the decuplet (see Fig. 3) lies lowest in energy. Furthermore, this mode, which corresponds to a perturbing term in the Hamiltonian transforming like the fifteenth component of the adjoint representation, leads to an equal spacing mass formula. In general, for any multiplet, this 15-dimensional splitting leads to the mass formula:

$$m \text{ or } m^2 = a + bZ + c(Z^2 - X) ,$$

where $X = \lambda^2 + \mu^2 + \lambda\mu + 3\lambda + 3\mu$ and $(\lambda\mu)$ is the usual notation for the SU_3 multiplet. **We** thus predict strange superneutral baryons and isobars in the region 1,600 - 2,000 MeV and new boson resonances preferably in the region 700 - 1,100 MeV.

III. WEAK INTERACTIONS

Cabibbo has suggested that the weak currents would transform like components of SU_3 octets, so that, for example, the vector current would be of the form:

$$V_\mu = g_F \{\cos \Theta \, V_\mu^F(\pi^+) + \sin \Theta \, V_\mu^F(K^+)\} ,$$

where experimentally $\Theta \simeq 0.26$.

This means essentially that the weak interactions are, in fact, strangeness conserving, but with a new strangeness direction. One way to illustrate this SU_3 rotation

$$\left.\begin{array}{l} p \rightarrow p \\ n \rightarrow n \cos \Theta + \Lambda \sin \Theta \\ \Lambda \rightarrow -n \sin \Theta + \Lambda \cos \Theta \end{array}\right\} \quad \begin{array}{l} \pi^+ = p\bar{n} \rightarrow p\bar{n} \cos \Theta + p\bar{\Lambda} \sin \Theta \\ = \pi^+ \cos \Theta + K^+ \sin \Theta \end{array}$$

is to use the matrix

$$\begin{pmatrix} 1 & 0 & 0 \\ 0 & \cos \Theta & \sin \Theta \\ 0 & -\sin \Theta & \cos \Theta \end{pmatrix}$$

in the p,n,Λ space.

The generalization of this formalism to SU_4 is straightforward, the idea being due to Gell-Mann and first published by Hara[11]. In the Λ_o^+, p_o^+, n_o^0, Z_o^0 space (which also corresponds to the lepton space $\mu^-, e^-, \nu_e, \nu_\mu$) we can use the matrix

$$\begin{pmatrix} 0 & 0 & -\sin & \cos \\ 0 & 0 & \cos & \sin \\ \sin & \cos & 0 & 0 \\ \cos & -\sin & 0 & 0 \end{pmatrix}$$

to give us, in addition to the current

$$J = (\bar{p}\cos\Theta + \bar{\Lambda}\sin\Theta)\, O_\alpha n = \pi^- \cos\Theta + K^- \sin\Theta$$

that transforms like an SU_3 octuplet, the current

$$J' = (-\bar{p}\sin\Theta' + \bar{\Lambda}\cos\Theta')\, O_\alpha Z = -\kappa^- \sin\Theta' + \lambda^- \cos\Theta'$$

that transforms like an SU_3 triplet.

For the leptonic decays of the known strongly interacting particles we do not get any new contribution because a triplet has no matrix elements between octuplets. Also, for the non-leptonic decays, we get no contribution from the crossed terms $J^\dagger J'$ and $J'^\dagger J$, but the term $J'^\dagger J'$ gives a pure $|\Delta T| = 1/2$ contribution which can be used to suppress dynamically the $|\Delta T| = 3/2$ part of $J^\dagger J$.

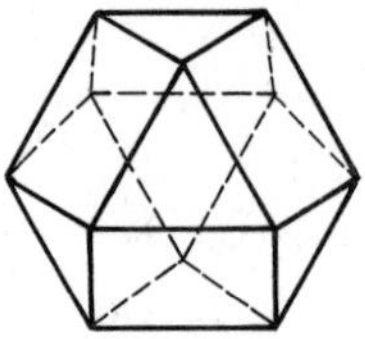

Fig. 1a

Number of states	SU_3 contents	Supercharge
3	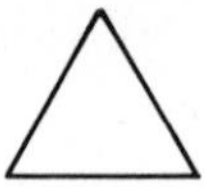	Z = -1
8 + 1	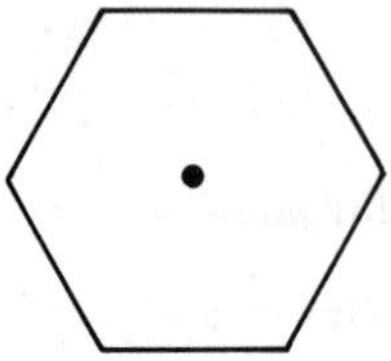	Z = 0
3	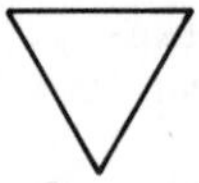	Z = 1
Σ = 15		

Fig. 1b

Fig. 1 The representation 15 of SU_4

Number of states	SU_3 contents	Supercharge
3		Z = -1
6 + 3		Z = 0
8	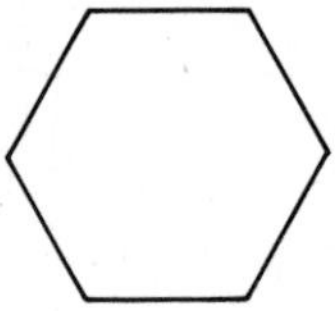	Z = 1
Σ = 20		

Fig. 2 The representation 20 of SU_4

Number of states	SU_3 contents	Supercharge
1	•	Z = -2
3		Z = -1
6	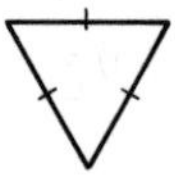	Z = 0
10	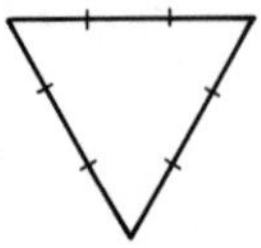	Z = 1
Σ = 20		

Fig. 3 The representation 20′ of SU_4

REFERENCES

1) P. Tarjanne and V.L. Teplitz, Phys.Rev.Letters 11, 447 (1963).

2) F. Gürsey and L.A. Radicati, Phys.Rev.Letters 13, 173 (1964).
A. Pais, Phys.Rev.Letters 13, 175 (1964).

3) R.E. Cutkosky, J. Kalckar and P. Tarjanne, Proc.Conf.High-Energy Physics, Geneva 1962, p. 653.

4) N. Cabibbo, Phys.Rev.Letters 10, 531 (1963), and 12, 62 (1964).

5) M. Ikeda, S. Ogawa and Y. Ohnuki, Progr.Theor.Phys. 22, 715 (1959).

6) See Dr. Zweig's lectures in this volume.

7) M. Gell-Mann, CTSL-20 (1961).
Y. Ne'eman, Nucl.Phys. 26, 222 (1961).

8) S. Okubo, Progr.Theor.Phys. 27, 949 (1962).

9) Pekka Tarjanne, Ann.Acad.Sci. Fennicae A VI Physica, 105 (1962).

10) P. Tarjanne (to be published in Physical Review).

11) Y. Hara, Phys.Rev. 134, B 701 (1964).

SOME PROPERTIES OF THE SU_n REPRESENTATION

L.C. Biedenharn*)

Theory Division, CERN

Summary : The methods of Weyl, Schwinger and Gelfand are discussed descriptively to illustrate the common structure of the SU_n representations in terms of diagrams. The idea of triality for SU_3 is discussed from this point of view as an example.

* * *

Low-energy nuclear physics has, particularly since the Princeton lectures of Racah (1951), increasingly applied group-theoretic techniques to construct nuclear wave functions; the accumulated experience in these symmetry methods can probably be of value to high-energy nuclear physics, now that SU_3 has become so important. I am indebted to Dr. Zichichi for the opportunity to discuss this with you. Let me hasten to point out that the emphasis on SU_n indicated in the title is not to be taken as implying a mathematical viewpoint, but rather to indicate that I wish to convey a view whereby one may grasp the structure of the problem - precisely in order to free oneself to concentrate on the physics.

There is a rather well-known story concerning the famous Berlitz School (of language instruction) which illustrates one of the peculiar pitfalls in the study of our subject. It seems that the owner of this School was desirous that his new heir be trained early for his future responsibilities, and he conceived the novel idea that each of the many relatives of this child speak to him in a different language. Thus the young Berlitz would learn from the beginning English, German, etc. The project was duly carried out, but the results were disastrous. It seems the poor child concluded that everyone had to invent his own private language -- and he was deeply disturbed that he could

*) NSF Fellow from Duke University, Durham, North Carolina, U.S.A.

not think up a new one! I am sure you see the relevance of this story to our problem, for it would appear to an objective observer that one of the coming-of-age-rites in physics is that one invents his own private language, that is, a new and different notation for the vector addition coefficients, ... ! Although the notation used below will probably be a bit unfamiliar I am pleased to say it was not invented by me. Nor are the results my own: they are gleaned from the classic -- and beautiful -- fundamental researches of Weyl, Wigner, Schwinger and Gelfand.

The model for all symmetry techniques in physics is based upon angular momentum, specifically SU_2. There are the familiar four 2×2 matrices to consider:

$$\begin{pmatrix} 1 & 0 \\ 0 & 1 \end{pmatrix} ; \begin{pmatrix} 0 & 1 \\ 0 & 0 \end{pmatrix} , \begin{pmatrix} 0 & 0 \\ 1 & 0 \end{pmatrix} , \tfrac{1}{2} \begin{pmatrix} 1 & 0 \\ 0 & -1 \end{pmatrix} .$$

$$\mathbb{1} \quad ; \quad e_{12} \qquad e_{21} \qquad h_1$$

Following Weyl essentially, we label these in the manner shown. (The last three matrices are collectively designated as $\{x_A\}$.)

The basic problem now is this: <u>to find all finite dimensional matrices*) that obey the same commutation rules as the</u> $\{x_A\}$. That is: one desires to make the association between two sets of matrices x_A and X_A such that:

$$\begin{array}{c} [x_A,\ x_B] \equiv (AB^C)\, x_C \\ \downarrow \quad \downarrow \qquad\qquad \downarrow \\ [X_A,\ X_B] \equiv (AB^C)\, X_C \end{array}$$

where the numbers (AB^C) are <u>identical</u> in the two cases.

*) To avoid trivial solutions, such as $\begin{pmatrix} a & 0 \\ 0 & b \end{pmatrix}$ where $\{a\}$ and $\{b\}$ are two solutions, one restricts attention to the irreducible cases, i.e. those that cannot be put in such a form.

Schwinger gave an elegant solution to this problem. Let us define creation-destruction operators a_1^*, a_1 and a_2^*, a_2. That is: $[a_i, a_j^*] = \delta_{ij}$, for i,j = 1,2. Then a solution to our problem is given by the association:

$$\begin{aligned} e_{12} &\to E_{12} = a_1^* a_2 \\ e_{21} &\to E_{21} = a_2^* a_1 \\ h_1 &\to H_1 = \tfrac{1}{2}(a_1^* a_1 - a_2^* a_2) . \end{aligned}$$

(The unit operator $\mathbb{1} \to N = a_1^* a_1 + a_2^* a_2$, i.e. the number of quanta.) It is clear that this satisfies the rules of the game.

Moreover, it is clear that the <u>states</u> which belong to a specific solution may be given in the (orthonormal) form:

$$|m_1 m_2\rangle = [m_1! m_2!]^{-1/2} (a_1^*)^{m_1} (a_2^*)^{m_2} |0\rangle ,$$

when $|0\rangle$ is the vacuum ket. For these states the operators H_1 and N are sharp

$$\begin{aligned} H_1 |m_1 m_2\rangle &= \tfrac{1}{2}(m_1 - m_2)|m_1 m_2\rangle \\ N |m_1 m_2\rangle &= (m_1 + m_2)|m_1 m_2\rangle . \end{aligned}$$

This result is just a symbolic transcription of the old "$\xi - \eta$ calculus" and is surely completely familiar. In terms of angular momentum (or rather SU_2) the more usual form is:

$$|JM\rangle = [(J+M)!(J-M)!]^{-1/2} (a_1^*)^{J+M} (a_2^*)^{J-M} |0\rangle .$$

From this it is a matter of a moment to obtain the result:

$$E_{12}|JM\rangle = [(J+M+1)(J-M)]^{1/2} |J,M+1\rangle ,$$

from which every solution to our problem is now explicitly given. Schwinger's famous monograph*) (1952) shows how this beautifully simple technique may be exploited to yield all of angular momentum theory.

---

*) To be published this year by Academic Press in "Selected Papers on the Quantum Theory of Angular Momentum".

Our purpose is rather different: we wish to play variations on this theme, and the next question is this: how can we diagram[†)] this state to make the structure obvious? The answer (given by Weyl and based on A. Young) is very simple:

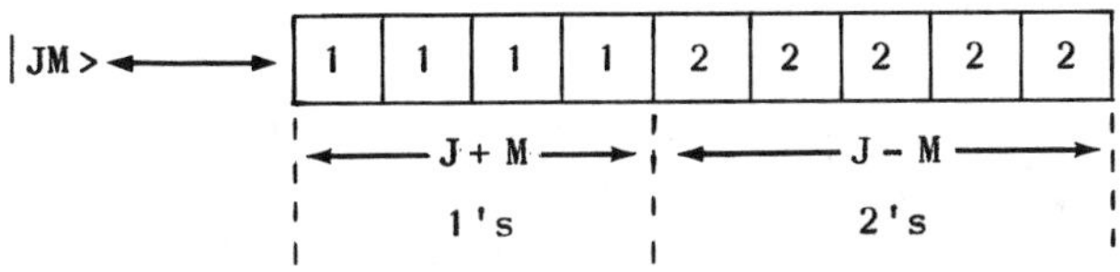

Note the essential point that we have ordered the entries in the boxes lexically.

Although we have hardly even indicated the proof, it is very familiar that the space of every solution to our problem is given by one such set of boxes of length 2J = 0, 1, 2, ...

Now let us generalize slightly. Consider two distinguishable, but otherwise identical, systems $a_i^{(1)}$ and $a_i^{(2)}$. Generalize the E_{ij},H, and N to include a sum on the upper index, i.e.

$$E_{12} = a_1^{(1)*} a_2^{(1)} + a_1^{(2)*} a_2^{(2)} \ .$$

The new feature is the possibility of the antisymmetric state: $(a_1^{(1)*} a_2^{(2)*} - a_2^{(1)*} a_1^{(2)*})|0>$, which clearly has E_{12}, E_{21}, $H_1 \to 0$ and $N \to 2$. This gives the complete basis for the solutions for U_2; i.e. the states:

$$|N,J,M> = (\text{Normalization})\ (a_{12}^*)^{N/2-J}\ (a_1^*)^{J+M}\ (a_2^*)^{J-M}\ |0> \ .$$

[It is convenient to denote by a_{12} the antisymmetric operator $a_1^{(1)} a_2^{(2)} - a_2^{(1)} a_1^{(2)}$.]

---

†) hommage à Feymann

Diagramatically this may be given in the form:

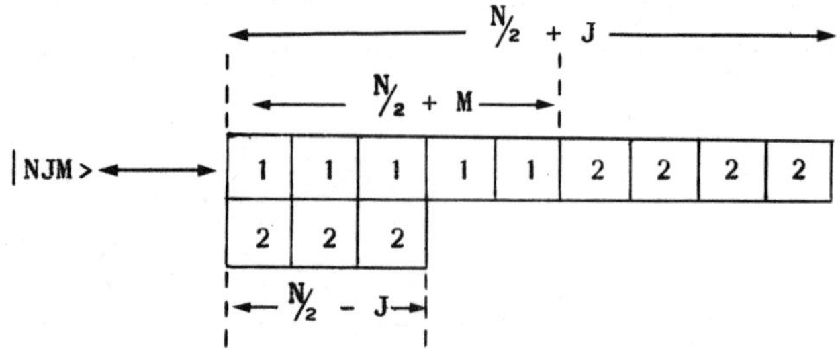

If one studies this diagram for a moment, it is clear that it is fully determined by <u>three positive</u> (including zero) <u>integers</u>, i.e.

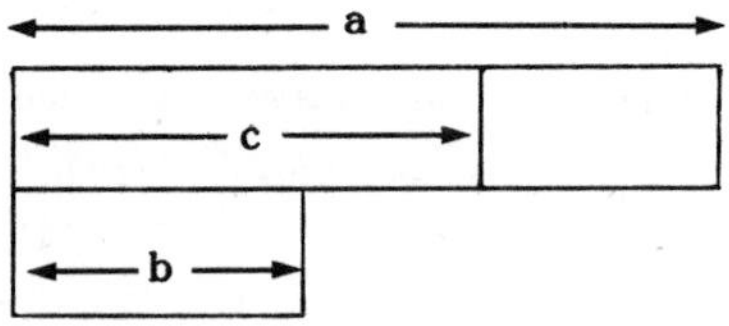

$a = N/2 + J,$

$b = N/2 - J,$ and

$c = N/2 + M$ = number of 1's in the top row.

The two integers a,b fully characterize the representation of U_2, while the integer c characterizes uniquely each <u>state</u> of the representation. One notes, too, that the antisymmetry condition forces c <u>to lie between</u> the integers a,b; that is, $a \geq c \geq b$.

Gelfand noted that this latter property may be indicated geometrically and we arrive at our next diagrammatic form - the "Gelfand pattern":

$$\begin{pmatrix} a & & b \\ & c & \end{pmatrix} \quad \text{a, b, c positive (including 0) integers}$$

$$a \geq c \geq b.$$

We may summarize these ideas now very succinctly. There are four equivalent ways to represent uniquely all states of all irreducible representations of U_2:

$$|NJM\rangle \longleftrightarrow \# \, (a_{12}^*)^{\cdots} (a_1^*)^{\cdots} (a_2^*)^{\cdots} |0\rangle \longleftrightarrow \begin{array}{|c|c|c|c|c|c|}\hline 1 & 1 & 1 & 1 & 2 & 2 \\ \hline 2 & 2 & 2 \\ \cline{1-3}\end{array} \longleftrightarrow \begin{pmatrix} a & & b \\ & c & \end{pmatrix}$$

abstract space	Schwinger realization of abstract space	Weyl basis vector	Gelfand basis vector

Each of these various ways has its own advantages and disadvantages; all are valuable.

The basic idea has now been achieved, the generalization to U_n (and SU_n) is probably quite obvious.

For U_n we consider the boson*) system a_i, where now $i = 1, 2, 3, \ldots n$. In order to get antisymmetric forms we must take n distinguishable, but otherwise identical, boson systems; then we may form the operators: a_{ij}, a_{ijk}, ..., $a_{ij\ldots,n}$ which are completely antisymmetric in their indices, i.e.

$$a_{ij..n} \equiv \sum_{\substack{\text{permutations}\\ \text{of } i,j,\ldots n \text{ indices}}} \epsilon^p P \left[a_i^{(1)} a_j^{(2)} \ldots a_n^{(\#)} \right] .$$

The operators $\{x_A\}$ are now the n^2 operators:

e_{ij} = (matrix with all zeros except for a 1 at ij, $i \neq j$),

$h_1 = \text{diag}\,(1 \; -1 \; 0 \; \ldots . \; 0) \times \frac{1}{2}$

$h_2 = \text{diag}\,(1 \; 1 \; -2 \; 0 \; \ldots . \; 0) \times \frac{1}{6}$

. . .

$h_{n-1} = \text{diag}\left(1 \; 1 \; \ldots . \; 1 \; -(n-1)\right) \times \frac{1}{n(n-1)}$,

and the $n \times n$ unit operator, $\mathbb{1}$.

(Note that $\mathrm{tr}\, x_A = 0$.)

---

*) One may actually re-do everything with fermions, but we stick to bosons here.

The problem - as earlier - is to construct all (irreducible) finite dimensional matrices that obey the same commutation relations as the $\{x_A\}$.

The 'Schwinger' solution is simply:

$$e_{ij} \rightarrow E_{ij} = \sum_{\alpha} a_i^{(\alpha)*} a_j^{(\alpha)} \quad \text{(where } \alpha \text{ is the index to distinguish the sets of bosons)}$$

and similarly for the H's. The states of the representations are now normalized products of the operators a_i^*, a_{ij}^*, etc., acting on the vacuum ket. Weyl and Gelfand basis vectors may now be constructed directly*).

The basic simplicity of the states of U_n and SU_n now becomes rather clearer: for the triangular Gelfand pattern $\begin{pmatrix} \cdot\cdot\cdot\cdot\cdot \\ \cdot\cdot\cdot\cdot \\ \cdot\cdot\cdot \\ \cdot\cdot \\ \cdot \end{pmatrix}$ of $n(n+1)/2$ integers uniquely characterizes each state of every irreducible representation of U_n (for SU_n put the uppermost right integer = 0). It is really astonishing how much information is contained in the Weyl and Gelfand diagrammatic forms for the states!

Let us note that in order to read off the quantum numbers, $H_i \rightarrow M_i$, from the Gelfand pattern one uses:

$$H_i \rightarrow M_i = \frac{\sum_{j=1}^{i} m_{j,i}}{i} - \frac{\sum_{j=1}^{i+1} m_{j,i+1}}{i+1} ,$$

where m_{ij} denotes the Gelfand pattern $\begin{pmatrix} m_{13} & \dot{m}_{23} & m_{33} \\ m_{12} & & m_{22} \\ & m_{11} & \end{pmatrix}$. (This formula is not nearly so complicated as it looks -- just the difference of the average values of adjacent rows.)

---

*) It is now that the Gelfand basis comes into its own, for the Weyl basis is no longer orthonormal in general.

To fix the ideas let us consider SU_3. The general state of the representation characterized by the two integers $[p,q]$ has the Gelfand pattern: $\begin{pmatrix} p & & q & & 0 \\ & a & & b & \\ & & c & & \end{pmatrix}$ where a,b,c stand for integers obeying the "between-ness" rule. In familiar terms one has the isospin and hyperchange quantum numbers:

$$I = \frac{a-b}{2}$$

$$I_z = c - \frac{a+b}{2}$$

$$Y = 2\left(\frac{a+b}{2} - \frac{p+q}{3}\right).$$

For example:

1. Triplets:

	100	100	100
	10	10	00
	1	0	0
I :	½	½	0
I_z :	½	-½	0
Y :	⅓	⅓	-⅔

The conjugate triplet has the pattern: $\begin{pmatrix} 1 & & 1 & & 0 \\ & 1 & & . & \\ & & . & & \end{pmatrix}$.

2. Octets:

	210	210	210	210	210	210	210	210
	21	21	20	20	20	10	10	11
	2	1	2	1	0	1	0	1
I :	½	½	1	1	1	½	½	0
I_z :	½	-½	1	0	-1	½	-½	0
Y :	1	1	0	0	0	-1	-1	0

It is clear that one can now generate by the most pedestrian arithmetic the complete (three-dimensional) lattice of quantum numbers associated with any desired representation. Moreover, one recognizes that the Weyl dimension formula (dim $[pq] = p - q + 1/1 \cdot p+2/2 \cdot q+1/1$) is simply the "volume" of this lattice, i.e. the number of points (each singly occupied) in the space of the three quantum numbers.

One interesting point arises immediately from the Gelfand pattern when written in terms of the quantum numbers I, I_z, Y. That is:

$$\begin{pmatrix} \cdot & \cdot & \cdot \\ & \cdot \ \ \cdot & \\ & \cdot & \end{pmatrix} = \begin{pmatrix} p & & q & & 0 \\ & I + \frac{Y}{2} + \frac{p+q}{3} & & -I + \frac{Y}{2} + \frac{p+q}{3} & \\ & & I_z + \frac{Y}{2} + \frac{p+q}{3} & & \end{pmatrix} .$$

This invites one to write the pattern directly in terms of the charge, as given by the Gell-Mann -- Nishijima rule $Q = I_z + Y/2$. One then finds that the pattern is:

$$\begin{pmatrix} p & & p & & 0 \\ & Q_{max} + \frac{p+q}{3} & & Q_{min} + \frac{p+q}{3} & \\ & & Q + \frac{p+q}{3} & & \end{pmatrix} ,$$

that is: the Gelfand pattern involves directly the charges of the multiplets shifted, however, by the value $p+q/3$. This number $p+q/3$ is just of the form such that the entries in the Gelfand pattern are integers*); expressed otherwise, the charges for general (p,q) are fractional --very familiar from quarks, aces, ... !

[Footnote on following page]

Alternatively one may say the charge is either integral, in which case the 3×3 operator is

$$Q = \begin{pmatrix} 1 & & \\ & 0 & \\ & & 0 \end{pmatrix} = (\tfrac{1}{3}\mathbb{1} + h_1 + \frac{h_2}{2})$$

$$Q \to I_z + \frac{Y}{2} + \frac{p+q}{3} ,$$

or one takes a quark model with the operator

$$\mathcal{Q} = \tfrac{1}{3}\begin{pmatrix} 2 & & \\ & -1 & \\ & & -1 \end{pmatrix}$$

$$\to I_z + \frac{Y}{2} \quad .$$

The physical predictions of these two operators are quite distinct [an example is given by the magnetic moments in the octet multiplets]. Note, too, that the octets, decuplets, ... are taken to have the average Q of a multiplet zero, so that for integral charge

$$Q \to I_z + \frac{Y}{2} + \tfrac{1}{3}[(p+q) \bmod 3] \ .$$

The curious occurrence of $p + q/3$ invites one to examine this point more generally. Consider the diagonal operator H_k. If two representations are multiplied together, the operator H_k for the resultant is again sharp, and is given by: $H_k^{(tot)} = H_k^{(1)} + H_k^{(2)}$. By considering U_n embedded in SU_{n+1}, and the result just given, it follows that one has the general result (for SU_n):

$$\sum_i m_{i,n}^{(tot)} \equiv \sum_i \left[m_{i,n}^{(1)} + m_{i,n}^{(2)} \right] \text{mod } n \ .$$

For SU_2 this is simply the familiar statement that:

($\mathcal{H}$ ≡ ½ integer angular momentum
I ≡ integer angular momentum).

$$\mathcal{H} + \mathcal{H} = I$$
$$\mathcal{H} + I = $$
$$I + I = I \ .$$

Thus the integer angular momenta form a sub-system of SU_2, i.e. the rotation group. The separation between integer and half-integer systems expressed by this rule is a super-selection principle.

In SU_3 one arrives at the interesting result that (similar to the two classes -- integer and half-integer -- in SU_2) there are three classes of representation in SU_3: $p + q = 3 \times \text{integer} + \begin{pmatrix} 1 \\ 0 \\ -1 \end{pmatrix}$.

(The number $t \equiv (p+q) \bmod 3$
$=, 1, 0, \text{ or } -1$
may be called the triality.)

One sees also that the representations $p + q = 3 \times$ integer form by themselves a sub-system, SU_3/C_3. All known multiplets are of this type, and it is this distinction which is involved in the more correct term for the Gell-Mann -- Neeman model "the eightfold way".

One sees at once that such properties readily generalize to all SU_n. Incidentally one also sees that if the triality is to be made a good quantum number (and not merely modulus 3) then either one must use U_3 or embed SU_3 in a higher group, such as SU_4. Both ideas have recently been put forward.

The methods of Weyl-Schwinger-Gelfand discussed in this lecture are extremely powerful, and they yield answers readily to a wide variety of specific applications. The small effort required to overcome the notational hurdle will be well repaid in results.

SUGGESTED BIBLIOGRAPHY

1) P. Jordan, ZS.f.Phys. 94, 531 (1935). (This is the original introduction of fermion and boson operators to discuss the U_n group.)

2) V. Bargmann, Rev.Mod.Phys. 34, 829 (1962). (An excellent account, and extension, of Schwinger's boson method for angular momentum.)

3) I.M. Gelfand and M.L. Tsetlin, Dokl.Akad.Nauk (SSSR) 71, 825 (1950). (Introduction of the Gelfand diagram.)

4) V. Bargmann and M. Moshinsky, Nucl.Phys. 23, 177 (1961); G.E. Baird and L.C. Biedenharn, J.Math.Phys. 4, 1449 (1963), and references cited in these papers. (Application of the boson calculus to U_n.)

POSSIBLE CONSEQUENCES OF THE $K_2^0 \to \pi^+ + \pi^-$ DECAY (CP VIOLATION AND OTHER INTERPRETATIONS)

N. Cabibbo
CERN, Geneva *)

In a recent paper, Christenson, Cronin, Fitch and Turlay (CCFT)[1] report the observation of the decay of the long-lived component of a K^0 beam into $\pi^+ + \pi^-$. They obtain a branching ratio of $(2 \pm 0.4)\ 10^{-3}$ over other charged decay modes. We will discuss here the possible interpretations of this result. Since these modify in one way or another our present picture of physics, some independent confirmation of the CCFT experiment is necessary.

In these lectures I will discuss some problems connected with this experiment, possible theoretical interpretations, and their experimental consequences. The first chapter will serve as an introductory review of the main decay modes of neutral K mesons; in the others I will speak of the matter of interest.

I. PHENOMENOLOGY OF K DECAYS (an outline)

1. $K \to 2\pi$

The final state has angular momentum J = 0, and therefore is spatially symmetric. Since pions obey Bose statistics, the state must be symmetric in I spin, which implies I = 0,2. The accessible final states are given in the following table (Table 1).

---

*) On leave of absence from the Laboratori Nazionali del CNEN, Frascati, Italy.

Table 1

Process	(I, I_z)	I spin wave function	CP	ΔI
$K^+ \to 2\pi$	(2,1)	$\frac{1}{\sqrt{2}}(\pi^+\pi^0 + \pi^0\pi^+)$	-	$3/2$, $5/2$
$K^0 \to 2\pi$	(0,0)	$\frac{1}{\sqrt{3}}(\pi^+\pi^- + \pi^-\pi^+ + \pi^0\pi^0)$	+ 1	$1/2$
or	(2,0)	$\frac{1}{\sqrt{6}}(\pi^+\pi^- + \pi^-\pi^+ - 2\pi^0\pi^0)$	+ 1	$3/2$, $5/2$

CP can be only defined for the neutral final states, which go into themselves under this operation.

As we will see in more detail in the following, the $K^0 - \overline{K^0}$ system splits into a short-lived component K_1 and a long-lived component K_2. The short-lived component decays mainly into 2π with a rate of $\Gamma^0_{2\pi} \approx 10^{10}$ sec^{-1}. The rate of $K^+ \to \pi^+ + \pi^0$ is smaller by a factor ≈ 700, $\Gamma^+_{2\pi} \sim 1.5 \times 10^7$. This difference can be understood if we assume the validity of the $\Delta I = 1/2$ selection rule. This rule forbids the decay of a K meson (which has $I = 1/2$) into states with I spin greater than 1. For detailed comparison of the predictions of $\Delta I = 1/2$ with experimental data, see R.H. Dalitz[2)], hereafter referred as D.

If the $\Delta I = 1/2$ rule holds exactly, we have the following consequences:

i) $K^+ \to \pi^+ + \pi^0$ is forbidden, and only happens via some electromagnetic effect. A difficulty is that this decay is not as suppressed as it should be under the above circumstances. However, we are not able to give a rigorous form to this criticism, and it should not be taken too seriously.

ii) In $K^0 \to 2\pi$ the preferred final state is $I = I_z = 0$. This leads to the following prediction for the rates

$$(K^0 \to \pi^+ + \pi^-) = 2(K^0 \to \pi^0 + \pi^0) \ . \qquad (1)$$

Equation (1) is to be modified by taking into account the correction to the phase space due to the $\pi^0 - \pi^+$ mass difference and an admixture of the I = 2 state, due to other e.m. corrections. The results of this analysis are in good agreement with experimental data (see D).

2. $K \to 3\pi$ (a simple account; for references to more detailed studies, see D).

The analysis of the angular momentum states can proceed in the following way. We first define the angular momentum of two pions, say π_1 and π_2, in their centre of mass, ℓ, and the angular momentum of the third one, π_3, in respect to the centre of mass of the first two, L

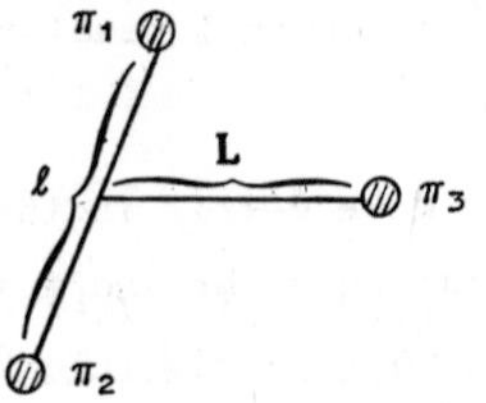

The two should then be combined to give the total angular momentum I = 0 (since the K has zero spin). This requires

$$\ell = L = 0,1,2,\ldots \quad (2)$$

The lowest choice $\ell = L = 0$ is highly favoured since the others given have 2,4, etc., centrifugal barriers. In the total decay rate (obtained by integrating the decay rate over the pion momenta) there will be no interference among the different sets (ℓ, L), so that the rate is dominated by $\ell = L = 0$.

The spatial wave function for $\ell = L = 0$ does not depend on the momenta of the three pions and is therefore completely symmetric under any exchange of π_1, π_2, π_3. The Bose statistic then requires that the I-spin wave function should also be symmetric. This restricts the I-spin values to be I = 1 or I = 3.†)

---

†) Problem 1 - Show this by use of G parity: remember that G = - 1 for an odd number of pions, and that for a system of isospin I,G is given by $C(-1)^I$ where C is the charge conjugation of the $I_3 = 0$ state of the system.

We can see this directly by enumerating the possible 3π states for different values of I_3. In the following table we enumerate the possible charge states (the exponent indicates the number of independent states n_i obtained by permutations) and the number of symmetric states.

Table 2

I_3	$(\pi_1\pi_2\pi_3)^{n_i}$	Number of symmetric states
+ 3	$(+\,+\,+)^1$	1 (I = 3)
+ 2	$(+\,+\,0)^3$	1 (I = 3)
+ 1	$(+\,+\,-)^3$, $(+\,0\,0)^3$	2 (I = 3, I = 1)
0	$(+\,-\,0)^6$, $(0\,0\,0)^1$	2 (I = 3, I = 1)

From the table we can readily reach our conclusion, remembering that the symmetry properties are the same for all the members of an I spin multiplet.

The final states in $K \to 3\pi$ are then limited by the $\Delta I = \frac{1}{2}$ rule to have I = 1. Let us denote these states by A^+ and A^0, respectively; we can write explicitely

$$A^+ = \frac{1}{\sqrt{15}}\left[2(+\,+\,-) + 2(+\,-\,+) + 2(-\,+\,+) + (+\,0\,0) + (0\,+\,0) + (0\,0\,+)\right]$$

$$A^0 = \frac{1}{\sqrt{15}}\left[(+\,-\,0) + (+\,0\,-) + (-\,+\,0) + (-\,0\,+) + (0\,+\,-) + (0\,-\,+) + 3(0\,0\,0)\right] . \tag{3}$$

A^0 has positive charge conjugation and, therefore, CP = - 1.†)

The $\Delta I = \frac{1}{2}$ rule has two classes of consequences in this simple

†) Problem 2 - Prove Eq. (3). Hint: build an I = 1 state by adding one pion to the I = 0 two-pion state, Eq. (1), and symmetrize. Check the normalization.

approximation of neglecting unsymmetric states ($\ell = L \geq 1$):

i) It determines the ratio of the different charge states in $K^+ \to 3\pi$ decay to be

$$\frac{(+\,+\,-)}{(+\,0\,0)} = \frac{4}{1} \times \frac{1}{1.295} \tag{4}$$

(the second factor is a correction for the difference in phase space) and in K^0 decays to be

$$\frac{(0\,0\,0)}{(+\,-\,0)} = \frac{3}{2} \times \frac{1.565}{1.336} \,. \tag{5}$$

ii) A relation between the amplitudes for $K^+ \to 3\pi$ and $K^0 \to 3\pi$. This is more subtle: the $\Delta I = \frac{1}{2}$ rule requires not only that I changes by $\frac{1}{2}$ in each decay, but that the Lagrangian for weak interactions behaves as an $I = \frac{1}{2}$ object. Let us build a phenomenological Lagrangian which describes the decays of K^+ and K^0 into the corresponding members of the A triplet, and behaves as a $I = \frac{1}{2}$ object:

$$L_{phen} = f\left[-\sqrt{\frac{2}{3}}\, A^- K^+ + \sqrt{\frac{1}{3}}\, A^0 K^0\right] + h.c., \tag{6}$$

(as usual, the <u>operator</u> A^- <u>creates</u> an A^+ state) this means a well-defined relation among the amplitudes:

$$-\, a(K^0 \to A^0) = a(K^+ \to A^+)/\sqrt{2} \,. \tag{7}$$

We cannot obtain from Eq. (7) any relation among the rates if we do not know more about the $K^0 - \bar{K}^0$ system. We will come back to this argument later.

3. <u>Leptonic decays</u>

We restrict the discussion to three-particle final states, since the $K \to \mu\nu$, $K \to e\nu$ modes are not available for neutral K's. Four-body decays ($K \to \pi + \pi + \ell + \nu$) are very interesting, but will not be discussed in these lectures.

As you heard from Feynman, there are good reasons to assume the validity of a $\Delta S = \Delta Q$ rule for strangeness-changing leptonic decays. This rule is a necessary consequence of the SU_3 theory of weak interactions, and is complemented by a $\Delta I = \frac{1}{2}$ selection rule*). In the following, we will assume the validity of both.

We have the following decays which obey the $\Delta S = \Delta Q$ rule:

$$\begin{aligned} &a) \quad K^+ \to \pi^0 + \mu^+ + \nu_\mu \\ &b) \quad K^0 \to \pi^- + \mu^+ + \nu_\mu \\ &c) \quad \bar{K}^0 \to \pi^+ + \mu^- + \bar{\nu}_\mu \\ &d) \quad K^- \to \pi^0 + \mu^- + \bar{\nu}_\mu \end{aligned} \tag{8}$$

and the corresponding electron modes. The $\Delta I = \frac{1}{2}$ rule implies the following relations among amplitudes:

$$\begin{aligned} a(K^+ \to \pi^0) &= \frac{1}{\sqrt{2}}\, a(K^0 \to \pi^-) , \\ a(K^- \to \pi^0) &= \frac{1}{\sqrt{2}}\, a(\bar{K}^0 \to \pi^+) . \end{aligned} \tag{9}$$

Let us discuss in more detail the structure of the matrix elements. In the V-A theory of weak interactions these will have the structure of a lepton current $\bar{\mu}\, \gamma_\lambda (1 + \gamma_5) \nu$ multiplied into a $K \to \pi$ transition current. Since this latter must be a function of the four-momenta of the pion and of the kaon, the most general form is:

$$f \left[(p_\lambda^{\,K} + p_\lambda^{\,\pi}) + \xi (p_\lambda^{\,K} - p_\lambda^{\,\pi}) \right] \ell_\lambda \tag{10}$$

where

$$\ell_\lambda = [\nu_\mu \gamma_\lambda (1 + \gamma_5) \mu] , \tag{11}$$

*) This is the $\Delta I = \frac{1}{2}$ rule for $\Delta S = \pm 1$ leptonic decays, different from the $\Delta I = \frac{1}{2}$ rule for non-leptonic decays.

for reaction (8a) and (8b), and

$$\ell_\lambda = [\mu\, \nu_\lambda (1+\gamma_5)\nu_\mu] \,, \tag{12}$$

for reactions (8c) and (8d). By the hypothesis of muon-electron universality the amplitudes for corresponding electron decays are obtained from these by substitutions

$$\begin{aligned} \mu, \bar{\mu} &\rightarrow e, \bar{e} \\ \nu_\mu, \bar{\nu}_\mu &\rightarrow \nu_e, \bar{\nu}_e \,. \end{aligned} \tag{13}$$

The conditions Eq. (9) imposed by the $\Delta I = \frac{1}{2}$ rule for leptonic decays can be written as

$$\begin{aligned} f(K^+ \rightarrow \pi^0) &= \frac{1}{\sqrt{2}} f(K^0 \rightarrow \pi^-) \\ \xi(K^+ \rightarrow \pi^0) &= \frac{1}{\sqrt{2}} \xi(K^0 \rightarrow \pi^-) .^{\dagger)} \end{aligned} \tag{14}$$

From momentum conservation we obtain

$$p_\lambda^{K} - p_\lambda^{\pi} = p_\lambda^{\mu} + p_\lambda^{\nu} \,, \tag{15}$$

so that the term proportional to ξ can be reduced by the use of the Dirac equation:

$$\begin{aligned} \xi(\bar{\mu}(\not{p}^\mu + \not{p}^\nu)(1+\gamma_5)\nu_\mu) &= i\xi m_\mu (\bar{\mu}(1+\gamma_5)\nu_\mu) \\ \xi(\bar{e}(\not{p}^e + \not{p}^\nu)(1+\gamma_5)\nu_e) &= i\xi m_e (\bar{e}(1+\gamma_5)\nu_e) \,. \end{aligned} \tag{16}$$

In electron decays the ξ term is completely negligible, while in muon decays it is not. The decay rates into electrons are simply proportional to $|f|^2$,

---

†) Problem 3 - Prove Eqs. (9) and (14). The technique can be similar to that used for proving equation (7). Remember that the $\Delta S = \Delta Q$ as well as the $\Delta I = \frac{1}{2}$ rule for leptonic decays relates to properties of the weak current of strongly interacting particles, not to the whole Lagrangian, since we do not attribute strangeness or I spin to the leptons.

those for muons are proportional to $|f|^2$ times a quadratic function of ξ. Since $|f|^2$ is the same (μ-e universality), the ratio is independent on f. For example, the ratio of the total rates for <u>each</u> of the decays in Eq. (8) and the corresponding electron modes is given by

$$\frac{K \to \pi \mu \nu}{K \to \pi e \nu} = 0.65 + 0.15 \text{ Re } \xi + 0.019 |\xi|^2 \ . \tag{17}$$

We see that the ratio is especially sensitive to the real part of ξ, not its imaginary part.

Time reversal invariance requires ξ to be real. Here, I will not derive the result, but simply outline the argument. The invariance under time reversal requires the equality of rate between any process and the one obtained from it by reversing <u>time</u> and as a consequence all motions, momenta, spins, etc.,

$$A \to B + C = C^T + B^T \to A^T . \tag{18}$$

The superscript T indicates reversal of $\vec{p}$'s and $\vec{\sigma}$'s. Mathematically

$$< B + C_{out} | A_{in} > \; = \; < A^T_{out} | C^T + B^T_{in} > \ . \tag{19a}$$

The subscripts <u>out</u> and <u>in</u> indicate the outgoing states (which are described by plane waves for $t \to +\infty$). In the absence of scattering (strong interactions in the initial or final state), a plane wave at $t = -\infty$ remains a plane wave at $t = +\infty$, and we can drop the <u>in</u> and <u>out</u> subscripts so that we get from T reversal invariance

<u>T with no final or initial interaction</u>

$$< B + C | A > \; = \; < B^T + C^T | A^T >^* . \tag{19b}$$

This is a sort of reality condition which, worked out in detail in our case, implies

$$\text{Im } \xi = 0 \ . \tag{20}$$

In the absence of scattering in the initial or final states, Eq. (18) implies a stronger condition (see Eq. 19b),

$$A \rightarrow b + C \underset{\text{}}{\overset{\underline{\text{T with no final or initial interaction}}}{=}} A^T \rightarrow B^T + C^T \; . \qquad (21)$$

This means that all correlations which can be described by a triple product of vectors should vanish. In the case of $K \rightarrow \mu 3$ decays we can build our correlation of this kind: $\vec{\sigma}_\mu \cdot (\vec{p}^\mu \times \vec{p}^\pi)$, namely, the polarization of the muon transverse to the decay plane.

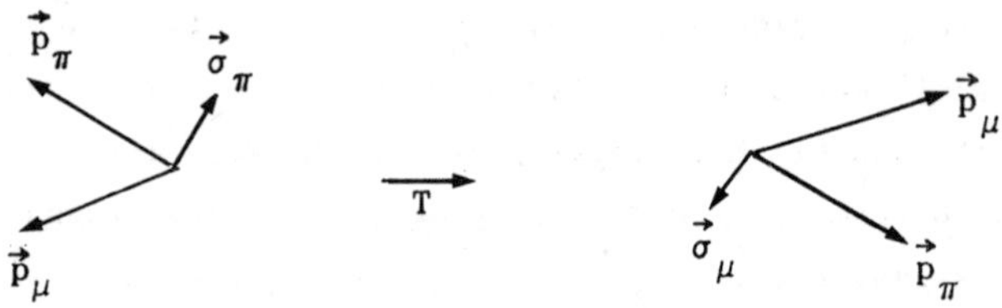

(22)

$$\vec{\sigma}_\mu (\vec{p}^\mu \times \vec{p}^\pi) \xrightarrow{\quad T \quad} - \vec{\sigma}_\mu (\vec{p}^\mu \times \vec{p}^\pi) .$$

By an explicit computation this component of the polarization is found (as we should by now expect) proportional to Im ξ.

A final remark: In writing an amplitude for any process there is some arbitrariness of phase. In the case of our $K \rightarrow \mu 3$ decay, the initial state could be taken to be $|K>$ or $e^{i\alpha}|K>$ without any physical consequence. Such a redefinition of phase produces a similar change in the amplitude. If Eq. (19a) could be made to hold by such a change, then T would hold, but such a phase change involves the phase of f, not that of ξ. Time reversal invariance requires the different parts of the amplitude to be relatively real (ξ real) but is not destroyed by an over-all phase.

II. THE $K^0 - \bar{K}^0$ SYSTEM

1. Decays and mass difference

It is well known that K_0 and $\bar{K}_0$ do not have definite lifetimes, while two combinations of them, usually called K_1 and K_2, do have definite lifetimes

$$\tau_{K_1} = 10^{-10}\ \text{sec}$$
$$\tau_{K_2} = 6 \times 10^{-8}\ \text{sec}\ . \tag{23}$$

The origin of the two lifetimes lies in the fact that K^0 and $\bar{K}^0$ have some decay channels in common, and in particular the 2π and the 3π channels. Consider, for example, the decays into two pions, to be more definite the decay into the I = 0 state. (This is the dominant one by the $\Delta I = \frac{1}{2}$ rule). This is a completely defined pure state: the two amplitudes

$$a(K_0 \to 2\pi,\ I = 0),$$
$$a(\bar{K}_0 \to 2\pi,\ I = 0), \tag{24}$$

are two well-defined numbers. In fact, they are defined up to a phase; we can take the liberty of making their phases equal by an appropriate choice of the phases for $|K^0\rangle$ and $|\bar{K}^0\rangle$. Furthermore, the CPT theorem, whose validity will be assumed, requires these two amplitudes to be equal in modulus so that we can put them equal:

$$a(K_0 \to 2\pi,\ I = 0) = a(\bar{K}_0 \to 2\pi,\ I = 0). \tag{25}$$

Suppose that at t = 0 we create a K_0; how will it develop in time, if we forget all other physical effects, except its decay into two pions (I = 0)? We can write

$$|K^0_{t=0}\rangle = \frac{1}{\sqrt{2}}\left[\,|K(+)\rangle + |K(-)\rangle\,\right]\ , \tag{26}$$

where

$$|K(\pm)> = \frac{1}{\sqrt{2}} [|K^0> \pm |\overline{K^0}>] . \qquad (27)$$

From Eq. (25), and the superposition principle, we have

$$\begin{aligned} a(K(+) \to 2\pi, I = 0) &= \sqrt{2}\, a(K^0 \to 2\pi \to I = 0) \\ a(K(-) \to 2\pi, I = 0) &= 0, \end{aligned} \qquad (28)$$

so that the K(+) part of the K^0 amplitude will decay while K(-) will live. After a time t the state will be

$$|K^0{}_t> = \frac{1}{\sqrt{2}} \left[|K(+)> e^{-\frac{\Gamma}{2}t} + |K(-)> \right], \qquad (29)$$

where Γ is the rate of decay of K(+) into two pions. After a long time $\Gamma \gg 1$, $|K^0>$ becomes $|K(-)>$, a mixture of $|K^0>$ and $|\overline{K^0}>$ in equal parts. This phenomenon, as well as those which we will meet when we go into more detail, has close optical analogues in the refraction and absorption of polarized light. We can think of the K^0, $\overline{K^0}$ as photons linearly polarized along fictitious axes x and y (see Fig. 1).

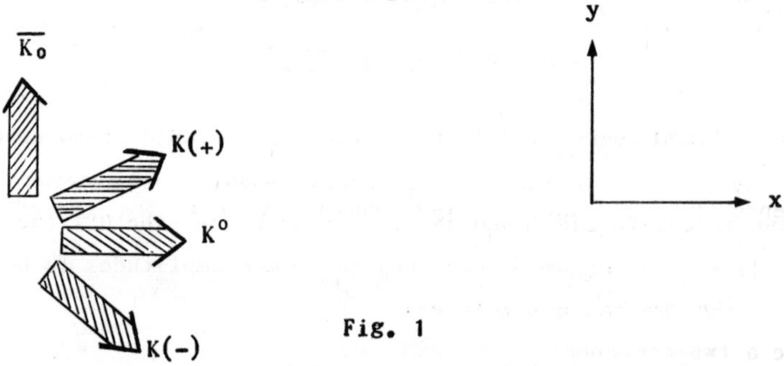

Fig. 1

The decay process is the equivalent of an absorption. The 2π (I = 0) decay has then an optical analogue in a "polaroid" filter with its axis at 45° from the x axis.

We will now continue our discussion under the hypothesis of CP invariance. If we apply CP to a K^0 we must obtain $\overline{K^0}$ (C sends particles into antiparticles)

$$CP|K^0> = e^{i\alpha}|\overline{K^0}> . \tag{30}$$

Note that here too we have a phase to choose. The phase is not arbitrary once we have chosen the phases of the amplitudes in Eq. (24) to be equal [see Eq. (25)]. The phase must be chosen in such a way that $|K(+)>$, which decays into two pions, has the same CP as the state into which it decays, namely CP = + 1. This implies $\alpha = 0$:

$$\begin{aligned} CP|K^0> &= |\overline{K^0}> \\ CP|\overline{K^0}> &= (CP)^2|K^0> = |K^0> \\ CP|K(\pm)> &= \pm\ |K(\pm)> . \end{aligned} \tag{31}$$

CP invariance now requires that $|K(+)>$ is the state which also decays into the $I = 2$, $I_z = 0$ 2π state, which also has CP = + 1. The decay into the symmetric 3π state, which has CP = - 1, should proceed through the $|K(-)>$ component.

It is convenient to rewrite the law of decay into 2π, $I = 0$ in the form of two differential equations:

$$\begin{aligned} \frac{d}{dt}\ |K(+)> &= -\frac{\Gamma}{2}\ |K(+)> \\ \frac{d}{dt}\ |K(-)> &= 0\ . \end{aligned} \tag{32}$$

We can condense the above into a single equation; if:

$$|\psi(t)> = a(t)\,|K^0> + b(t)\,|\overline{K^0}> , \tag{33}$$

we introduce a two-component wave function:

$$\psi(t) = \begin{pmatrix} a\ (t) \\ b\ (t) \end{pmatrix} . \tag{34}$$

Examples:

$$K^0 = \begin{pmatrix} 1 \\ 0 \end{pmatrix} ; \quad K(\pm) = \frac{1}{\sqrt{2}}\begin{pmatrix} 1 \\ \pm 1 \end{pmatrix} . \tag{35}$$

In terms of this ψ the law of decay into two pions can be written (in the rest system, τ being the proper time)

$$\frac{d\psi}{d\tau} = -\frac{1}{2}\,\boldsymbol{\Gamma}_{2\pi}\psi \,, \tag{36}$$

where $\boldsymbol{\Gamma}$ is a two-by-two matrix

$$\boldsymbol{\Gamma}_{2\pi} = \frac{1}{2}\begin{pmatrix}\Gamma & \Gamma\\ \Gamma & \Gamma\end{pmatrix} = \Gamma\,\frac{1}{2}\,(1+\sigma_x)\ . \tag{37}$$

If CP is conserved, $\boldsymbol{\Gamma}_{2\pi}$ describes the whole of two-pion decays. The decay into symmetric state of 3π, A^0, is also described by a similar matrix:

$$\boldsymbol{\Gamma}_{3\pi} = \frac{1}{2}\begin{pmatrix}\Gamma_{3\pi} & \Gamma_{3\pi}\\ \Gamma_{3\pi} & \Gamma_{3\pi}\end{pmatrix} = \Gamma_{3\pi}\,\frac{1}{2}\,(1-\sigma_x)\ . \tag{38}$$

Note that $\boldsymbol{\Gamma}_{2\pi}$ and $\boldsymbol{\Gamma}_{3\pi}$ are respectively proportional to $(1 \pm \sigma_x)$, the projection operators for $K(\pm)$ states. Let us come to leptonic decays. Under the $\Delta S = \Delta Q$ selection rule, K^0 and $\overline{K^0}$ decay into independent channels ($\pi^- + \ell^+ + \nu$ and $\pi^+ + \ell^- + \bar{\nu}$, respectively) with rates which are equal by CPT. The ensemble of these decays is therefore described by a matrix

$$\boldsymbol{\Gamma}_{lep} = \begin{pmatrix}\Gamma_{lep} & 0\\ 0 & \Gamma_{lep}\end{pmatrix} = \Gamma_{lep}\ \mathbf{1}, \tag{39}$$

Γ_{lep} being a sum of muon and electron rates. Note that in writing this we only use $\Delta S = \Delta Q$ and CPT, not CP. In conclusion, the decay of a free neutral K is governed in its rest system by the equation:

$$\frac{d}{d\tau}\,\psi = -\frac{1}{2}\,\boldsymbol{\Gamma}\psi \,, \tag{40}$$

where

$$\boldsymbol{\Gamma} = \boldsymbol{\Gamma}_{2\pi} + \boldsymbol{\Gamma}_{3\pi} + \boldsymbol{\Gamma}_{lep} + \cdots \tag{41}$$

The operation CP can be represented by the matrix [verify that this is equivalent to Eq. (31)],

$$CP\ \psi = \begin{pmatrix} 0 & 1 \\ 1 & 0 \end{pmatrix} \psi = \sigma_x \psi \,. \tag{42}$$

If CP is conserved, Γ must commute with σ_x [this is, in fact, the case for Eqs. (37), (38) and (39)] so that Eq. (40) splits into two independent equations for the two CP states $|K(+)\rangle$ and $|K(-)\rangle$. (Note however, that the form of $\Gamma_{2\pi}$ in Eq. (37) was obtained without the use of CP, so that it commutes with σ_x independently of CP.) These two states would then correspond to the experimental K_1 and K_2. Since $\Gamma_{2\pi} \approx 10^3(\Gamma_{3\pi}, \Gamma_{lep})$ the K_1 has a lifetime which is indeed 10^3 times shorter than a K_2. It is clear from the above that CP invariance requires $|K_2\rangle \equiv |K(-)\rangle$ which is then absolutely forbidden to decay into two pions.

We have forgotten an important factor in the time development of free neutral K's, namely their masses. From the point of view of strong interactions, K_0 and $\bar{K}_0$ have the same mass, say M_s. Weak interactions will give contributions to the masses through self-energy diagrams like

Fig. 2

If CP is conserved, intermediate states with CP = ± 1 will contribute to the mass of K(+) (or K_1) and K(−) (or K_2), respectively, but cannot connect the two. Since the intermediate states are different, the two masses will be shifted by different amounts from M_s. The masses can again be described by a matrix

$$\mathbf{M} = M_1 \frac{1}{2}(1 + \sigma_x) + M_2 \frac{1}{2}(1 - \sigma_x) \,. \tag{43}$$

Now we have to correct Eq. (40) to take into account the fact that ψ, apart from the decreases due to decays, suffers an oscillation: it is convenient to rewrite it as a Schrödinger equation:

$$i \frac{d\psi}{d\tau} = H\,\psi \tag{44}$$

where

$$H = M - i\,\Gamma/2 . \tag{45}$$

If CP is conserved, $[H, \sigma_x] = 0$, and we can write

$$H = \eta^0 + \xi^0 \sigma_x , \tag{46}$$

where

$$\begin{aligned} \eta^o &= \frac{1}{2}\left[(M_1 + M_2) - i\,\frac{1}{2}\,(\Gamma_1 + \Gamma_2)\right] , \\ \xi^0 &= \frac{1}{2}\left[(M_1 - M_2) - i\,\frac{1}{2}\,(\Gamma_1 - \Gamma_2)\right] , \end{aligned} \tag{47}$$

where Γ_1 and Γ_2 are the total decay rates of K_1 and K_2. As one could expect, the eigenvalues of this Hamiltonian are:

$$\lambda_{1,2} = M_{1,2} - i\,\frac{1}{2}\,\Gamma_{1,2} ,$$

corresponding to eigenvectors K(+) and K(−). The general solution of Eq. (44) is:

$$|\psi(\tau)\rangle = a\,|K(+)\rangle\,\ell^{-i\tau(M_1 - \frac{i}{2}\Gamma_1)} + b\,|K(-)\rangle\,\ell^{-i\tau(M_2 - \frac{i}{2}\Gamma_2)} \tag{48}$$

Orders of magnitude

$\Gamma_1 \approx 10^{10}\ s^{-1}$ corresponds to an energy $\hbar\Gamma_1$ of about 10^{-5} eV. $(M_1 - M_2)$ has been measured many times and values range from 0.5 to $1.5\times \hbar\Gamma_1$, the best value being $\approx 0.8\ \hbar\Gamma_1$, also $\sim 10^{-5}$ eV. $\Gamma_2 \approx \Gamma_{3\pi} \approx \Gamma_{lep}$ are smaller by a factor 1000:

$$\Gamma_1 \approx 10^{-5} \text{ eV}$$

$$M_1 - M_2 \approx 10^{-5} \text{ eV} \tag{49}$$

$$\Gamma_2 \approx 10^{-8} \text{ eV} .$$

2. Regeneration in matter

Let us consider a beam of kaons which passes through matter. We will forget those kaons which are scattered out of the beam, and focus our attention on those which continue in the forward direction. The matter acts on the beam in two ways: it acts as an absorber, through scattering, nuclear reactions, etc., and also as a refracting medium, through the average potential K^0's and $\overline{K^0}$'s in the presence of nuclei. These two effects can be described by introducing a new term in the Hamiltonian, H'. Since K^0 and $\overline{K^0}$ have definite – and different – nuclear properties, H' will have the general form:

$$H' = \eta' + \zeta'\sigma_z . \tag{50}$$

The real parts of η' and ζ' correspond to potential energy, the imaginary parts to absorption.

Orders of magnitude

Matter can be considered, from the point of view of K^0 mesons, an assembly of potential wells (the nuclei) of radius $\sim 10^{-13}\, A^{1/3}$ and depth of the order of 100 MeV. Of these wells there are $\approx 6\times 10^{23}\rho/A$ per cm^3 (ρ = density in gm/cc). The average potential energy of either K^0 or $\overline{K^0}$ [Re $(\eta' \pm \zeta')$] is then of the order of

$$\rho \times 10^{-7} \text{ eV} .$$

This is also the order of magnitude of both η' and ζ'. The proportionality of η' and ζ' to the density is generally true for amorphous materials. In liquid hydrogen, for example, $\zeta' \approx 10^{-8}$ eV .

Let us write again the Schrödinger equation in a material for a K of energy $E_k = \gamma M_k$. In passing from the rest system to the lab system $\tau = t/\gamma$; $d/d\tau = \gamma d/dt$. The equation becomes

$$i \frac{d\psi}{dt} = (\eta + \xi \sigma_x + \zeta \sigma_z) \psi , \tag{51}$$

where

$$\eta = \frac{\eta^0}{\gamma} + \eta' \\ \xi = \frac{\xi^0}{\gamma} , \ \zeta = \zeta' . \tag{52}$$

The Hamiltonian is now apparently CP violating (it does not commute with σ_x). Apparently, because the K are not isolated from the material they go through, CP should also act on this material (send it to antimatter). The Eq. (51) still admits two lifetimes. The Hamiltonian has two eigenvalues

$$\lambda_1' = \eta + (\xi^2 + \zeta^2)^{1/2}, \\ \lambda_2' = \eta - (\xi^2 + \zeta^2)^{1/2}, \tag{53}$$

to which correspond solutions:

$$\psi_1(t) = (1 + |\epsilon|^2)^{-1/2} [\,|K(+)> + \epsilon|K(-)>\,] e^{-i\lambda_1' t} , \\ \psi_2(t) = (1 + |\epsilon|^2)^{-1/2} [\,|K(-)> - \epsilon|K(+)>\,] e^{-i\lambda_2' t} . \tag{54}$$

$$\epsilon = \frac{(\xi^2 + \zeta^2)^{1/2} - \xi}{\zeta} \tag{55}$$

If $\zeta << \xi$, $\eta' << \eta^0$ (as is the case, for example, in liquid hydrogen or in a gas) we can develop these to the first order in ζ:

$$\lambda_{1,2} \approx (\eta^0 \pm \xi^0)/\gamma , \tag{56}$$

$$\epsilon = \frac{\gamma}{2} \frac{\zeta}{\xi} = \frac{\gamma \zeta}{(M_1 - M_2) - i/2\,(\Gamma_1 - \Gamma_2)} . \tag{57}$$

What is the physical meaning of these equations? In a low-density material the two lifetimes are essentially unchanged, but they do not correspond to eigenvalues of CP. The long-lived component, which can be obtained by producing neutral K's and waiting for a few K_1^0 lifetimes, will now contain an admixture ϵ of $K(+)$. It will decay into 2π with a branching ratio

$$R = \frac{2\pi}{3\pi + \text{lept}} = \frac{\text{fraction of } K(+) \times \text{rate for } K(+) \to 2\pi}{\text{fraction of } K(-) \times \text{rate for } K(-) \to 3\pi, \text{ lept}} = \frac{|\epsilon|^2 \Gamma_1}{\Gamma_2} . \tag{58}$$

Put $|\zeta| \approx 10^{-8}$ eV (liquid hydrogen), $\gamma \sim 2$ (1 GeV),

$$|\epsilon| = \frac{\gamma}{2} |\zeta| \, [(M_1 - M_2)^2 + (\Gamma_1 - \Gamma_2)^{2/4}]^{-1/2} \approx 10^{-3}$$

$$R \approx 10^{-3}$$

III. ARE K_0's AN ISOLATED SYSTEM ?

A decay of $K_2^0 \to 2\pi$ can happen under one of the following circumstances:

i) the K_2^0 is not an isolated system;

ii) CP is not conserved.

One example of the first circumstance is given by the case where K_2^0 is not locally isolated, namely it interacts with matter, discussed above. If CP is conserved, the result of CCFT

$$\frac{K_2^0 \to \pi^+ + \pi^-}{K_2^0 \to \text{other charged modes}} = (2 \pm 0.4)\ 10^{-3} , \tag{59}$$

requires an admixture of the form

$$K_2^0 = (1 + |\epsilon|^2)^{-1/2} \, [\,|K(-)> - \epsilon|K(+)>\,] \; ,$$

where $|\epsilon| \approx 2\times 10^{-3}$. This can be understood if in the experimental set-up of CCFT the K_2^0 are not isolated, but interact with the external world in a way that introduces an effective Hamiltonian of the form

$$H' = \zeta\sigma_z \; . \tag{60}$$

[This implies a difference in potential energy (Re ζ) and/or absorption (Im ζ), between K^0 and $\overline{K^0}$.] To get the observed effect we need

$$|\zeta| \approx 10^{-8} \text{ eV} \; . \tag{61}$$

In the experimental set-up of CCFT the K's traversed He gas at normal pressure, which has a density of $\approx 10^{-4}$ g/cm^3. According to the rough evaluation given in the last lecture, this gives $|\zeta| \approx 10^{-11}$ eV, so that the coherent regeneration in He is too small by a factor $\sim 10^6$ (it is proportional to $|\zeta|^2$, see above). The same conclusion is reached by CCFT with a more accurate analysis.

Other effects connected with the presence of He atoms (for example, electromagnetic) have been considered but have also been found to be exceedingly small. However, any effect due to atomic or nuclear regeneration increases with the square of the density and would cause a regeneration about 10^6 as large in liquid hydrogen, which is not observed (see CCFT).

We will now discuss a different possibility, proposed by J.S. Bell and J.K. Perring, and by J. Bernstein, T.D. Lee and the author[3]. It could be that even if K_2^{-0} are locally isolated from nearby matter (i.e. He gas) to all practical extent, they are not isolated from the world at large. That is, suppose there is some sort of long range field, which interacts with K^0 and $\overline{K^0}$ in opposite ways, and whose source is normal matter as found in the universe. For example, this field could be coupled to hypercharge, or to I_3 (in the stellar matter there seems to be an excess of protons over neutrons). It is interesting to note that this hypothesis brings to definite experimental predictions of two kinds which come from:

i) reality character of the potential;

ii) tensor character.

1. Reality character

Any long-range force gives rise to a potential energy difference but not to an absorption. If the potential energy of K^0 is $+\frac{1}{2}V$, that of $\overline{K^0}$ is $-\frac{1}{2}V$, the Hamiltonian for free kaons is to be modified by a term

$$H' = \tfrac{1}{2} V \sigma_z \, . \tag{62}$$

This is similar to normal regeneration, with

$$\zeta = \tfrac{1}{2} V \, . \tag{63}$$

This implies that the experimental K_2^0 is a mixture of K(-) and K(+) as in Eq. (54), with

$$\epsilon = \frac{\Upsilon}{2} \frac{V}{(M_1 - M_2) - i/2\,(\Gamma_1 - \Gamma_2)} \, . \tag{64}$$

Since the magnitude of $|\epsilon|$ is measured by CCFT, ϵ is now completely determined.

2. Consequences of reality character

i) Ratio $K_2^0 \to \pi^- \ell^+ \nu / K_2^0 \to \pi^+ \ell^- \nu = R_\ell ; (\ell^\pm = e^\pm \text{ or } \mu^\pm)$.

Assuming the $\Delta S = \Delta Q$ rule this is equal to

$$R_\ell = \frac{\text{content of } K^0 \text{ in } K_2^0}{\text{content of } \overline{K^0} \text{ in } K_2^0} = \left|\frac{1-\epsilon}{1+\epsilon}\right|^2 \approx 1 - 4 \operatorname{Re} \epsilon \, . \tag{65}$$

The deviation from 1 is given by

$$4 \operatorname{Re} \epsilon = 4|\epsilon| \frac{(M_1 - M_2)\, V}{[(M_1 - M_2)^2 + 1/4\,(\Gamma_1 - \Gamma_2)^2]^{1/2} |V|} \tag{66}$$

The sign is determined by the sign of $V(M_1 - M_2)$. Since the sign of $(M_1 - M_2)$ can be measured independently, this effect can, in principle, give the sign of V. Using the CCFT result and other known numbers we get

$$|R_\ell - 1| \approx 0.6\% \ . \tag{67}$$

This is too small to be easily checked. However, a different result would rule out this interpretation of the CCFT result. On this point a word of caution is needed: a value of $(R_\ell - 1)$ much larger than 1% is improbable, even if the CCFT effect is due to CP violation.

ii) $\pi^0\pi^0/\pi^+\pi^-$ ratio = $R\pi$

The CCFT effect is due (under the above hypothesis) to the decay of the $|K(+)>$ component in the K_2^0 state. This should therefore be equal to the decay of the $|K(+)>$ which is the main component of K_1^0 [see Eq. (54)]. Therefore, we predict:

$$R_\pi\Big|_{K_2^0} = R_\pi\Big|_{K_1^0} \ . \tag{68}$$

iii) Interference with coherent regeneration in matter

Suppose we have a material for which we know the value of $\zeta = \zeta_{mat}$ including its phase, and we can vary its density. ζ_{mat} will depend linearly on ρ:

$$\zeta_{mat} = \rho\chi_{mat} \ . \tag{69}$$

The total ζ will be given by

$$\zeta = \zeta_{mat} + \tfrac{1}{2} V = \rho\chi_{mat} + \tfrac{1}{2} V \ . \tag{70}$$

The branching ratio into 2π will then be proportional to $|\zeta|^2$ [see Eqs. (57) and (58)],

$$|\zeta|^2 = \tfrac{1}{4} V^2 + V\rho \ \mathrm{Re}\ (\chi_{mat}) + \rho^2 |\chi_{mat}|^2 \ . \tag{71}$$

The regeneration as function of ρ is uniquely predicted, apart from the sign of V

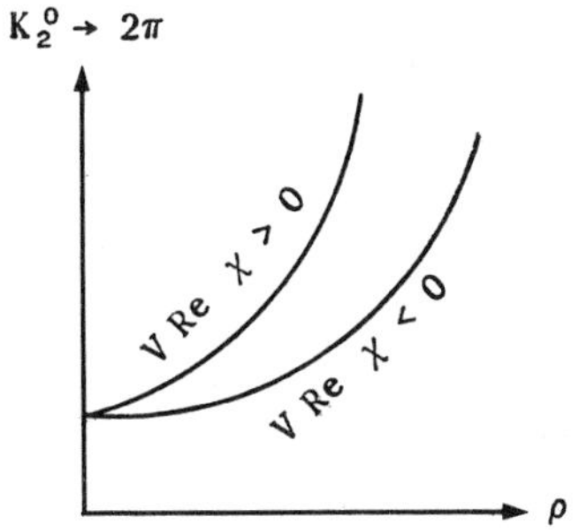

3. Consequences of tensor character

There are different possibilities. The potential V can arise from interactions with:

i) a scalar field φ;

ii) the time component of vector field φ_4;

iii) the 4,4 component of tensor field φ_{44};

iv) higher tensors.

The second case would imply a field analogous to the e.m. field; we would have

$$V = \varphi_4 \, f \, , \tag{72}$$

f being the coupling constant of this field with the K meson (analogous to electric charge). V would be independent on the K energy.

The third case is analogous to the gravitational potential; it would give rise to a potential energy proportional to the total energy of the K^0

$$V = \varphi_{44} \, f \, \frac{E_K}{M_K} = \varphi_{44} \, f \, \gamma \, . \tag{73}$$

In the first case the potential energy would be inversely proportional to the total energy of the K meson

$$V = \varphi f \frac{1}{\gamma} . \tag{74}$$

Consequently, we get [see Eq. (57)],

ϵ independent of γ (scalar field),

$\epsilon \propto \gamma$ (vector field),

$\epsilon \propto \gamma^2$ (tensor field),

$\epsilon \propto \gamma^n$ (n-th order tensor field $\varphi_{44\ldots4}$). †)

The interesting fact is that <u>it is difficult to arrange V to change sign from K^0 to $\overline{K^0}$ unless the tensor order of the field is odd</u>, in any sensible field theory, so that V should probably be given by a vector field. In this case, the CCFT effect should be <u>proportional to the square of the K energy</u>. This is a crazy prediction, but easy to check: at 10 GeV the branching ratio should rise from 2×10^{-3} to $\sim 30\%$. With a little bit of imagination one could also think of a vector part $\vec{\varphi}$ which would give rise to dependence of the effect on the direction of flight of K^0's, diurnal variations, etc.

Since the source of the potential V could be the whole galaxy, a very small coupling constant f is necessary to produce a potential V of $\sim 10^{-8}$ eV, $f^2 \sim 2.5\times 10^{-49}$. A vector field of this kind would give rise to a small difference between inertial and gravitational mass, which is too small by many orders of magnitude to be detected in the Eotvos-Dicke experiments.

---

†) <u>Problem 4</u> - Show this directly by use of special relativity. Hint: consider the problem in the rest system of the K. How do φ, φ_4, φ_{44} transform when we go from lab to rest system? (Consider $\varphi_{1,2,3} = 0$, or $\varphi_{12}, \varphi_{13}, \ldots, \varphi_{34} = 0$.)

Note

S. Weinberg[4] has pointed out a difficulty with the explanation of the CCFT through a vector field presented in this lecture; namely, both hypercharge and I_3 are not exactly conserved quantities. As a consequence, the mass of the vector field could not be exactly zero. The difficulty arises from the fact that in processes where Y (or I_3) is not conserved (ex. $\Sigma^+ \to p + \pi^0$), one should observe with large probability the emission of spin 1 particles associated with the vector field.

A second class of theories which involve a long-range interaction is possible, in which the field induces a $\Delta S = 2$ transition $K^0 \to \overline{K^0}$. These theories require, to explain the CCFT effect, a field which behaves as a tensor of even order (scalar, tensor, etc.). The $K_2^0 \to 2\pi$ branching ratio could then (for a scalar field) be independent of γ. Other consequences are similar to those discussed above[5].

IV. CP VIOLATION IN K_2^0 DECAYS

We have examined in the previous chapter one of the possibilities to explain the CCFT effect, namely that the observed K_2^0 are not an isolated system, and the experimental consequences, some of them rather striking, of the existence of some kind of long-range force which could indeed make K^0's not isolated. We now go to a different, and perhaps simpler interpretation, namely the hypothesis that CP is violated in weak interactions.

Consequences of this hypothesis for the $K^0 - \overline{K^0}$ system are not as definite as those of the alternative considered in the previous chapter.

1. $K_2^0 \to 2\pi$ decays, regeneration in matter

If CP is violated, the Hamiltonian H will not commute with σ_x, and will contain σ_z and σ_y terms which are there even if K^0's are isolated We still get two particles with definite mass and lifetime, corresponding to the experimentally observed K_1^0 and K_2^0. This can be easily proved (the case in which we introduce a σ_z term is completely analogous to that discussed earlier, of an artificial regeneration, and a σ_y term can be treated in a similar way).

The long-lived state $|K_2^0>$ will be a mixture of $|K(+)>$ and $|K(-)>$,

$$|K_o^2> = (1 + |\epsilon|^2)^{-1/2} [|K(-)> + \epsilon^0 |K(+)>] . \tag{75}$$

Since ϵ^0 is determined by intrinsic properties, it does not depend on γ. $|K(+)>$ can decay into 2π, I = 0 (it is, in fact, defined to do so), with an amplitude

$$a_{I=0}^{(+)} = a(K(+) \rightarrow 2\pi, I = 0) . \tag{76}$$

However, we have also to consider a 2π, I = 2 state (see chapter I). Both K(+) and K(-) can decay into this, if CP is violated. If $\Delta I = 1/2$ is only violated by e.m. interactions, these amplitudes will be smaller ($1/20$ to $1/100$) of that in Eq. (76). $|\pi^+\pi^->$ and $|\pi^0\pi^0>$ are combinations of I = 0 and I = 2:

$$|\pi^+\pi^-> = \frac{1}{\sqrt{3}} [\sqrt{2}|I = 0> + |I = 2>] ,$$

$$|\pi^0\pi^0> = \frac{1}{\sqrt{3}} [|I = 0> - \sqrt{2}|I = 2>] . \tag{77}$$

Let us write down the amplitudes for decay of K_2^0 (Eq. (75) into these two channels:

$$a(K_2^0 \rightarrow \pi^+\pi^-) = \frac{1}{\sqrt{3}} \left[a_{I=2}^{(-)} - \sqrt{2}\, \epsilon^0 a_{I=0}^{(+)} \right] ,$$

$$a(K_2^0 \rightarrow \pi^0\pi^0) = \frac{1}{\sqrt{3}} \left[-\sqrt{2}\, a_{I=2}^{(-)} - \epsilon^0 a_{I=0}^{(+)} \right] . \tag{78}$$

We neglected here terms like $\epsilon^0 a(K(+) \rightarrow 2\pi, I = 2)$, which are negligible in respect to $\epsilon^0 a_{I=0}^{(+)}$. Assume that the amplitudes are normalized in such a way that their modulus square gives directly the decay rates. For example:

$$\Gamma_1 = \Gamma(K_1^0 \to 2\pi) = |a_{I=0}^{(+)}|^2 \; . \tag{79}$$

Let us also define

$$\delta = a_{I=2}^{(-)} \Big/ a_{I=0}^{(+)} \; . \tag{80}$$

We find then

$$\begin{aligned} \Gamma(K_2^0 \to \pi^+ + \pi^-) &= \frac{\Gamma_1}{3} |\delta - \sqrt{2}\, \epsilon^0|^2 \; , \\ \Gamma(K_2^0 \to \pi^0 + \pi^0) &= \frac{\Gamma_1}{3} | + \sqrt{2}\, \delta + \epsilon^0|^2 \; . \end{aligned} \tag{81}$$

These two rates need not be in the ratio 2 : 1, as in the case of K_1^0 decays. We do not get here a definite prediction as we did before on the assumption that the K^0 are not isolated system, but CP is microscopically conserved.

CCFT find $\Gamma(K_2^0 \to \pi^+ + \pi^-) = 2\times 10^{-3} \times 0.8 \times \Gamma_2$ (0.8 is the branching ratio for charged decay modes of K_0^2) from which $|\delta - \sqrt{2}\,\epsilon^0| \approx 2.8\times 10^{-3}$. Barring a cancellation among relatively large numbers, either $|\epsilon^0|$ or $|\delta|$ or both are of the order of 2×10^{-3}. Further experiments are needed to decide whether the dominant effect is due to CP mixing in K_0^2 (ϵ^0) or to CP violation in the I = 2 channel (δ), or to a mixture of the two.

Even the measurement of the two rates r is not sufficient to determine uniquely ϵ^0 and δ which are, in general, complex numbers. A complete determination of ϵ^0 and δ would be obtained by measuring the two-decay rates in a light material of known regenerating properties. In such a material we would get a differerent K(+) admixture in K_2^0 (see chapter II):

$$\epsilon = \epsilon^0 + \epsilon_{mat} \; . \tag{82}$$

We have then

$$\Gamma(K_2^0 \to \pi^+\pi^-)_{mat} = |\delta - \sqrt{2}\,\epsilon^0 - \sqrt{2}\,\epsilon_{mat}| =$$

$$= |\delta - \sqrt{2}\,\epsilon^0|^2 + 2|\epsilon_{mat}|^2 - 2\sqrt{2}\ \mathrm{Re}\ \epsilon^*_{mat}(\delta - \sqrt{2}\,\epsilon^0)) \qquad (83)$$

$$\Gamma(K_2^0 \to \pi^0\pi^0)_{mat} = |+\sqrt{2}\,\delta + \epsilon^0|^2 + |\epsilon_{mat}| + 2\ \mathrm{Re}\ \epsilon^*_{mat}(\sqrt{2}\,\delta + \epsilon^0).$$

The measurement of these quantities and of the two r ates in vacuo, coupled with the knowledge of ϵ_{mat} are sufficient to a complete determination of ϵ and δ, up to a discrete number of ambiguities which can be solved by using different regenerators.

2. Ratio of leptonic decays in K_2^0, R_ℓ

The ratio of leptonic decays is given by [see Eq. (65)]

$$R_\ell = 1 - 4\ \mathrm{Re}\ \epsilon^0 . \qquad (84)$$

$|R_\ell - 1|$ is not expected to be much larger than 1%, although it could be much smaller (if $|\epsilon^0| << |\delta|$ or if ϵ^0 is nearly imaginary).

3. If CP is violated, how strongly so?

The discussion of this requires a certain care. If CP is violated in weak interactions, the operation is not well defined. We have seen [see Eq. (30)] that CP for K^0, $\overline{K^0}$ is only defined up to a phase α. This liberty of definition arises from the fact that given a definition of CP, say $(CP)^0$ defined by putting, for example, $\alpha = 0$, there is an infinity of others

$$CP = (CP)^0\ e^{i\alpha Y} \qquad (85)$$

where Y is the hypercharge operator. †)

---

†) Problem 5 - Verify that if $(CP)^0|K^0\rangle = |\overline{K^0}\rangle$ then $CP|K^0\rangle = e^{i\alpha}|\overline{K^0}\rangle$.

All these definitions are completely equivalent from the point of view of strong interaction, since Y is there conserved. With CP violated in weak interactions, no choice of α is a priori better than others. As a useful definition we will keep Eq. (31), i.e. we put CP = + 1 for the physical state K(+) which goes to the 2π, I = 0 state. Let us now write the total Hamiltonian:

$$H = \mathbf{M} - i\,{}^1\!/_2\,\Gamma\,. \tag{86}$$

This can be divided into a part which commutes with σ_x and one which anticommutes with it, which we will call the CP violating part. CCFT's results require this part to be of the order of 10^{-8} eV.

$$\Gamma = \Gamma_{2\pi,I=0} + \Gamma_{lept} + \Gamma_{3\pi} + \text{smaller contributions.} \tag{87}$$

$\Gamma_{2\pi,I=0}$ commutes with σ_x by definition, Γ_{lept} does the same if the $\Delta S = \Delta Q$ rule is valid *). What remains is of the order of $\sim 10^{-8}$ eV. Moreover, the results on 3π decay, discussed below, suggests that only a small part of it $\lesssim 10^{-9}$ eV can be CP violating. The situation is much worse for the M part. We can divide contributions to M according to the different intermediate states:

$$\mathbf{M} = M_s \cdot \mathbb{1} + \mathbf{M}_{2\pi,I=0} + \mathbf{M}_{3\pi} + \text{other contributions.} \tag{88}$$

The "other contributions" are not <u>necessarily</u> small. A large contribution could be given by the intermediate state of a single η meson, which is not available as a possible decay channel. It is not possible to affirm anything about the commutation properties of any part of M with σ_x (except of course, the M_s part). Even the $\mathbf{M}_{2\pi,I=0}$ part could have a substantial CP violating contribution. In fact, $\mathbf{M}_{2\pi,I=0}$ gets contributions from virtual 2π states, and even if we adjust the phases of K^0 and $\overline{K^0}$ so that Eq. (25) holds for physical pions, the two amplitudes could grow (if CP is violated) a different phase when we go from physical states to others which are far from the energy shell.

---

*) R. Sachs has proposed that CP is violated in leptonic decays with $\Delta S = -\Delta Q$. We will not discuss further this possibility and refer the interested reader to Sach's paper[6].

In this sense, the CCFT result could appear too small to be compatible with "full" CP violation.

4. Decay into 3π

We restrict here the discussion to the decay into the symmetrix state, A^0 (see chapter I). If CP is violated both K(+) and K(-) can decay into the A^0 state. It is convenient to remember again that K(+) and K(-) have been defined in chapter II on the base of the 2π, I = 0 state, using only CPT (not CP) invariance.

Define

$$a(K^0 \to A^0) = a\, e^{i\varphi}$$
$$a(\bar{K}^0 \to A^0) = a' e^{i\varphi'} , \tag{89}$$

where a and a' are positive real numbers. By CPT

$$a = a' . \tag{90}$$

If CP were conserved, we would get in addition $\varphi = \varphi'$.

Let us assume only CPT, we obtain

$$a(K(+) \to A^0) = \frac{1}{\sqrt{2}}\, a \left[e^{i\varphi} - e^{i\varphi'}\right] = \sqrt{2}\; i\, a \sin\left[\frac{\varphi - \varphi'}{2}\right] \exp\left[i\, \frac{\varphi + \varphi'}{2}\right],$$
$$a(K(-) \to A^0) = \frac{1}{\sqrt{2}}\, a \left[e^{i\varphi} + e^{i\varphi'}\right] = \sqrt{2}\; a \cos\left[\frac{\varphi - \varphi'}{2}\right] \exp\left[i\, \frac{\varphi + \varphi'}{2}\right]. \tag{91}$$

Since we are assuming the $\Delta I = \frac{1}{2}$ rule we obtain the relation (5) among $\pi^0\pi^0\pi^0$ and $\pi^+\pi^-\pi^0$ for both K(+) and K(-), and any of their combination.

If we assume $(\varphi - \varphi')$ to be non-negligible, we can neglect the small admixtures ϵ^0 of K(-) in K_1^0 and of K(+) in K_2^0 .

The $\Delta I = \frac{1}{2}$ selection rule has another prediction, Eq. (7) which can now be written as:

$$a = |a(K^+ \to A^+)| 1/\sqrt{2} \ . \tag{92}$$

The rates for $K_2^0 \to \pi^+\pi^-\pi^0$ and $K_1^0 \to \pi^+\pi^-\pi^0$ are given by

$$\begin{aligned} \Gamma[K_2^0 \to \pi^+\pi^-\pi^0 \ (A^0)] &= \tilde{\Gamma} \cos^2 \left(\frac{\varphi - \varphi'}{2}\right) , \\ \Gamma[K_1^0 \to \pi^+\pi^-\pi^0 \ (A^0)] &= \tilde{\Gamma} \sin^2 \left(\frac{\varphi - \varphi'}{2}\right) , \end{aligned} \tag{93}$$

where

$$\tilde{\Gamma} = \tfrac{1}{2} \times 1.336 \times \Gamma(K^+ \to \pi^+\pi^+\pi^-). \ ^{\dagger)} \tag{94}$$

The more recent experimental results on $\Gamma(K_2^0 \to \pi^+\pi^-\pi^0)$ are in good agreement with the predictions of $\Delta I = \frac{1}{2}$ and CP, i.e. they are consistent with $\cos^2(\frac{\varphi - \varphi'}{2})$ being equal to one within $\approx$ 15%. This does not leave much space for CP violation in 3π decays.

In conclusion, the evidence from both 2π and 3π decays does not seem to point to a "large" violation of CP in non-leptonic weak interaction, but to a rather small one. However, our ignorance of the mechanism of non-leptonic decays does not allow us to exclude the possibility that the smallness of CP violation in these decays is due to some dynamical effect*).

---

†) Problem 6 - Derive these last equations; the 1.336 is the ratio of $\pi^+\pi^-\pi^0/\pi^+\pi^+\pi^-$ phase spaces, as quoted in D.

*) As an example we do not understand why parity is nearly conserved in the $\Sigma^+ \to p + \pi^0$ and $\Sigma^- \to n + \pi^-$ decays.

V. CP VIOLATION IN WEAK INTERACTIONS, LEPTONIC DECAYS

1. Re-examining the results reached in the previous lecture, we must conclude that if there is CP violation, it misses three occasions of showing large effects in K^0 decays:

i) and ii) In $K_2^0 \to \pi^+\pi^-$ both δ and ϵ^0 are (barring cancellations) of order $\leq 10^{-3}$. $\delta \approx 10^{-3}$ is 10 - 20 times smaller than what you expect for a $\Delta I = 3/2$ amplitude, so that CP violation is there restricted to $1/10 - 1/20$. Values of ϵ^0 (amplitude mixing in K_2^0) much larger than 10^{-3} could be expected from the M term.

iii) In $K_2^0 \to 3\pi$ predictions based on $\Delta I = 1/2$ and CP are in agreement with experiment within 10 - 15%. This leaves little space for CP violation in this process.

These facts leave us with an uneasy feeling, not much more than that, given our ignorance of non-leptonic decays.

In leptonic decays we have a good test of T symmetry (equivalent to CP if CPT is valid, as we assume).

This comes from an experiment of Telegdi et al.[7] on the decay of free polarized neutrons.

If we write

$$G_A/G_V = |G_A/G_V| e^{i\varphi} \tag{95}$$

then T symmetry requires $\varphi = 0$. From the absence of any correlation between the neutron polarization $\vec{P}_n$ and the normal to the decay plane $\vec{p}^e \times \vec{p}^\nu$, Telegdi et al. conclude that

$$|\varphi| < 8° . \tag{96}$$

2. In this chapter I will describe a possible theory of weak interactions with CP and T violation[8] based on a simple extension of our present ideas. This theory leads to definite predictions on the form that the violation should take in leptonic decays. As we will see, it is not in

disagreement with the result given in Eq. (96).

We will maintain the scheme of current-current interactions discussed in Feynman's lectures:

$$\frac{G}{\sqrt{2}} (J_\lambda + \ell_\lambda)(J_\lambda + \ell_\lambda)^* + (\text{neutral currents, perhaps}). \tag{97}$$

The * indicates the hermitian conjugate for the space components, and (- 1)× the hermitian conjugate for the fourth. This corrects the change of sign due to the i in the fourth component (x_4 = it):

$$\ell^*_{1,2,3} = \ell^+_{1,2,3}; \quad \ell^*_4 = - \ell^+_4 . \tag{98}$$

The known form of the lepton current ℓ_λ is based on good experimental evidence, and we will not change it. It has definite behaviour under CP:

$$CP\ \ell_\lambda (CP)^{-1} = \ell^+_\lambda .$$

To obtain CP violation, J_λ, current of the strong interacting particles, should have a mixed behaviour under CP:

$$J_\lambda = J^{(+)}_\lambda + J^{(-)}_\lambda \tag{99}$$

where

$$CP\ J^{(\pm)}_\lambda (CP)^{-1} = \pm\ J^{(\pm)+}_\lambda . \tag{100}$$

3. We want to assume that J_λ and J^*_λ are members of the same octet of currents J^i_λ (see Feynman's lectures) (i = 1,...,8)

$$\left.\begin{matrix} J_\lambda \\ J^*_\lambda \end{matrix}\right\} = \cos\Theta(J^1_\lambda \pm iJ^2_\lambda) + \sin\Theta(J^4_\lambda \pm iJ^5_\lambda) . \tag{101}$$

Since J_λ and J_λ^* are connected by hermitian conjugation, the currents J_λ^i should be hermitian:

$$J_\lambda^{i*} = J_\lambda^i \,. \tag{102}$$

This octet should have <u>mixed</u> CP behaviour. We write

$$J_\lambda^i = J_\lambda^{i(+)} + J_\lambda^{i(-)} \tag{103}$$

and then (see appendix)

$$\begin{aligned} CP\ J_{1,2,3}^{i(\pm)}\ (CP)^{-1} &= \pm\ \epsilon(i)\ J_{1,2,3}^{i(\pm)} \\ CP\ J_4^{i(\pm)}\ (CP)^{-1} &= \pm\ \epsilon(i)\ J_4^{i(\pm)}. \end{aligned} \tag{104}$$

$J_\lambda^{i(+)}$ and $J_\lambda^{i(-)}$ will be called, respectively, CP conserving and CP violating.

4. The different octets $J_\lambda^{i(\pm)}$ give rise to different kinds of form factors in baryon leptonic decays. To see this let us focus our attention on those members of the octet J^i which correspond to the I spin, i = 1,2,3, and divide them into vector and axial parts, and then again according to their transformation properties under CP:

$$J_\lambda^i = V_\lambda^{i(+)} + A_\lambda^{i(+)} + V_\lambda^{i(-)} + A_\lambda^{i(-)} \,. \tag{105}$$

The four parts so obtained behave differently under G parity:

$$G = C\ e^{i\pi I_2} \,.$$

More precisely

$$\begin{aligned} V_\lambda^{i(\pm)} &\text{ has } G = \pm 1 \\ A_\lambda^{i(\mp)} &\text{ has } G = \mp 1. \end{aligned} \tag{106}$$ †)

Therefore, according to the definition of Weinberg[9)], the "CP conserving" currents $V_\lambda^{i(+)}$, $A_\lambda^{i(+)}$ and the "CP violating" ones belong, respectively, to the first and second classes.

---

†) <u>Problem 7)</u> - Prove Eq. (106).

Following Weinberg's argument we can show that in matrix elements among nucleon states, e.g. $< p|J_\lambda^1 + iJ_\lambda^2|n>$, first and second class currents give rise to different form factors: (k_ν = momentum transfer)

	CP conserving (first class)	CP violating (second class)
Vector	γ_μ, $\sigma_{\mu\nu}k_\nu$	ik_ν
Axial	$\gamma_\mu\gamma_5$, $k_\mu\gamma_5$	$i\sigma_{\mu\nu}k_\nu\gamma_5$

The i in front of CP violating terms ensures that they are also T violating, and is due to the hermiticity condition [Eq. (102)]. Time reversal violations will arise from the interference among terms which are relatively complex and is therefore restricted in this theory to interference among first class and second class form factors. The latter are forbidden contributions, i.e. they are proportional to the available energy in decay processes, so that T violation is expected to be very small in low Q value decays (as is the case in neutron decay).

In the limit of exact SU_3 symmetry the validity of the table is extended to all the leptonic decays of baryons with both $\Delta S = 0,1$.

If this theory is correct, T reversal violations can only be detected in decays of high Q values, like some nuclear β decays and the β decays of hyperons. Another possible place to look for T violation effects is in neutrino experiments, where it is possible to reach large momentum transfers.

5. Another interesting case is that of $K \to \mu + \nu + \pi$ decays. The matrix element for these (see Chapter I) contains two terms:

$$f[(P_\lambda^K + P_\lambda^\pi) + \xi(P_\lambda^K - P_\lambda^\pi)]\ \mu\gamma_\lambda(1+\gamma_5)\ .$$

It is easy to prove that, in the limit of exact SU_3 (and in this theory), the two terms arise from the CP conserving and the CP violating parts, respectively. Moreover, the parameter ξ is expected, in this limit, to be purely imaginary; this is natural because the CP violating part should also be T violating. This decay seems promising for a search for T violation effects because if, for example, we put $|\xi| \approx 1$, the two terms in the amplitude are of comparable size.

APPENDIX

CP INVARIANCE AND SU_3

Let us discuss briefly the definition of CP for an octet. First of all the structure of SU_3 should be invariant under CP. The structure equations of the group,

$$[F^\ell, F^m] = i f_{\ell mn} F^n, \tag{A1}$$

should go into themselves. This means that if

$$CP\, F^\ell (CP)^{-1} = - \epsilon(\ell)\, F^\ell , \tag{A2}$$

we have a condition on the $\epsilon(\ell)$:

$$\epsilon(\ell)\, \epsilon(m) = - \epsilon(n) \quad \text{if} \quad f_{\ell mn} \neq 0. \tag{A3}$$

We want a solution with $\epsilon(3) = \epsilon(8) = 1$, since charge and hypercharge are odd under CP. Among the four possible solutions of this type we select one:

$$\epsilon = +1 \text{ for } \ell = 1,3,4,6,8$$
$$\epsilon = -1 \text{ for } \ell = 2,5,7. \qquad \dagger)$$

An octet, O^ℓ, transforms in the same way as the generators. Therefore, we have a set of commutation rules (remember those of a vector with the angular momentum)

$$[F^\ell, O^m] = i f_{\ell mn}\, O^n . \tag{A5}$$

---

†) Problem 8 - Check this solution and find others. Show that necessarily $\epsilon(3) = \epsilon(8)$. $f_{\ell mn} \neq 0$ if $(\ell mn) =$

$= (123), (147), (156), (246), (257), (345), (367), (458), (678).$

There are then two possibilities for CP which leave these [as well as Eq. (A1)] invariant

$$\mathrm{CP}\ 0^{\ell(\pm)}(\mathrm{CP})^{-1} = \pm\ \epsilon(\ell)\ 0^{\ell}\ . \qquad \text{(A6)}$$

The discussion above is similar to that of C symmetry[10].

REFERENCES

1) J.H. Christenson, J.W. Cronin, V.L. Fitch and R. Turlay, Phys.Rev. Letters 13, 138 (1964).

2) R.H. Dalitz, "Proceedings of the Brookhaven Conference on Fundamental Aspects of Weak Interactions", page 378 (1963).

3) J.S. Bell and J.K. Perring, Phys.Rev.Letters 13, 348 (1964).
J. Bernstein, N. Cabibbo and T.D. Lee, Phys.Letters 12, 146 (1964).

4) S. Weinberg, Phys.Rev.Letters 13, 495 (1964).

5) F. Gürsey and A. Pais, "Speculations on CP invariance and the 2π modes of long-lived neutral K particles". Unpublished.

6) R.G. Sachs, Phys.Rev. Letters 13, 286 (1964).

7) M.T. Burgy, V.E. Krohn, T.B. Novey, G.R. Ringo and V.L. Telegdi, Phys.Rev.Letters 1, 324 (1958).

8) N. Cabibbo, "Possibility of large CP and T violation in weak interactions" Phys.Letters 12, 137 (1964).

9) S. Weinberg, Phys.Rev. 112, 1375 (1958).

10) N. Cabibbo, Phys.Rev.Letters 12, 62 (1964); and
M. Gell-Mann, Phys.Rev.Letters 12, 83 (1964).

METHODS FOR ASSIGNING SPIN AND PARITY TO BARYON RESONANCES

J. Ashkin
Carnegie Institute of Technology,
Pittsburgh, Pennsylvania, U.S.A.

I. DETERMINATION OF THE SPIN AND PARITY OF BARYON RESONANCES. METHOD OF BYERS AND FENSTER

With the discovery during the past few years of many resonant states involving the baryons and mesons, the problem arises of determining their spins and parities. As in low-energy nuclear physics, it is a matter of making a detailed examination of angular distributions in transitions from one state to another.

For the case of the baryon resonances a useful general analysis has recently been given by Byers and Fenster[1)]. Since the proposed procedure has been used in a number of experiments[2-4)], and promises to be of some importance, it may be helpful for experimentalists to have it discussed here. For bubble chamber experiments, where limitations due to statistics are often important, the procedure has the advantage that it may utilize events in which the resonant Y^* is produced over a range of angles and energies.

In idealized form, the problem is as follows. Let the resonant baryon state Y^* be produced and undergo strong decay in the reaction

$$\begin{array}{l} a + b \rightarrow Y^* + c \\ \qquad\qquad \hookrightarrow \underset{(\text{spin } 1/2)}{Y} + \underset{(\text{spin } 0)}{\text{meson}} \end{array} \qquad (1)$$

where, in the two-body decay, $Y^* \rightarrow Y + \text{meson}$, the Y is a hyperon of spin $1/2$ and the meson has spin zero. Suppose in addition, that in the weak decay of the Y ($\Lambda \rightarrow p + \pi^-$, $\Sigma^+ \rightarrow p + \pi^0$, $\Xi^- \rightarrow \Lambda + \pi^-$, $\Xi^0 \rightarrow \Lambda + \pi^0$)

$$Y \rightarrow \text{baryon} + \text{pion} \ , \qquad (2)$$

the intrinsic asymmetry parameter due to parity violation is large, so that in effect, the decay serves to measure the polarization of the Y. The idealization consists of assuming (with the help of a Dalitz plot, for example) that

i) over the range of effective masses M (Y, meson) covering the Y^* peak the only important amplitude for the final state Y + meson + c is the amplitude for Y^* + c and,

ii) that the Y^* lives long enough so that when it decays it is far enough from particle c for the Y^* − c interaction to be neglected.

Assumption (i) especially is not easy to check and may well be a source of trouble in a given experiment. We will have a little to say about this question later, but it is unfortunately very difficult to make any remarks which are generally useful.

We continue, therefore, with the discussion of the idealized problem.

<u>Decay from a particular spin state of the Y^*</u>

Consider a particular state $|Jm>$ of the Y^* (in its rest frame) characterized by total angular momentum J and component $J_z = m$ along some z axis. Denote by

$$< p \vartheta \varphi \ \text{spin} \ |T| Jm > ,$$

the matrix element of the transition operator T giving the amplitude for decay leading to a spin $1/2$ hyperon Y of momentum p in the direction $(\vartheta \varphi)$ and a spin zero meson in the opposite direction. We wish to show in an elementary way that given the angular momentum J of the Y^*, the decay amplitudes are completely determined in their angular dependence by two complex numbers $\Gamma(+)$ and $\Gamma(-)$ whose magnitudes $|\Gamma(+)|^2 + |\Gamma(-)|^2$, give the decay rate and whose relative phase $\Gamma(+)/\Gamma(-)$ gives the parity of the Y^*.

To completely specify the decay amplitude it is necessary to indicate some projection of the spin $\vec{s}$ of the hyperon Y in the final state. Since the spin angular momentum is not separately conserved in the decay, it is awkward to use a representation based on the z component of the hyperon spin. Instead, it is very convenient to work with the "helicity" spin states specified by the projection $\lambda = \vec{s} \cdot \hat{p}$ of the spin in the direction of the momentum (unit vector $\hat{p}$)[5]. If $|p00\lambda>$ corresponds to the Y moving in the positive z direction with a given helicity, or circular polarization, $\lambda(= \pm \tfrac{1}{2})$ (and the meson moving with opposite momentum in the direction $-z$) we may describe a state of the same helicity λ for the particles moving in the directions $+\hat{n}(\vartheta,\varphi)$ and $-\hat{n}(\vartheta,\varphi)$ by a rotation

$$|p\vartheta\varphi\lambda> = R|p00\lambda>$$

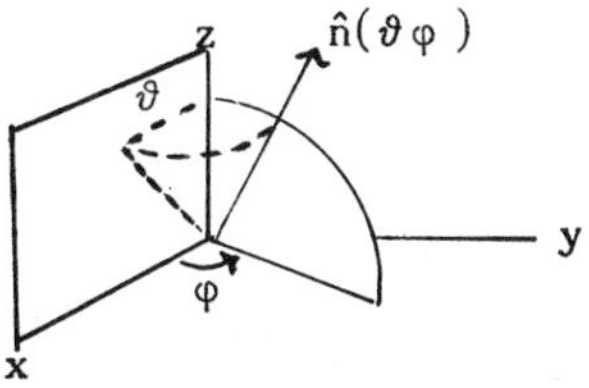

where

$$R = R_{\varphi\vartheta 0} = e^{-i\varphi J_z} \, e^{-i\vartheta J_y} ,$$

corresponds to successive rotations (of momentum and spin together) of angle ϑ about the y axis and φ about the z axis.

Now, it should be clear physically that if we were to have chosen as axis of spin quantization for the Y^*, the direction $\hat{n}$ of the decay products the set of amplitudes for decay from these spin states would suffice to completely determine the amplitudes for decay from the states $|Jm>$ with z as axis of quantization. The two sets of states are, of course, linearly related by the appropriate matrix for the rotation of a system with angular momentum J. But the decays in the direction of the Y^* spin are particularly simple to discuss. To say the same thing formally, the transition operator T conserves the total angular momentum and is therefore invariant under rotations:

$$R^+TR = T \quad \text{or} \quad R^+T = TR^+ .$$

We therefore find

$$\begin{aligned} \langle p\vartheta\varphi\lambda\,|T|\,Jm\rangle &= \langle p00\lambda\,|R^{+}_{\varphi\vartheta 0}T|\,Jm\rangle \\ &= \langle p00\lambda\,|TR^{+}_{\varphi\vartheta 0}|\,Jm\rangle \\ &= \sum_{m'=-J}^{J}\langle p00\lambda\,|T|\,Jm'\rangle\,\langle Jm'|R^{+}_{\varphi\vartheta 0}|\,Jm\rangle \quad , \end{aligned}$$

an expression which shows how the angular dependence of the decay amplitudes is entirely contained in the well-known unitary matrices for rotation of a system of total angular momentum J

$$D^{*J}_{mm'}(\varphi\vartheta 0) = \langle Jm'|R^{+}_{\varphi\vartheta 0}|Jm\rangle \; .$$

The dynamics of the decay enters only through the amplitudes for decay in the z direction. In this case, the spins of the Y^* and of the Y have necessarily equal projections. The sum over m′ thus reduces to a single term with $m' = \lambda$. As the basic amplitudes we have therefore the two quantities

$$\begin{aligned} \Gamma(+) &\equiv \langle p00\ {}^1\!/_2|T|J,{}^1\!/_2\rangle \\ \Gamma(-) &\equiv \langle p00{-}{}^1\!/_2|T|J,-{}^1\!/_2\rangle , \end{aligned} \tag{3}$$

in terms of which the amplitudes for decay in an arbitrary direction are given by

$$\begin{aligned} \langle p\vartheta\varphi,\lambda = +{}^1\!/_2\;|T|Jm\rangle &= \Gamma(+)D^{*J}_{m,\,1/2}(\varphi\vartheta 0) \\ \langle p\vartheta\varphi,\lambda = -{}^1\!/_2\;|T|Jm\rangle &= \Gamma(-)D^{*J}_{m,\,-1/2}(\varphi\vartheta 0) \; . \end{aligned} \tag{4}$$

[Note: All relevant properties of the matrices $D^{J}_{mm'}$ may be found, for example, in Brink and Satchler[6].]

Assuming that the reaction which prepares the Y^* initially leads to an unequally weighted mixture of states $|Jm\rangle$, we hope to determine J by examining the angular distribution of the decay products. To see how the parity of the Y^* is to be determined, we must consider the behaviour of the two basic amplitudes under space reflections. Consider reflections in the x-z plane

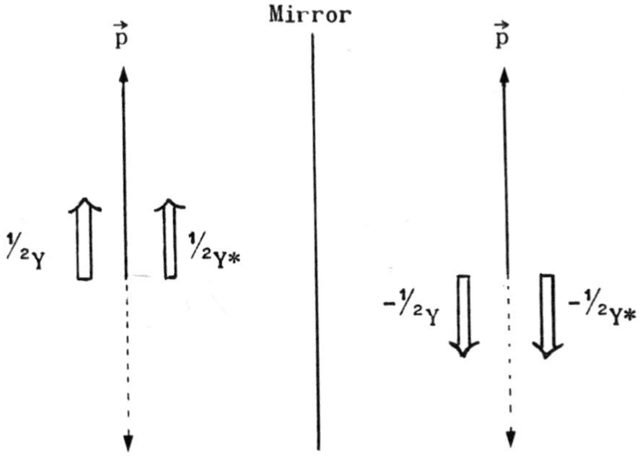

bringing the configuration of momentum and spins for the $\lambda = +\frac{1}{2}$ decay into coincidence with those for the $\lambda = -\frac{1}{2}$ decay. Invariance of the transition operator under reflection, valid for the strong interactions, shows that except for a relative phase the two amplitudes $\Gamma(+)$ and $\Gamma(-)$ are equal. Examination of the reflection properties of the states (see Jacob and Wick) shows readily that

$$\frac{\Gamma(+)}{\Gamma(-)} = \eta_Y \, \eta_{meson} \, \eta_{Y*}(-)^{J-\frac{1}{2}} = \begin{cases} +1 \\ -1 \end{cases}, \qquad (5)$$

where the product of three η's gives the relative intrinsic parity of the resonant state Y^* with respect to its decay products. A measurement of the sign of the ratio $\Gamma(+)/\Gamma(-)$ is therefore required for the parity determination. Looked at in a different way, it is not difficult to see that $\Gamma(+) + \Gamma(-)$ and $\Gamma(+) - \Gamma(-)$ are the relative amplitudes for decay into states of different "orbital" parity, $(-1)^{J-\frac{1}{2}}$ and $(-1)^{J+\frac{1}{2}}$, respectively. For reflection invariance, one or the other of these must vanish. Non-relativistically this corresponds to the selection of orbital angular momentum $\ell = J - \frac{1}{2}$ or $\ell = J + \frac{1}{2}$.

II. DECAY FROM A STATISTICAL MIXTURE OF SPIN STATES; DENSITY MATRICES FOR Y^* AND Y

We come now to the description of the initial spin states produced in the production reaction which prepares the resonant state Y^*. If we do not keep track of the spins of the initially colliding particles in the production reaction (1), the Y^* with which we have to deal in the decay reaction is not described by a pure spin state but rather by a statistical mixture of states. For experimental reasons, it is likewise useful to accept a sample of Y^* which may be produced over some range of production angles and possibly some range of production energies. Referring each event to the appropriate rest frame of the Y^*, we obtain a statistical mixture of spin states of the Y^*, $|\chi_1>$, $|\chi_2>$ .... with relative weights P_1, P_2,.., best described in terms of the density matrix

$$\rho(Y^*) = \sum_n |\chi_n > P_n < \chi_n| \tag{6}$$

$$<\chi_n|\chi_n> = 1; \quad \sum_n P_n = 1 .$$

As is well-known (Dirac, Third Edition, p. 132), all statistical questions concerning measurements made on the mixture of states are expressible in terms of ρ. Thus if Q is any observable, the expectation value of measurements of Q over the mixture is given by

$$< Q > = \frac{\text{Trace } (Q\rho)}{\text{Trace } (\rho)} .$$

The decay of the Y^* gives rise to a statistical mixture of states of the decay products, Y + meson, denoted symbolically as $T|\chi_1>$, $T|\chi_2>$,... By this is meant that the amplitude for finding the helicity state $|p\vartheta\varphi\lambda>$ in the state $T|\chi>$ is

$$< p\vartheta\varphi\lambda |T|\chi> = \sum_{m=-J} < p\vartheta\varphi\lambda |T|Jm> <Jm|\chi> .$$

The density matrix for the mixture of decay states is evidently

$$\begin{aligned}\rho(Y) &= \sum_n T|\chi_n > P_n < \chi_n|T^+ \\ &= T\ \rho(Y^*)\ T^+ .\end{aligned} \tag{7}$$

Its four matrix elements

$$\begin{aligned}\rho(Y)_{\lambda\lambda'} &= \sum_{mm'} < p\vartheta\varphi\lambda\ |T|\ Jm > \rho(Y^*)_{mm'} < Jm'\ |T^+|\ p\vartheta\varphi\lambda' > \\ &= \Gamma(\lambda)\ \Gamma^*(\lambda') \sum_{mm'} D^{*J}_{m\lambda}(\varphi\vartheta 0)\ D^J_{m'\lambda'}(\varphi\vartheta 0)\rho(Y^*)_{mm'}\end{aligned} \tag{8}$$

are linear expressions in the $(2J+1) \times (2J+1)$ matrix elements of $\rho(Y^*)$. From this expression we may, for example, obtain the intensity or angular distribution of the decay products by taking the trace (expectation value of the unit operator). Since $\lambda = \lambda'$ in the trace, it is clear that the intensity angular distribution gives information about J but no information at all about the parity of the Y^*.

At this point it is useful to notice that although there are many different ways of parametrizing the initial density matrix $\rho(Y^*)$, there is one which is particularly convenient. As a Hermitian matrix $(2J+1) \times (2J+1)$, $\rho(Y^*)$ is specified by $(2J+1)^2$ real quantities, or equivalently by the expectation values of a total of $(2J+1)^2$ independent real physical operators for the mixture of initial spin states. A general operator for spin states of a particle of spin J takes the form

$$\Lambda = \sum_{m_1 m_2} w_{m_1 m_2} |Jm_1 > < Jm_2|$$

where the weighting factors $w_{m_1 m_2}$ are arbitrary constants. For the present purpose, it is useful to choose $w_{m_1 m_2}$ so that the resulting operator transforms in a simple way under rotations. Recalling that the bra-vector $< Jm|$ transforms in the same way as the ket $(-1)^{J-m}|J,-m>$, we may evidently use the Clebsch-Gordan coefficients to construct a set of operators U_L^M with $-L \leq M \leq L$ transforming under rotations in the same way as the spherical harmonics Y_L^M:

$$U_L^M \equiv \sum_{m_1 m_2} |Jm_1> <Jm_2|(-1)^{J-m_2} < J J m_1 - m_2|LM> . \tag{9}$$

It is important to notice that the vector addition of J with J leads to L ranging in integer steps from 0 to 2J, so that the U_L^M vanish identically for $L > 2J$. There are thus altogether $(2J+1)^2$ operators U_L^M and it is easy to verify using the orthogonality of the Clebsch-Gordan coefficients, that they satisfy the relations

$$\begin{aligned}
&< Jm_1|U_L^M|Jm_2> = (-1)^{J-m_2} < J J m_1 - m_2|LM> ,\\
&U_L^{M^+} = (-1)^M U_L^{-M} ,\\
\text{Trace } &U_{L'}^{M'} U_L^{M^+} = \delta_{LL'}\delta_{MM'} ,\\
&U_L^M \equiv 0 \text{ for } L > 2J ,\\
&U_0^0 = \frac{1}{\sqrt{2J+1}} 1 .
\end{aligned} \tag{10}$$

Taking the density matrix for the Y^* as normalized to unity, and using the trace property Eq. (10), we see that $\rho(Y^*)$ is expressible as

$$\begin{aligned}
\rho(Y^*) &= \sum_{LM} < U_L^M >^* U_L^M ,\\
< U_L^M > &\equiv \text{Trace } \rho(Y^*) U_L^M .
\end{aligned} \tag{11}$$

Using Eq. (10) it is clear that the $< U_L^M >$ although not real, are expressible in terms of exactly $(2J+1)^2$ real quantities. For L = 1 the three quantities $< U_1^M >$, M = - 1,0, + 1 transform as a vector and are equivalent to the (spherical) components of the polarization of the Y^* for the selected sample. For larger L the $< U_L^M >$ describe higher order tensor polarizations of the Y^*. [For more general discussion of the expression of the density matrix in orthogonal operators see, for example, U. Fano[7].]

To see the convenience of the parametrization Eq. (11), we may substitute into Eq. (8). From Eq. (10) and the Clebsch-Gordan decomposition

$$D^{j_1}_{m_1 n_1} D^{j_2}_{m_2 n_2} = \sum_{JMN} < j_1 j_2 m_1 m_2 | JM > D^J_{MN} < JN | j_1 j_2 n_1 n_2 > ,$$

together with the orthogonality of the Clebsch-Gordan coefficients we obtain the basic relation

$$\rho(Y)_{\lambda\lambda'} = \Gamma(\lambda)\Gamma^*(\lambda')(-1)^{J-\lambda'} \sum_{LM} < U_L^M >^* < JJ\lambda - \lambda'/L, \lambda - \lambda' > D^{*L}_{M,\lambda-\lambda'}(\varphi \vartheta 0) . \tag{12}$$

III. INTENSITY DISTRIBUTION

$$I(\vartheta,\varphi) = \text{Trace } \rho(Y) = \sum_{\lambda} \rho(Y)_{\lambda\lambda}$$

$$= \sum_{\substack{\lambda \\ LM}} |\Gamma(\lambda)|^2 (-1)^{J-\lambda} < JJ\lambda - \lambda | L0 > < U_L^M >^* \underbrace{D^{*L}_{M0} (\varphi \vartheta 0)}$$

$$D^{*L}_{M0} (\varphi \vartheta 0) \rightarrow \sqrt{\frac{4\pi}{2L+1}}\, Y_L^M (\vartheta,\varphi) .$$

Recalling that $|\Gamma(+)|^2 = |\Gamma(-)|^2$, the normalized angular distribution is given simply by

$$I(\hat{n}) = I(\vartheta,\varphi) = \sum_{\substack{\text{even } L \\ M}} \sqrt{\frac{2J+1}{2L+1}}\, n_{L0} < U_L^M >^* Y_L^M(\vartheta,\varphi) \tag{13}$$

$$n_{L0} \equiv (-1)^{J-\frac{1}{2}} \sqrt{\frac{2J+1}{4\pi}} < JJ\ \tfrac{1}{2} - \tfrac{1}{2} | L0 >$$

The restriction to even L in the summation is the result of an identity connecting the Clebsch-Gordan coefficients for $\lambda = +\frac{1}{2}$ and $\lambda = -\frac{1}{2}$. Physically this expresses the obvious fact that with parity conservation the angular distribution must be invariant to spatial inversion of the momenta of the decay products. In a similar way, the transformation properties of the $< U_L^M >^*$ and Y_L^M insure the invariance of the angular distribution $I(\hat{n})$ against a rotation of the co-ordinate system. In terms of experimentally measured "moments" of spherical harmonics over the angular distribution,

$$< Y_L^M > \equiv \int d\Omega\, I(\vartheta,\varphi)\, Y_L^M(\vartheta,\varphi) \ , \tag{14}$$

and the abbreviation

$$t_L^M \equiv \sqrt{\frac{2J+1}{2L+1}} < U_L^M > \ , \tag{15}$$

we may give the result in the form

$$< Y_L^M > = \begin{cases} n_{L0}\ t_L^M , & L \text{ even} \\ 0 , & L \text{ odd} \end{cases} \tag{16}$$

and

$$< Y_L^M > \equiv 0 \text{ for } L > 2J.$$

As an important consequence we see that if $J = \frac{1}{2}$ and parity is conserved, the angular distribution of decay products must be isotropic. Anistropy necessarily implies $J > \frac{1}{2}$.

IV. ANGULAR DISTRIBUTION OF THE POLARIZATION OF Y

To discuss the polarization of the Y in the decay $Y^* \rightarrow Y +$ meson, it is simplest to consider the spin states of the Y in an appropriate rest frame, where the spin direction has an unambiguous meaning. This is accomplished by transforming to a Lorentz frame (ξ, η, ζ) moving in the direction of the Y momentum (ζ direction) with velocity equal to that of the Y in the Y^* rest frame

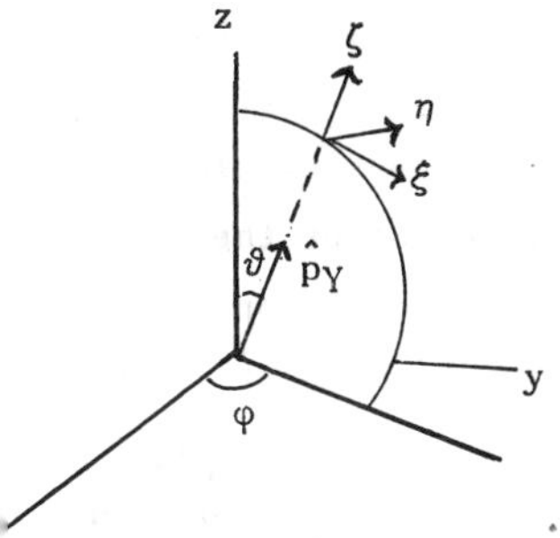

$\hat{\zeta}$ in direction $\hat{n} \equiv \hat{p}_Y$

$\hat{\xi}$ in plane of $\hat{z}$, $\hat{\zeta}$

$\hat{\eta}$ perpendicular to plane of $\hat{z}, \hat{\zeta}$

Under such a Lorentz transformation it is clear that apart from a normalization factor independent of λ, the helicity states $|p\,\vartheta\,\varphi\,\lambda>$ go over into the spin states $|\tfrac{1}{2}\,\lambda>$ for the Y at rest in the (ξ, η, ζ) frame with ζ as axis of quantization. Absorbing the change of normalization, unimportant for our purposes, we see that Eqs. (8) and (12) serve equally well to define the density matrix for the spin states of the Y in the Y rest frame (ξ, η, ζ).

The polarization of the Y is then obtained as

$$\vec{P}(\vartheta,\varphi) = <\vec{\sigma}> = \frac{\text{Trace } \rho(Y)\vec{\sigma}}{\text{Trace } \rho(Y)} ,$$

or

$$I(\vartheta,\varphi)\,\vec{P}(\vartheta,\varphi) = \text{Trace } \rho(Y)\vec{\sigma} .$$

Experimentally, $\vec{P}$ is found from the angular distribution of the parity violating weak decay of the Y.

1. Longitudinal polarization $\vec{P}\cdot\hat{n}$

$$\vec{P}\cdot\hat{n} = \langle\sigma_\zeta\rangle = \frac{\text{Trace } \rho(Y)\sigma_\zeta}{I(\vartheta,\varphi)} .$$

Remembering that σ_ζ has only diagonal matrix elements, and defining moments of the angular distribution of $\vec{P}\cdot\hat{n}$, we find

$$\begin{aligned} \langle \vec{P}\cdot\hat{n}\, Y_L^M \rangle &\equiv \int d\Omega I(\vartheta,\varphi)\, \vec{P}\cdot\hat{n}\, Y_L^M(\vartheta,\varphi) \\ &= \begin{cases} n_{L0}\, t_L^M , & L \text{ odd} \\ 0 , & L \text{ even} \end{cases} \end{aligned} \tag{17}$$

The dependence on odd L only corresponds to the fact that under spatial inversions $\vec{P}\cdot\hat{n}$ goes over into $\vec{P}\cdot(-\hat{n})$.

2. Transverse polarization

Here, the important point to notice is that σ_ξ and σ_η have only off diagonal matrix elements, $\lambda \neq \lambda'$. From Eq. (12) we see then that the transverse components of the polarization necessarily involve the products $\Gamma(+)\,\Gamma(-)^*$ and $\Gamma(-)\,\Gamma(+)^*$ where the relative phases are important. For practical applications it is best to express the transverse polarization in terms of its components in the original (x,y,z) co-ordinate frame. The final result, after some reductions involving the orthogonality of the functions $D^{*L}_{m,-1}(\varphi\vartheta 0)$, gives another relation for $\langle U_L^M \rangle$, L odd, in terms of the parameter

$$\gamma \equiv \frac{\Gamma(+)^*\Gamma(-) + \Gamma(+)\,\Gamma(-)^*}{|\Gamma(+)|^2 + |\Gamma(-)|^2} = \begin{cases} +1 \\ -1 \end{cases} \text{or} \tag{18}$$

and moments of the spherical components of the polarization P^m:

$$P^{\pm 1} = \mp (P_x \pm iP_y)/\sqrt{2}, \quad P^{0} = P_z$$

$$\gamma(2J+1)n_{LO}t_L^M = (L+1)\sqrt{\frac{L}{2L+1}} \sum_{m=-1}^{1} \langle P^m Y_{L-1}^{M-m} \rangle \langle 1L-1\, m\, M-m | LM \rangle \tag{19}$$

<u>L odd</u>

$$+ L \sqrt{\frac{L+1}{2L+1}} \sum_{m=-1}^{1} \langle P^m Y_{L+1}^{M-m} \rangle \langle 1L+1\, m\, M-m | LM \rangle$$

V. LORENTZ FRAMES IN WHICH TO MEASURE THE DECAY OF Y^* AND Y

It is clear that the Y^* decay is to be described in some rest frame of the Y^*, and the same for the Y decay. There may, however, be some confusion in the choice of these co-ordinate systems. A convenient choice is as follows.

For definiteness let us take as the reactions (1) and (2)

i) $K^- + p \rightarrow Y_1^{*+} + \pi^-$
ii) $Y_1^{*+} \rightarrow \Lambda + \pi^+$
iii) $\Lambda \rightarrow \pi^- + p$
($Y_1^* = Y_1^*(1385)$ for example)

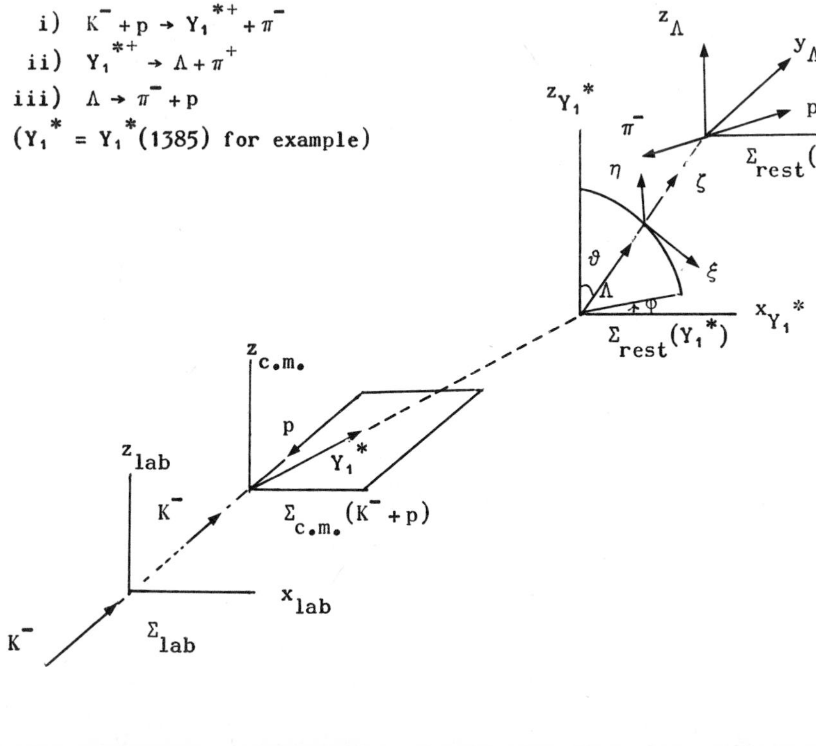

We take the incident K^- along the y direction in the lab. frame (Σ_{lab}) with the target proton at rest, and define z_{lab} as the normal to the production plane. The Y_1^* (and π) are then in the xy plane. From Σ_{lab} we go to the centre-of-mass $\Sigma_{c.m.}(K^- + p)$ by a Lorentz transformation, without rotation, along the direction of the K^-. Now the production amplitudes for the Y_1^* may be expressed in terms of helicity states for the Y_1^* in the c.m. frame. These states are, in effect, described in $\Sigma_{c.m.}(K^- + p)$ as corresponding to a z axis in the direction of Y_1^* and x,y axes defined by the standard rotation which rotates helicity states from $z_{c.m.}$ to the Y_1^* direction. We next transform Y_1^* to rest by a pure Lorentz transformation along the Y_1^* direction, and subsequently, for convenience make a counter rotation to bring the z axis (now called $z_{Y_1^*}$) back to parallelism with $z_{c.m.}$. The net effect is a Lorentz transformation $Z(\hat{Y}_1^*)$("direct" Lorentz transformation) from $\Sigma_{c.m.}(K^- + p)$ to $\Sigma_{rest}(Y_1^*)$, leaving components of vectors transverse to the direction $\hat{Y}_1^*$ invariant. Symbolically,

$$\Sigma_{rest}(Y_1^*) = Z(\hat{Y}_1^*)\ \Sigma_{c.m.}(K^- + p),$$

and it is this rest frame of the Y_1^* which is good to use for describing its decay angular distribution [angles ϑ,φ in Eq. (13)].

Exactly the same kind of transformation applies to the description of the density matrix of the Λ [Eqs. (8) and (12)], first in terms of helicity states (axes ξ,η,ζ introduced before in the discussion of the polarization of the Y or Λ) and subsequently in terms of axes in a frame $\Sigma_{rest}(\Lambda)$ "parallel" to the axes in $\Sigma_{rest}(Y_1^*)$:

$$\Sigma_{rest}(\Lambda) = Z(\hat{\Lambda})\ \Sigma_{rest}(Y_1^*)\ .$$

The Λ polarization $\vec{P}\ (\vartheta,\varphi)$ in Eqs. (17) and (19) is therefore understood as expressed in the co-ordinate system $\Sigma_{rest}(\Lambda)$ obtained in this way.

Each "direct" Lorentz transformation is to be taken in succession (for each production and decay event in turn):

$$\Sigma_{lab} \to \Sigma_{c.m.}(K^- + p) \to \Sigma_{rest}(Y_1^*) \to \Sigma_{rest}(\Lambda) \;.$$

For example, we must not go to a Λ rest frame directly from the lab. This would result in a different rest frame for the Λ with axes rotated from the one obtained by successive transformation. It would, however, be equally good to go in one step by "direct" Lorentz transformation from Σ_{lab} to a Y_1^* rest frame and proceed from there as before.

VI. RESTRICTIONS ON THE t_L^M

It is useful to notice a number of conditions which must be satisfied by the tensor polarizations t_L^M of the Y^*.

i) a) If the z axis in $\Sigma_{c.m.}$ (production) or in $\Sigma_{rest}(Y^*)$ is chosen normal to the production plane,

b) if the Y^* is selected without regard to possible spin directions of other particles produced along with it in the production reaction (average over spins and directions of other particles), and

c) if the initial particles are unpolarized, then rotation and reflection invariance shows that

$$t_L^M = 0 \text{ for odd } M \;. \tag{20}$$

(After making an inversion of all momenta in the production reaction consider the effect of a rotation of 180° around the z direction.) For L = 1 the statement is equivalent to the condition that in reactions involving unpolarized particles the vector polarization of any of the particles in the final state is necessarily normal to the production plane.

ii) As a Hermitian matrix with non-negative eigenvalues the density matrix $\rho(Y^*)$ obeys the condition that Trace $(\rho^2) \leqq$ (Trace $\rho)^2$. Expressed in terms of the t_L^M, [Eqs. (10), (11) and (15)] this gives the requirement

$$\sum_{LM} (2L+1)|t_L^M|^2 \leq (2J+1) \ . \tag{21}$$

iii) There are other inequalities based on the particular form for the t_L^M. For example, from the fact that

$$t_1^0 = \frac{1}{\sqrt{J(J+1)}} < s_z > ,$$

where $< s_z >$ is the average of the spin operator s_z over the ensemble of Y_1^* states, it easily follows from Eq. (17) that the longitudinal polarization of the Y is restricted by

$$-\frac{1}{2J(J+1)} \leq < \vec{P} \cdot \hat{n} \cos \vartheta > \leq \frac{1}{2J(J+1)} \ . \tag{22}$$

If by good fortune the production reaction for the Y^* should yield a large value for $< \vec{P} \cdot \hat{n} \cos \vartheta >$, this would impose a useful upper limit on the magnitude of J.

As another example, for L = 2 and M = 0 it can be shown that

$$t_2^0 = \frac{3 < s_z{}^2 > - J(J+1)}{\sqrt{J(J+1)(2J-1)(2J+3)}} \equiv N_2(3 < s_z{}^2 > - J(J+1)) \ .$$

Since

$$0 \leq < s_z{}^2 > \leq J^2 ,$$

it follows that

$$- N_2 \ J(J+1) \leq t_2{}^0 \leq N_2(3J^2 - J(J+1)) \ . \tag{23}$$

In general there is a class of inequalities for each hypothesis J which are similar to those first considered by Lee and Yang[8)] in their discussion of parity violating decays of hyperons. They are rather complicated and we shall not write them down here, but it would be interesting to apply them to the experimental data available for the strong decays of the $Y_1^*(1385)$ and the $\Xi^*(1529)$.

VII. SUMMARY OF PROCEDURE FOR SPIN PARITY DETERMINATION

For L even and odd, the t_L^M are found from the experimental decay distributions:

(A) $n_{L0}\ t_L^M$ .... L even; from decay angular distribution;

(B) $n_{L0}\ t_L^M$ .... L odd; from distribution of longitudinal polarization;

(C) $\gamma(2J+1)\ n_{L0}\ t_L^M$, L odd; from distribution of transverse polarization.

The quantities listed are expressed directly in terms of the experimental moments of the distributions through Eqs. (16), (17) and (19). For a given choice of J the coefficients n_{L0} are fixed, so one can see if the resulting t_L^M are statistically consistent with zero for $L > 2J$ and satisfy the inequalities Eqs. (21), (22), (23) and their generalizations for $L \leq 2J$. From a comparison of (B) and (C) for the same (odd) L and M there is another check on the hypothesis J and a determination of the sign of γ. Equation (5) then gives the parity of the Y^*. In fact, if the statistical accuracy is good enough the comparison of (B) and (C) should in itself fix J and the parity.

VIII. BACKGROUND INTERFERENCE

The procedure outlined gives a value for J in any one experiment which depends, of course, on the extent to which the production reaction leads to a density matrix $\rho(Y^*)$ with fully developed tensor polarization parameters t_L^M. Since it may happen under given circumstances that the t_L^M begin to be very small for L's below the maximum allowed value 2J, the procedure is likely to give only a lower limit on J. It is, in general, advisable to repeat the procedure for a variety of different ranges of energy and angle at production of the Y^*, and possibly for different production reactions with the expectation that in some of the experiments $\rho(Y^*)$ will fully develop its allowed complexity.

Finally, it is important to decide if the experimental evidence justifies the assumption that there is no non-resonant background amplitude which interferes significantly with the resonant Y^* production amplitude in the production reaction Eq. (1). An interfering non-resonant amplitude might be expected to distort the resonance peak in the effective mass plot for the Y^* and possibly to distort the angular distribution of the decay $Y^* \to Y + \text{meson}$ so that it exhibits a forward backward asymmetry [appearance of odd L in the decay angular distribution Eq. (13)]. A reasonable criterion would be to require that these distortion effects be very small. This is the case for the $\Xi^*(1529)$ [Schlein et al.[2]] mentioned earlier but not entirely obvious for the $Y_1^*(1385)$ where there is a forward-backward asymmetry. It is clear that the matter is delicate and that it will, in general, be necessary to find agreement in spin parity assignments based on several different experiments before considering the results established.

* * *

REFERENCES

1) N. Byers and S. Fenster, Phys.Rev.Letters 11, 52 (1963).

2) P.E. Schlein, D.D. Carmony, G.M. Pjerrou, W.E. Slater, D.H. Stork and H.K. Ticho, Phys.Rev.Letters 11, 167 (1963).

3) J.B. Shafer, J.J. Murray and D.O. Huwe, Phys.Rev.Letters 10, 179 (1963).

4) E. Malamud and P.E. Schlein, Phys.Letters 10, 145 (1964).

5) M. Jacob and G.C. Wick, Annals of Physics 7, 404 (1959).

6) D. Brink and G.R. Satchler, Angular Momentum, Oxford University Press (1962).

7) U. Fano, Rev.Mod.Phys. 29, 74 (1957).

8) T.D. Lee and C.N. Yang, Phys.Rev. 109, 1155 (1958).

GENERAL REVIEW OF NEUTRINO PHYSICS

G. Bernardini
University of Rome

Probably, it is well known to everybody that the experiments which extended the study of leptonic interactions to the domain of momentum transfers of the order of 1 GeV stemmed from a suggestion made by Pontecorvo at the Kiev Conference in 1959[1)], and by Schwartz in early 1960[2)]. The idea is the following: π's and K's of a few GeV, which are produced quite abundantly by the multi-GeV accelerators at Brookhaven, CERN, Hamburg, Argonne, Cambridge, and soon at other places, decay in flight and produce neutrinos in their more common decay modes. Because of the centre-of-mass velocity of the parent particle these neutrinos may have fairly high energies, of the order of several GeV. For equivalent momenta the kaons produce neutrinos of higher energy than the pions.

The maximum and minimum momenta of the neutrino are given by:

$$P_{max} = \gamma\, P^{*}(1+\beta)$$
$$P_{min} = \gamma\, P^{*}(1-\beta)\ ,$$

where P^{*} is the momentum of the neutrino in the centre of mass of the parent.

β, γ refer to the parents kinematics

$P^{*} \simeq 35$ MeV/c for pions

$\simeq 340$ MeV/c for kaons.

From this we see that the neutrino from a pion has

$$E_{max} \approx \tfrac{1}{2}(\text{energy of parent pion})$$

$$E_{max} \approx \text{(energy of parent kaon)} .$$

Of course both spectra are uniform and go down to almost zero energy.

The angle of the neutrinos relative to the parent's direction is small because of the Lorentz contraction. The forward half hemisphere in the centre-of-mass system is contracted in the laboratory frame to angles less than $1/\gamma$. With the available average parent energies of several GeV, the angular spread of neutrinos emitted in the forward direction is not greater than one degree.

The advantages of using high-energy neutrinos are that for the first time there is the possibility of studying the inverse neutrino reactions at very high momentum transfers and that at high incident momenta there is a large phase space factor. The famous experiment of Reines-Cowan concerning the reaction

$$\bar{\nu} + p \rightarrow n + e^{+}$$

was done with pile-neutrinos, i.e. at momentum transfers which were almost zero. Compared to this, the phase space in the present experiments is higher by several orders of magnitude. Of course, the cross-section does not increase quadratically with momentum, as it would if only the phase space were involved, because the nucleon has a structure. The form factors which describe the structure are equal to unity at momentum transfers which are small compared with the mass of the nucleon. As the momentum is increased, the cut-off in the momentum becomes more and more severe and the cross-section levels off as it could be crudely shown with the following argument.

Neglect the mass of the muon. Take the energy of the electron and neutrino equal to the average momentum of the two particles. Then the four-momentum transfer becomes

$$q^2 = - m_e^2 + 2E_\nu(E_e - p_e \cos\Theta)$$

$$\underset{m_e \to 0}{\approx} 2E_\nu E_e \sin^2\frac{\Theta}{2} \approx 2p_\nu^2 \sin^2\frac{\Theta}{2} \,.$$

Now, the cross-section, expressed roughly, is

$$\sigma \approx G^2(p^2\Omega)\cdot F,$$

where G is the coupling constant, F is the form factor, p is the neutrino momentum and Ω is the solid angle $\propto 2\sin^2\Theta/2$. Therefore, $p^2\Omega = q^2$. At low q^2, $F = 1$, $\sigma \approx G^2q^2$; at high q^2, $F \approx \text{const}/q^2$. Since for $q^2 \gtrsim M^2$, where M = nucleon mass, certainly the form factors start to decrease, if we take const = M^2, which gives

$$\sigma \approx G^2 \cdot q^2 \times \frac{M^2}{q^2} = G^2M^2 \,,$$

one has

$$\sigma \approx 10^{-38}\ \text{cm}^2 \,.$$

The variation in cross-section with incident neutrino momentum will look like

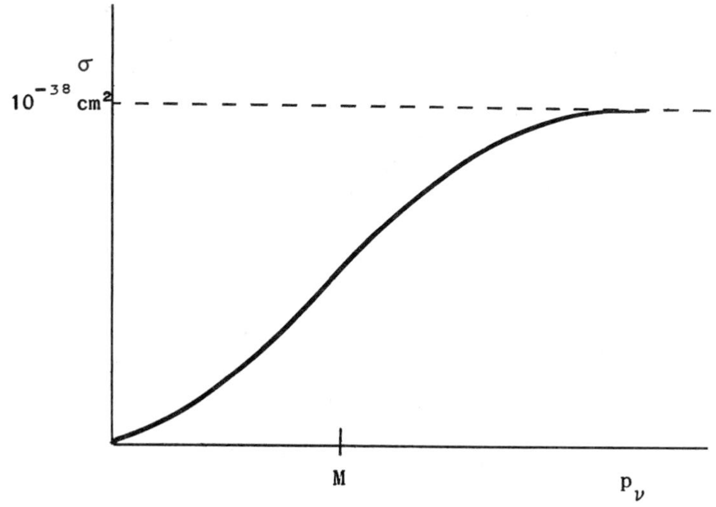

In spite of this asymptotic limiting, the increase in cross-section relative to the Reines-Cowan experiment is five orders of magnitude. This is the basic advantage of using high-energy neutrinos.

The first experiment at high-energy was done by the Columbia group at Brookhaven (led by Lederman, Schwartz and Steinberger), and if you are familiar with this fundamental paper[3], you will remember that there were essentially two results, one, of course, by far more significant than the other.

For ν_μ *) interacting with neutrons; the main result of Brookhaven is that the rates of these two possible process

$$\begin{aligned} n + \nu_\mu &\to p + e^- \\ &\to p + \mu^- \end{aligned}$$

was found drastically different.

Their analysis proceeded in the following way. They compared 32 tracks which were almost unambiguously muons above 300 MeV (from range measurement), with all other events. They had 24 or 26 mixed-up events which we now know were the rather complicated inelastic processes which were neglected and also 6 events with a few sparks. By comparing the latter with calibrations done with electrons of known energy, these 6 events might hardly be electrons with energy up to 300 MeV. Then the ratio

$$R = \frac{\nu_\mu + n \to p + e^-}{\nu_\mu + n \to p + \mu^-} \lesssim \frac{1}{5}$$

from which it was concluded that $\nu_\mu \neq \nu_e$. In a subsequent paper with Lee[4], they answered some criticisms made by Lapidus[5] and other about some possible attenuation of the electron events with respect to the μ events

*) To avoid confusion in terminology, I will call the neutrino, ν_μ, which is produced in association with a muon a μ neutrino, and that, ν_e, associated with an electron e-neutrino.

due to the pseudoscalar term, different axial form factors, etc. The minimum expected number of electrons was calculated using the conserved vector current hypothesis (assuming that other terms can only increase the cross-section), using the fact that about half ν_μ and half $\bar{\nu}_\mu$ were present in the used μ neutrino spectrum. Under these conditions the Vector-Axial interference term, which depresses $\sigma_{\bar{\nu}}$ and enhances σ_ν, is practically eliminated and the rate is proportional to

$$\sigma_{\text{effective}} = \frac{1}{2}\,\sigma_{\nu} + \frac{1}{2}\,\sigma_{\bar{\nu}} > \sigma_V \ .$$

With the vector form factors borrowed from electron-proton scattering, the minimum number of electrons expected would be 12 [with $\simeq$ 30% uncertainty due to the $(\nu_\mu + \bar{\nu}_\mu)$ spectrum] while the very maximum found*) was 6.

Thus, this first experiment showed that the μ neutrino and the e neutrino were different. At the same time this experiment showed that the rate of the events attributable to ν_μ elastic interaction was of the right order of magnitude. The second experiment, at CERN in 1963, was designed to improve this information and in fact the situation has been substantially improved.

An outstanding feature of the CERN experiment was the neutrino beam which is the merit of the engineers and in particular of Van der Meer and co-workers who designed a huge conical magnetic mirror - the horn, in such a way that particles produced at the target in its apex were focused onto the neutrino detectors. The particles (pions and kaons) were produced by the external proton beam which was also a masterpiece, since the efficiency of extraction was 95 - 97%.

The action of the horn is illustrated below. It consists of two concentric cones. A strong current flows through the inner cone

*) Most of the six possible electron events were found when the operating conditions were not yet too satisfactory.

and returns through the outer one. The magnetic field is circular in a plane perpendicular to the beam direction.

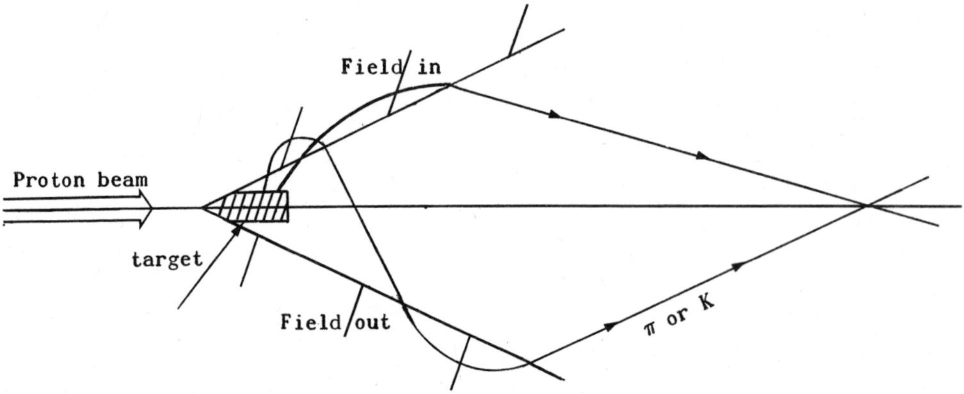

The effect of this set-up is tabulated below

Target	Horn	Total flux
internal target	no horn	1
external target	no horn	> 10
external target	with horn	> 50

So far, the spectrum of neutrinos could not be measured because of lack of time and statistics. The calculated spectrum according to an elaborate but straightforward combination of orbits and kinematical rules is shown below. The ordinate is neutrinos/(GeV/c)m² circulating proton, with the horn adjusted to focus positive particles at a distance of 31 m behind the shielding wall which separated the horn from the apparatus.

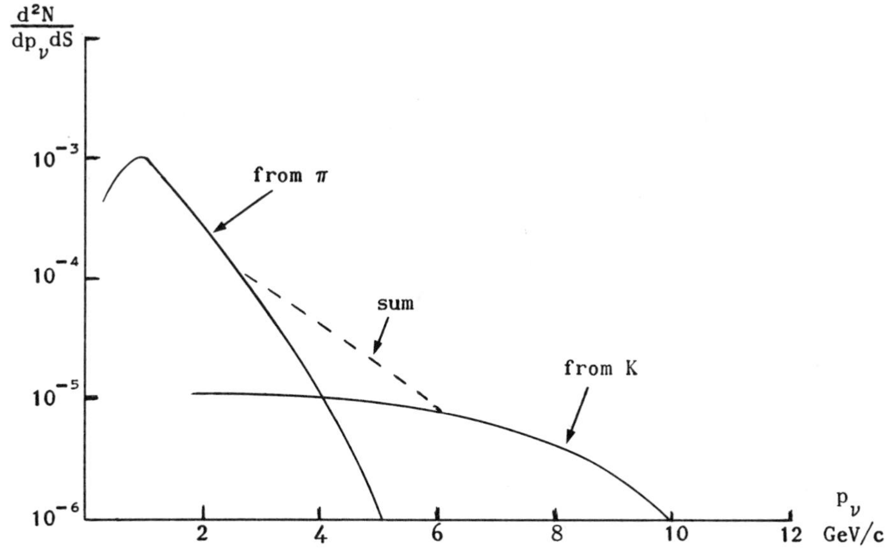

It may be seen that the pions contribute most up to about 4 GeV, and then the kaons extend the spectrum up to about 10 GeV. In fact, there were two versions of the horn. The first gave a maximum energy of 9 GeV, and the second of 11 GeV. The latter was constructed so as to extend upwards the lower limit of the intermediate boson mass - about which we will speak later. The calculated spectra are effected by several errors, the most important of which lies in the uncertainty of emission angles and momenta of π's and K's from the target. The part above 4 GeV is particularly uncertain.

Apparatus

The experiment was carried out in two complementary parts using:

i) a bubble chamber;

ii) spark chambers.

The freon bubble chamber had the following characteristics:

radiation length	= 11.5 cm
nuclear interaction mean free path	= 68 cm

fiducial volume	≈ 200 litres or larger depending upon the type of event selected
	~ 0.3 ton
magnetic field	27 kgauss

The physicists concerned in this part of the work were: H. Bingham, M. Block, H. Burmeister, D. Cundy, B. Eiben, C. Franzinetti, P. Innocenti, J. Keren, R. Møllerud, G. Myatt, M. Nikolić, A. Orkin-Lecourtois, M. Paty, D. Perkins, C. Ramm, K. Schultze, H. Sletten, K. Soop, R. Stump, W. Venus and H. Yoshiki.

In the bubble chamber, the discrimination of the tracks was the standard one using ionization, momentum measurements, delta rays, etc., except that multiple scattering caused some troubles in measuring momentum. The discrimination between protons and mesons was quite neat, but of course, it was impossible to distinguish muons from pions.

Those concerned in the spark chamber experiment were: H. Bienlein, A. Böhm, G. von Dardel, H. Faissner, F. Ferrero, J.-M. Gaillard, H.J. Gerber, B. Hahn, V. Kaftanov, F. Krienen, C. Manfredotti, M. Reinharz, R.A. Salmeron, P.G. Seiler, A. Staude, H.J. Steiner, J. Stein and myself.

There were two versions of the spark chamber experiment, but the principle in both cases was the same. They were made as follows:

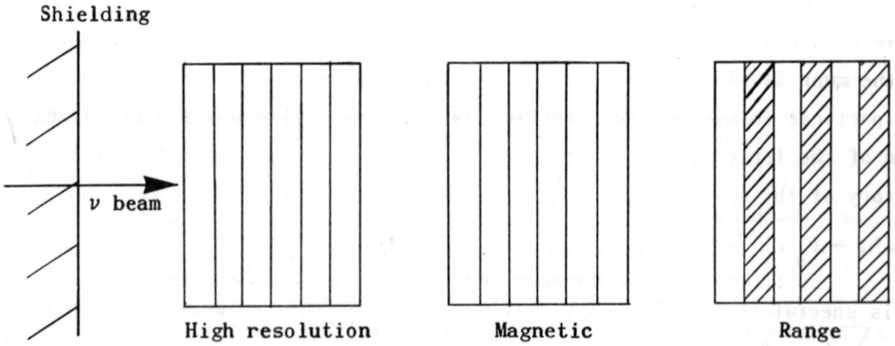

The first part had thin (0.5 cm) plates to have high resolution in order to see as much as possible the short-range proton and particularly the showers' development. This was followed by a magnetic region and then by the range chamber to give a measurement of the range of particles eventually stopping.

In the first run, the set-up was designed to see to what limit ν_μ was different from ν_e, and so a mixed array of brass and aluminium plates was used so as to see a sizable multiplication of the shower. The magnetic field was produced by a Helmholtz coil magnet kindly loaned to us by Saclay.

In the second run, this was replaced by a huge set of 25 magnetized iron plates, each 5 cm thick and with spark chambers between them. Here, the magnetic field allows a sign determination for particles with ranges ≥ 200 g/cm^2, and allows a 25% momentum of determination for particles between 1 and 30 GeV.

Separation of events into elastic and inelastic

For this, the bubble chamber was the best because the spark chamber, although it gives higher statistics, gives very poor information on the nature of a single event.

Concerning the sign of the muon, in elastic or inelastic events, if we assume a μ-leptonic number conservation law to hold, then the sign of the muon is always negative. This is true for any assignment particle-antiparticle for the muons, and for any self-consistent assignment of the sign of the lepton number to muons. To prove this, simply consider the history of the process from the time the pion is in free motion:

$$\pi^+ + N_1 \rightarrow \nu_\mu + \mu^+ + N_1 \longrightarrow \mu^+ + N^* \rightarrow \mu^+ + \mu_2 + N_2 + \text{hadrons}$$

N_1 is spectator $\longleftrightarrow$ μ^+ is spectator, N^* is some intermediate state.

$$\sum L_\mu = 0$$

Applying $\sum L_\mu = 0$ to the final state, we see that μ_2 must have opposite L_μ number to μ^+, i.e. it must be a μ^- provided that the μ^- is the anti-particle of the μ^+.

These assumptions have been verified in both the spark chamber and bubble chamber measurements. The muon sign analysis of all events having a muon crossing the magnet for the two runs gave, in the spark chambers :

			Expected	Found
1963:	positive mesons focused by horn	μ^+/μ^-	6%	(8 ± 4)%
1964:	"	"	3%	(2.5 ± 1)%

In the 1963 measurements, the statistics were limited by the aperture of the Saclay magnet.

The expected ratios are not zero because negative pions which travel along the axis of the horn are not defocused and so are available for producing $\bar{\nu}_\mu$ contamination.

The bubble chamber results are completely equivalent except that there is less chance of misinterpreting events. Hence, there one may also see if a process $\nu_\mu + N \rightarrow N +$ something not μ^- is possible. At energies above 1 GeV the possible events of this type are less than 2% of the total events and look very much like events originated by neutrons coming from the recoils of the events induced in the shielding by neutrinos.

We have seen above that if the μ lepton number is conserved, the muon produced is always negative. From the same equations, it follows by charge conservation that if the event is elastic - i.e. no hadrons are present, then the first nucleon must be a neutron and the product nucleon a proton.

In the inelastic events, there are many possibilities for the hadrons, and the target nucleon may be either a proton or a neutron. The largest part of the events is of the type :

$$\nu + N \rightarrow N + \mu^- + n\,\pi \, .$$

The cases where strange particles are produced are very few, $\lesssim 3\%$. Taking into account the efficiency of the chamber for detecting them, the few events which have been observed (7 out of 459) are compatible with associated production.

Recognition of elastic events

The elastic process is

$$\nu_{\mu} + N - P + \mu^{-} .$$

The recognition of this type of event is made somewhat less definite by the fact that the process takes place inside a heavy nucleus. Let us follow what happens. The ν_{μ} hits a neutron inside the nucleus and then the muon comes out without interacting, but the proton can interact coming out and so produce a nucleonic cascade. Worse still, the event may be inelastic with pion production, with subsequent absorption of the pion inside the nucleus to produce, for example, a pair of nucleons - the most common result of absorbing a pion in nuclear matter. The resultant event then looks like a muon, several protons, but no pions.

The first discrimination made against inelastic events is a brutal one, call inelastic, all those events in which one sees pions. Pions are discriminated from other particles using the criterium: there should be one negative track of mesonic character, which is identified as the μ. If other mesonic tracks are present, they are called pions. This is checked by the fact that, on the average, they interact like pions in the bubble chamber.

A further selection is now necessary to see which of the non-pionic events are elastic. Several kinematic tests were made, and in spite of the fact that they are not extremely neat, they are comforting.

Assume that the muon does not interact in the nucleus. The direction of the neutrino is known to about one degree. By range measurement, the momentum of the muon is known. Hence, assuming a two-body interaction, the kinematics are completely determined.

The energy of the neutrino is given by

$$E_\nu = \left(E_\mu - \frac{m_\mu^2}{2M}\right) \Big/ \left(1 - \frac{E_\mu}{M}\left[1 - \beta_\mu \cos\Theta\right]\right) = E_{calc}$$

using only the muon data. An independent estimate of this quantity is obtained from the visible energy: $E_{vis} = E_\mu + T_p$. A scatter diagram of E_{calc} against E_{vis} should cluster around the line $E_{vis} = E_{calc}$, with a spread caused by the nucleons Fermi-motion.

The results are indicated below. Only eight or nine events deviate from the line by more than twice the Fermi momentum of 270 MeV/c. The inelastic events fall asymmetrically on the diagram cluster around the region indicated by the crosses.

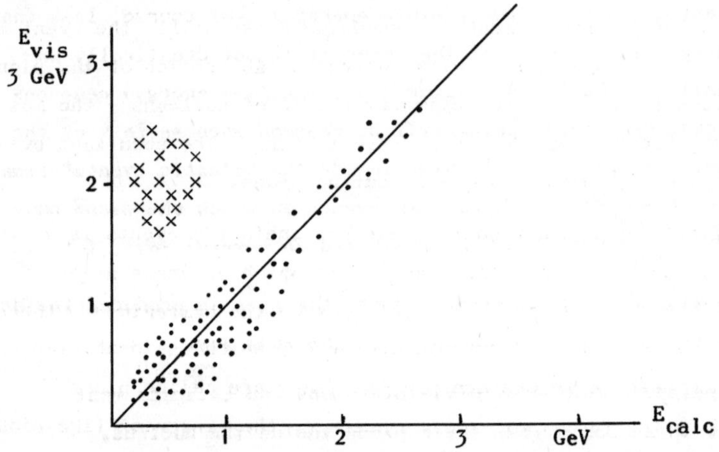

It is quite significant that when from the non-pionic cases the eight or nine events now mentioned are taken away, the total number of the points on the left side of the 45° line is the same (within the expected fluctuations) as the total number on the right. Another test has been done by taking the invariant mass of the particle which has been produced by the collision - call this N^*. For the non-pionic events, i.e. the so-called elastic events, the values of N^* cluster around the nucleon mass.

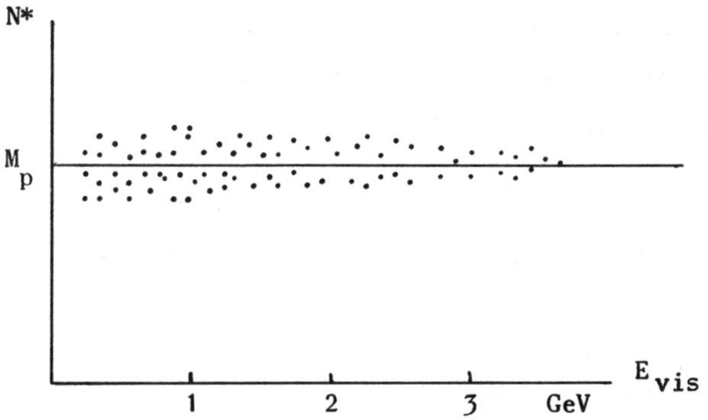

This is quite a crude method and not independent from that previously mentioned but it gives us some information which is quite relevant concerning the idea of using the visible energy as an estimate of E_ν for the elastic events and inelastic events. The visible energy is, of course, less than the neutrino energy, but in most of the cases it is not drastically so because essentially what we do not observe are the (low energy) neutrons of the nuclear cascade. This point will be resumed when we talk of the inelastic events. Inspite of all this, inside the "elastic events" remains an appreciable contamination of inelastic events in which the pions have been reabsorbed. This number may be estimated in several ways, for example:

i) Comparison with photoproduction. Here, the pion is produced inside nuclear matter and may be reabsorbed in the same way.

ii) Take the inelastic events with visible pions and estimate what fraction of these could lose their pions inside the nucleus.

These give plausible estimates, but my personal opinion at the moment is that this contamination of inelastic events could be of the order of 20%.

The elastic events may be used to compare the predicted and experimental cross-sections, and, in particular, to compare the q^2 dependance of the axial vector form factor with the vector form factor.

The idea is that we are sure of the 'conserved vector current' theory, so we may take the vector form factor as known and equal to the form factor from electron scattering.

The cross-section may be written as [6]

$$\frac{d\sigma}{dq^2} = \frac{G^2}{32\pi} \frac{1}{E_\nu^{\ 2}} [A \pm B(s-u) + C(s-u)^2] , \qquad (1)$$

where $q^2 = 2M[E_\nu - E_\mu] = 2MT$ is the four-momentum transfer and where T is the kinetic energy of the nucleon. $s-u$ is the usual scattering variable, which in our case could be written:

$$= 4ME_u - q^2$$
$$= 2M(2E_\nu - T)$$

if the muon mass is neglected, and the nucleon is at rest.

The term linear in $(s-u)$ comes from the interference between the vector and pseudovector amplitudes, and its sign is + for neutrinos and - for antineutrinos. At high energy the interference term becomes small compared with the term in $(s-u)^2$, i.e. the cross-sections for neutrino and antineutrino become equal. For further discussion of the interference, see the notes of Feynman's discussion sessions.

To evaluate q^2, since as we have seen before, the direct measurement of T is not very accurate, we use $T = (E_{vis} - E_\mu)$. This is more or less an integral of the total energy involved in the event, minus the energy of the muon. The value of q^2 can thus be determined experimentally within the limits of the error in the visible energy relative to the neutrino energy.

The bubble chamber group has used the following simple trick to remove the uncertainty due to the poorly known neutrino spectrum and to obtain the q^2 dependence of the pseudovector form factor:

the q^2 spectrum of events is given by

$$\frac{dN}{dq^2} = \int \varphi(E_\nu) \frac{d\sigma(E_\nu)}{dq^2} \cdot dE ,$$

where $\varphi(E_\nu)$ is the neutrino flux as a function of energy. If one divides the events into energy intervals, ΔE, one can write

$$\Delta N(E_{vis}) = \varphi(E_\nu)\ \sigma(E)\ \Delta E$$

and hence

$$\frac{dN}{dq^2} = \sum \frac{\Delta N(E_{vis})}{\sigma(E)} \frac{d\sigma(E)}{dq^2} .$$

Now the cross-section $\sigma(E)$ and $d\sigma(E)/dq^2$ can be expressed in terms of the form factors in the constants A, B, and C of Eq. (1). The vector form factor results of electron scattering are inserted in these, and the pseudovector form factor was left as a free parameter which was fitted using the maximum likelihood method.

The result was that for the vector form factor given by

$$F_V(q^2) = \left[1 + \left(\frac{q}{0.84}\right)^2\right]^{-2}$$

the best fit to the pseudoscalar form factor was

$$F_A(q^2) = \left[1 + \left(\frac{q}{M_A}\right)^2\right]^{-2}$$

with MA = $1.05 \begin{smallmatrix} +\ 0.35 \\ -\ 0.2 \end{smallmatrix}$. The range of q^2 is up to about $1 (\mathrm{GeV}/c)^2$. Above this the statistics are not sufficient.

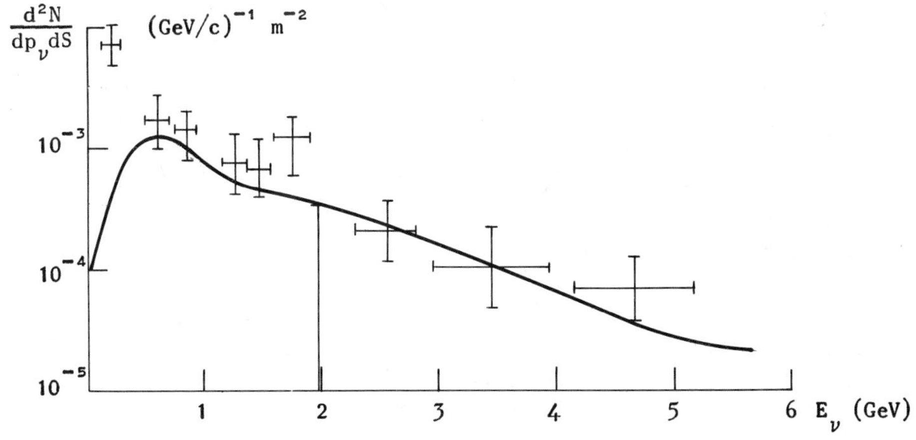

The slide indicates the results obtained by the reciprocal procedure. The form factors were used to calculate the neutrino spectrum which is then compared with the spectrum calculated by Van der Meer. There is only one point which is erratic and we are able to explain it *).

A similar result was obtained from the spark chambers on the basis of the angular distribution. There, the identification of the events on the basis of visible energy is lost. The only thing to do is to select events which show one μ-like track and at most one additional track compatible with a proton. The compatibility was checked by comparing the presumed proton's range with the one inferred from the muon's angle and momentum (if measured). For longer tracks also multiple scattering could be used to discriminate protons against π's from inelastic reactions.

One of the events is sketched below:

The independent value of M_A which was obtained from the spark chamber angular distribution was $M_A \approx 1$ GeV.

In the thin-walled spark chambers, about 6,000 events were observed in the two runs. Besides the elastic events described above, elastic events of the type $\nu_e + n \rightarrow p + e^-$, which is really the inverse of the Reines-Cowan reaction, were observed. In the spark chamber, the sign is not recognized, but the shower is seen very clearly:

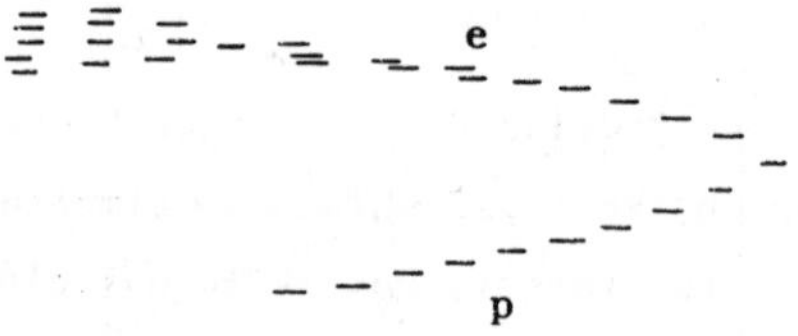

*) It is very likely due to the secondary sources of slow π' and K' which originated in the target, the walls of the horn, in the shielding, etc.

The ν_e are produced by the decay mode $K^+ \rightarrow \pi^0 + e + \nu$. Assuming the Universal Fermi Interaction and its extension up to very high momentum transfers, and using the estimated K^+ spectrum, the expected number of events is of the order of (0.5 - 1)% and the number found was (1.2 ± 0.4)%.

The inelastic events

There are many types of inelastic events, and they may be studied properly only in the bubble chamber. Of 430 events in the fiducial volume, more than half are inelastic. Most of the inelastic events are very complicated so only the inelastic events with one pion have been examined in detail. The (3/2, 3/2) isobar is supposed to play a dominant role in one-pion events. This is shown quite clearly in the mass distribution. To avoid too much distortion of the spectrum by the phase space factor, only events with E_{vis} > 1.5 GeV are considered. The result is shown below and shows at least as good evidence for N^* production as that presented for quite a few resonances.

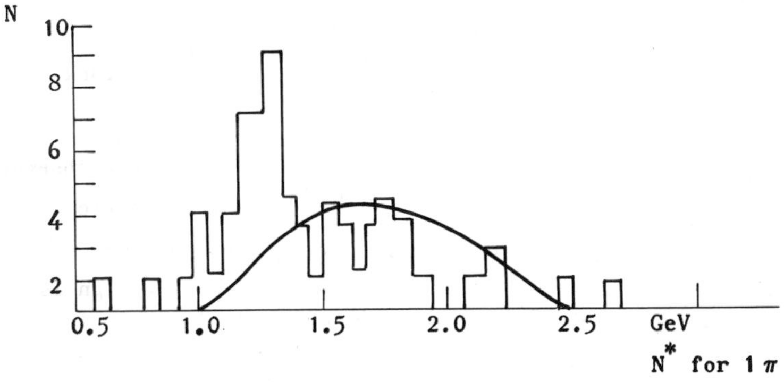

The relative cross-section for this process has recently been calculated by Berman and Veltman. The experimental rate is a factor of two lower than the theory, but it is not clear if this is a fault of the theory or of the experiment. It is possible that pion reabsorption will account for an appreciable part of this difference.

The N^* production may also be examined by taking the π^+/π^0 ratio

$$\nu + N \rightarrow \mu^- + N^*$$
$$N^* \rightarrow N + \pi^+$$
$$N^* \rightarrow p + \pi^0 \, .$$

For this ratio, one expects five and finds three. The number of π^- should be negligible. The numbers found instead were

π^+	π^0	π^-
42	17	14

These numbers would appear to show the large influence of secondary interactions in nuclear matter. We will now talk about the general questions which are answered by the CERN experiment.

1) To what level can we say that $\nu_\mu \neq \nu_e$.

In the spark chamber, by selecting only the through elastic events, one obtains a direct result:

$$\frac{\nu_\mu + N \rightarrow N + e^-}{\nu_\mu + N \rightarrow N + \mu^-} \approx 0.01.$$

A similar result can be obtained from the bubble chamber.

Out of 459 events, five single electrons have been observed. All these electrons are above 400 MeV. Then, as one does not assume any symmetry between ν_e and ν_μ, the conclusion is simply that

$$\frac{\nu_\mu + N \rightarrow N + e^- + \ldots}{\nu_\mu + N \rightarrow N + \mu^- + \ldots} \approx \frac{1}{100} \, .$$

If instead, we assume UFI but $\nu_\mu \neq \nu_e$, and ν_μ always giving rise to a muon and ν_e to an electron, then, according to the estimated fluxes and the rates of the μ events, one expects the following electron events

1.1 elastic   2 are observed

2.2 inelastic   3 are observed;

which are in excellent agreement with what is found (with better statistics) considering the elastic events in the spark chamber. Hence, summing up all the results previously discussed, the simplest conclusion is that UFI holds up to momentum transfer of the order of 1 GeV but ν_μ and ν_e carry an independent quantum number in all their interactions with hadron currents. The limit of any mixing is less that 1%. Both ν_μ and ν_e can be related to lepton numbers, L_μ and L_e, respectively, for each of which an additive conservation law holds*).

2. Neutral currents

The bubble chamber was suitable to give reliable information about the process

$$\nu + p \rightarrow \nu + p$$

which involves the neutral current. We ask what is the ratio of this process to the elastic events $\nu + n \rightarrow p + \mu$. In the bubble chamber one looks for recoil protons. As said before, there is a background of knock-on protons from neutrons which are produced by neutrino reactions

---

*) The limit established for L_μ conservation is probably better than that known at present for L_e. One may remember that a total additive rule could be valid, $\Sigma\,(L_e + L_\mu)$ = const., and that the difference between the μ and e lepton could be related to a new different quantum number, say an intrinsic lepton parity. I am grateful to Dr. Zichichi for a clarifying discussion concerning this point and its relation to muonium-antimuonium transition.

in the shielding. The shielding is so thick that effectively no neutrons produced by the machine filter through. To remove this type of background, it was necessary to impose a lower limit of 250 MeV on the energy of the proton. Above this limit, the ratio found is

$$\frac{\nu + p \to \nu + p}{\nu + n \to \mu^- + p} \leq 3\% \; .$$

Here, the $\nu + p \to \nu + p$ possible cases are due to the few events where E_{vis} $E_{vis} > 250$ MeV and no μ^- candidate was visible. They are quite certainly high-energy neutron stars.

In parallel to the bubble chamber a counter experiment was made by Faissner et al.[7]. The detector was a set of 12 large liquid organic scintillation counters weighing a few tons. The bias of them corresponded to ≈ 15 MeV stopping protons. In addition the time-of-flight of the initiating particles was measured utilizing the sharp bunch structure of the ejected 24.8 GeV/c proton beam.

Taking into account the bound and unbound protons of the detector liquid and assuming an energy independent cross-section σ_0 for the reaction

$$\nu_\mu + p \to \nu_\mu + p$$

it was found

$$\sigma_0 < 2 \times 10^{-37} \; cm^2 \; .$$

This limit does not say too much but it is a few orders of magnitude better than the others established before.

3. W. Intermediate vector bosons

Since the electron and the muon have similar properties except that we find this drastic difference for the associated neutrinos, it would be very nice to imagine something which will re-establish the symmetry.

This could be obtained with the introduction of a vector boson, similar to the photon in electromagnetic interactions, which will make the interaction local, yet mediated.

For example the μ decay will look as follows:

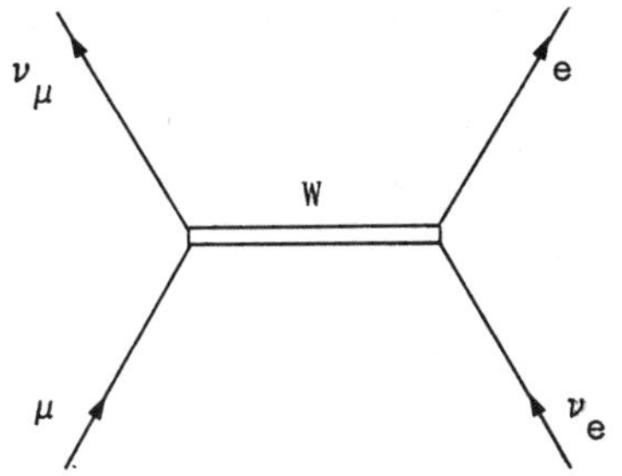

The advantage will be that one has two independent currents $(\mu\ \nu_\mu)$ and $(e\ \nu_e)$ but the two vertices are identical, let us say because the weak charge is the same in both cases.

The W should be rather heavy, at least heavier than the mass of the K, because otherwise the K would decay via semi-weak interactions; for instance according to $K^+ \rightarrow W + \gamma$ with a mean life between 10^{-17} and 10^{-18}, according to the value of its mass[8,9].

Thus we know, from the very short range of the weak interactions, that the W is massive and also that it is more massive than the K. The W should also be charged (see above diagram, or consider the similar diagram for neutron decay).

When one considers strange currents, strange decays, one has to introduce a neutral W and according to the way one uses $\Delta S = \Delta Q$ and $\Delta S = \frac{1}{2}$ rules, the properties of the W are changed. This will, I think, be discussed by Feynman.

If the W is simply the mediator of the μ decay and β decay processes, of course it has to decay leptonically. That is, if it is produced in a real state it has to go into $(e + \nu_e)$ or $(\mu + \nu_\mu)$. Note, this is not the only way in which it can decay because, via semi-weak interactions, it can also decay via pion-kaon modes. If its mass is close to one of the resonances, its decay via these modes can be dominant with respect to the leptonic modes. Thus, in setting a limit to the mass, one has to consider the possibilities of pionic or leptonic decays.

It was pointed out at Kiev by Pontecorvo and Rindin[10] that if the mass M_W of the W had been of the order of the proton mass, with the beams of ν_μ neutrinos available at BNL and at CERN, the production of W would have been possible. A complete theory of this process was given in 1960 by Lee and Yang[8, 9].

The basic diagrams, of which the second is dominant are as follows:

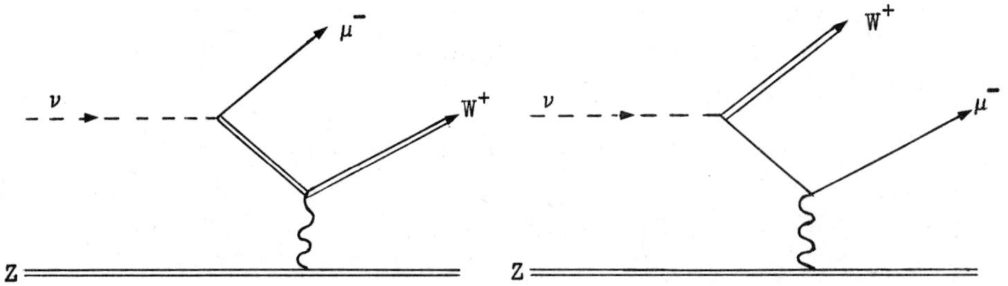

The order of magnitude of the cross-section for this semi-weak process is $\sigma \sim G_\alpha^2 \approx 10^{-5}\ M^{-2}\ \alpha^2 \approx 10^{-37}\ cm^2$.

Note that this is ten times higher than the asymptotic value of the cross-section for $\nu_\mu + n \rightarrow p + \mu$, so if the energy of the neutrinos is sufficiently high relative to the mass of the W, the production of the W should be readily observable.

The created boson would then decay with a mean-life between 10^{-17} and 10^{-18} into either a lepton pair or a system of pions and/or kaons. In the first decay mode, the final state of the over-all reaction

$$\nu_\mu + Z \rightarrow Z(\text{or } Z^*) + \mu^- + W^+ \rightarrow Z(\text{or } Z^*) + \begin{array}{l} \mu^- + e^+ + \nu_e \\ \mu^- + \mu^+ + \nu_\mu \end{array}$$

contains two opposite charged leptons; the positive leptons being an electron or a muon with equal probability.

The nuclear charge may act "coherently" or "incoherently" according to the incident ν_μ energy and the value of M_W. This is determined by the minimum momentum of the exchanged photon, which is:

$$Q_{min} \simeq \frac{M_W^2}{2E} .$$

For $M_W > 1$ GeV, the "incoherent" process dominates up to $E \leq 8$ GeV. In all cases, Q is a small fraction of M_W on the average, and, similarly to a two-body decay, the energy of the μ produced first is peaked around.

$$E_\mu = E_\nu [m_\mu / M_W] .$$

As shown by Bell and Veltman[11] and Überall[12], the W, which has spin 1, is strongly left-hand longitudinally polarized around the direction of the incident μ neutrino. The second positively-charged lepton is then forced to be polarized in the same direction and it is preferably pushed backwards in the c.m. of the W. Consequently, in the lab. system, the largest fraction of the W energy goes to the second neutrino, and the second μ is fairly slow. Actually the ratio of the momenta of the first and second muons is only about 1.5. At the same time, the angular distribution of the positive lepton is broader than that of the first μ .

Extensive calculations have been made on the energy dependence of the production cross-section for several nuclei by Lee et al.[13], Solov'ev et al.[14], Bell and Veltman[15], von Gehlen[16] and, more recently, by Wu et al.[17]. The shape of the curve $\sigma_W(E_\nu)$ sketched below does not change appreciably with M_W, but of course the threshold does. It is around 2 GeV for $M_W \simeq 1$ GeV and $\simeq 5$ GeV for $M_W \simeq 2$ GeV. Then the production rate depends drastically on the ν_μ spectrum. Instead, the kinematical features of the lepton pairs mentioned above slowly vary with M_W.

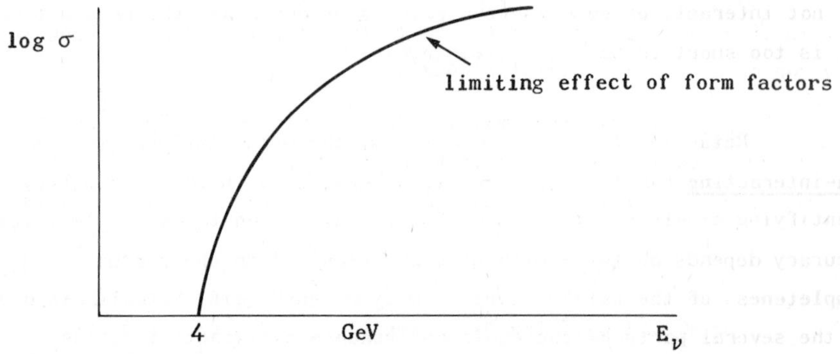

The search for these lepton pairs has been divided between the bubble chamber and the spark chamber. The spark chamber is better for this and, in particular, the 1964 experiment was designed specially to establish the limit of the W mass. However, only the leptonic decays can be seen in the spark chamber. The search for pion and kaon modes is a job for the bubble chamber.

In the bubble chamber a leptonic decay event should look like:

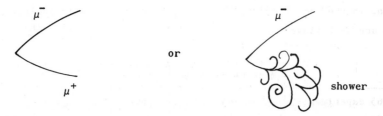

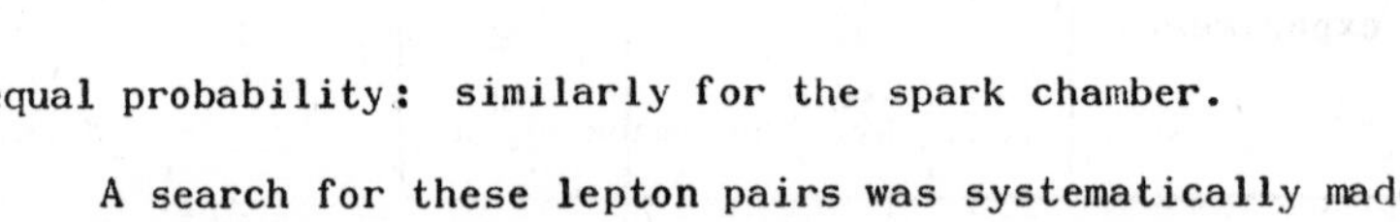

with equal probability: similarly for the spark chamber.

A search for these lepton pairs was systematically made on the spark chamber pictures obtained with the 1963 and 1964 set-up. For the muon pairs, the problems were:

a) to identify a muon track unambiguously; and

b) to distinguish this type of event from, say, a large momentum transfer elastic neutrino process, where the proton comes out and does not interact, or even where a pion is produced and the proton track is too short to be clearly visible.

Returning to the first problem, the distinction between a non-interacting (or μ track) and all others, lies in the possibility of identifying single scatterings or "stars" along the track. Then, its accuracy depends on the length of each track and on the goodness and completeness of the calibrations. Only recently did the calibrations of the several parts of the equipment reach a satisfactory status.

Once the mean-free path, Λ, was established via calibrations for a visible interaction of pions, protons and kaons, a sample of possible (μ,μ) pairs was considered. The sample of about 350 events was made selecting events with two tracks, each long enough to make a search for interactions*) possible. Obviously, the matter was to see if, in this sample, the total number of interactions was less than what should be expected assuming (with all possible configurations) that one of the two tracks was a μ and the other was not a μ but a proton, pion or kaon, in the proportion indicated by the bubble chamber analysis. The results are as follows :

	Minimum expected	Observed
1963 experiment	63	56
1964 experiment	33	36
	96	92

The conclusion is obvious.

*) For further details, see Gaillard's report, Dubna 1964.

A similar and somewhat easier analysis was made for the possible (μ,e) pairs. Out of 1,700 events produced in aluminium, five candidates with a shower corresponding to an energy E > 500 MeV were found. The other track is larger than the 0.8 nuclear geometrical mean-free path Λ and non-interacting.

According to kinematics with this cut-off on E_e, the sample should include 70% of the (μ,e) decay mode.

However, if one takes into account the correction due to π^0's and the fact that the total non-electronic track length obtained, summing up all the events, is only about 2Λ, one has to conclude that the possible (μ,e) have to be reduced from five down to three, at the most.

In the bubble chamber [where (μ,μ) pairs are not identifiable because the total track length of the possible candidates is always too short with respect to the interaction mean-free path], there is one possible case of (μ^-,e^+) pair, but the negative non-interacting mesonic track is only 40 cm long and could also be a π^-.

The previous results concerning the (μ,e) pairs allow a first lower limit for M_W. With the assumption that the branching between leptonic decay and pionic decay of the W is $^5/_{50}$, and with $M_W \lesssim 1.8$ GeV, one has for the (μ,e) pairs:

	Expected	Found
Spark chamber	$\simeq$ 11	$\leq$ 3
Bubble chamber	$\simeq$ 3	$\leq$ 1

The result of the (μ,μ) pair analysis is obviously consistent with the conclusion one may derive from that of the (μ,e) pairs.

However, a more precise and significant limit on the W mass was established by making use of the sign identification of the tracks for the (μ,μ) pairs, that is, by using the information provided by the magnetized-iron regions. This method thus uses events which are produced in the first part of the spark chamber system, pass through the magnetized region and stop before the last range chamber. According to what was said before, the kinematics of the W decay depends very little on M_W. Of the two μ's, the positive track has a higher momentum than the μ^- on the average. As already stated the average momenta are roughly in the ratio

$$\frac{< p^+ >}{< p^- >} \simeq 1.5 \ .$$

Bell and Veltman have calculated in detail the angular and momentum distribution of this decay mode. On the basis of these calculations, one can choose a sample of (μ, μ) candidates and see if they correspond to the range and sign requirements. The sampling was done by looking for events with two μ-like tracks of which one was longer than 7 Λ_0 and the other > 2.4 Λ_0. If one again comes to a decision regarding the branching between leptonic and pionic modes, then the Bell and Veltman calculations allow the determination (according to sign, ranges and geometrical biases) of the expected rates for several mass values with a branching ratio $^{50}/_{50}$. The results are indicated in the following table.

M_W(GeV)	Expected		Observed
	v.d.M.	$q^2 < 0.2$	
1.3	21	51	none
1.5	11	26	
1.8	4	9	

In the second column, the rates are calculated according to the Van der Meer spectrum. In the third column, the rates have been roughly estimated on the basis of the energy distribution of ~ 70 events which did not show any visible track besides the μ and which, accordingly, show a q^2 value roughly smaller than $\simeq 0.2$. For such small values of q^2, one may consider the relative probabilities for all processes (elastic or inelastic) independent of the incident energy and also of the cut made by the Pauli principle (the estimate of which depends on the nuclear models used). Consequently, from the energy distribution of those events, one may derive the shape of the ν_μ spectrum. Of course, in this manner one gets the shape of the spectrum and not the absolute flux, but what is relevant here is the proportion of the μ neutrino above 4 GeV with respect to the total flux*). The shape of the spectrum obtained by this method compared with the calculated Van der Meer spectrum seems to show that, in the energy region above 4.5 GeV, there are about twice the μ neutrinos expected. This result, if confirmed with reasonable statistics, will also imply some modifications concerning the energy dependence of the total inelastic cross-section, the rate of the ν_e elastic events, etc. The above table confirms that among the spark chamber events collected in the 1964 experiment, there is not any evidence of lepton pairs.

The absence of any evidence in favour of the lepton pairs is not adequate to prove that $M_W \geq 1.8$. The mesonic decay mode could well be largely dominant. But in this case, some indication of this should be evident in the bubble chamber events.

The analysis was limited to the few events with $E_{vis} \geq 6$ GeV in total 23. For a $M_W \geq 1.5$ GeV, the calculated production cross-section $\sigma_W(E_\nu)$ becomes larger than $\simeq 10^{-38}$ cm² when $E_\nu \geq 6$ GeV, and it is then expected to compete successfully with all other processes.

Of the 23 events, only 14 have a total mesonic charge of + 1. (These are selected because the W must of course be charged.) The plot of their corresponding effective masses is shown below.

*) As shown by M. Block (letter submitted to Physical Review) and previously by T.D. Lee in his 1961 lectures at CERN (CERN 61 - 30, page 89) the absolute flux could be determined if one would be able to discriminate the <u>true</u> low q^2 elastic events.

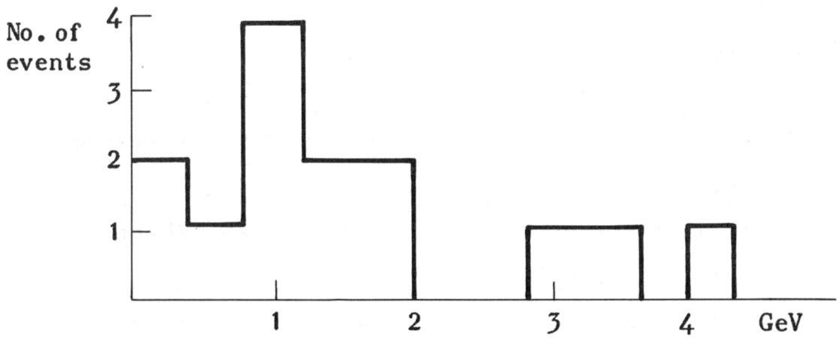

If one makes the extreme assumption that the mesonic decay mode is 100%, a value $M_W \leq 1.3$ is excluded because one should observe 20 - 50 events, the leptonic decay being absent.

For $M_W \simeq 1.5$, one would expect 11 events in the region between 1 and 2 GeV. As can be seen eight events at the most can be grouped around $M_W \simeq 1.5$ when allowance is made for the errors in the mass measurements; but it is likely that they are complicated multipion events corresponding to a high excitation of the struck nucleon. Hence, although it seems quite inprobably, a lower limit such as $M_W \simeq 1.5$ cannot be completely excluded.

One should notice that the above numbers are derived from the calculated Van der Meer ν_μ spectrum. According to what is indicated in the table on page 337 , it may well be that the spectrum contains a higher proportion of neutrinos above 6 GeV than that used for the numbers quoted above.

In conclusion, disappointingly, there is no evidence for any heavy boson with a mass $M_W \leq 1.3$, and it is very likely that the lower limit should be placed around 1.5 - 1.8 *).

*) Note added in proof. According to a re-examination of all data (see final CERN neutrino paper in print), the CERN results are consistent with a value of $M_W \geq 1.8$ GeV.

REFERENCES

1) B. Pontecorvo, Proceedings of the International High-Energy Conference in Kiev 1959, and JETP (USSR) 37, 1751 (1959).

2) M. Schwartz, Phys.Rev.Letters 4, 306 (1960).

3) G. Denby, J.-M. Gaillard, K. Goulianos, L.M. Lederman, N. Mistry, M. Schwartz and J. Steinberger, Phys.Rev.Letters 9, 36 (1962).

4) G. Danby, J.-M. Gaillard, K. Goulianos, L.M. Lederman, T.D. Lee, N. Mistry, M. Schwartz and J. Steinberger, Phys.Rev.Letters 10, 260 (1963).

5) L.I. Lapidus, JETP (USSR) 44, 755 (1963).

6) M. Gourdin and A. Martin, CERN Preprint, 4804 - TH.261 (1962).

7) H. Faissner, J. Kjellman and A. Staude, Nuovo Cimento 32, 782 (1964).

8) T.D. Lee and C.N. Yang, Phys.Rev.Letters 7, 429 (1961).

9) T.D. Lee and C.N. Yang, Phys.Rev.Letters 4, 307 (1960).

10) B. Pontecorvo and S. Rindin, Report of the Kiev Conference on High-Energy Physics, 1959.

11) J.S. Bell and M. Veltman, Phys.Letters 5, 151 (1963).

12) H. Überall, Phys.Rev. 133, 444 (1964).

13) T.D. Lee, P. Markstein and C.N. Yang, Phys.Rev.Letters 7, 429 (1961).

14) V.V. Solov'ev and I.S. Tsukerman, JETP 15, 868 (1962).

15) J.S. Bell and M. Veltman, Phys.Letters 5, 94 (1963).

16) G. von Gehlen, Nuovo Cimento 30, 859 (1963).

17) C.T. Wu, C.N. Yang, K. Fuchel and S. Heller, Phys.Rev.Letters 12, 57 (1964).

FUTURE EXPERIMENTS IN NEUTRINO PHYSICS

M.M. Block,

Northwestern University,
Evanston, Illinois

This lecture will briefly summarize the present planning of the CERN neutrino bubble chamber group, as well as describe possible new spark chamber experiments using deuterium targets.

The CERN group has proposed that the next experiment in the recently enlarged heavy liquid chamber be a survey of antineutrino reactions in freon. A list of possible antineutrino interactions expected is given below:

$$\bar{\nu} + p \to n + \mu^+ \quad \text{"elastic scattering"} \qquad (1)$$
$$\bar{\nu} + n \to \Sigma^- + \mu^+ \qquad (2)$$
$$\bar{\nu} + p \to \Sigma^0 + \mu^+ \qquad (3)$$
$$\bar{\nu} + p \to \Lambda^0 + \mu^+ \qquad (4)$$
$$\bar{\nu} + n \to N^{*-} + \mu^+ \qquad (5)$$
$$\bar{\nu} + p \to N^{*0} + \mu^+ \qquad (6)$$
$$\bar{\nu} + n \to Y_1^{*-} + \mu^+ \qquad (7)$$
$$\bar{\nu} + p \to Y_1^{*0} + \mu^+ \qquad (8)$$
$$\bar{\nu} + p \to Y_0^{*0} + \mu^+ \qquad (9)$$

Reactions (1) to (4) are examples of unitary octet-octet transitions, whereas (3) to (8) are examples of unitary octet-decuplet transitions, and (9) is a unique case, the octet-singlet transition. A detailed analysis of these reactions, using a model called unitary universality, is given in a paper by Block, Phys. Rev. Letters, 1964, and is not repeated here due to lack of time. However, it should be pointed out that independent of any model, in the $\Delta S = +\Delta Q$ reactions (2) and (3), the cross-section for (2) to (3) must be in the ratio 2 : 1, if the $\Delta I = \frac{1}{2}$ law is valid. Further, for the $\Delta S = 0$ transitions (5) and (6), the ratio of the cross-sections for (5) to (6) must be in the ratio 3 : 1 if the $\Delta I = 1$ law is to be valid. In addition, the rates of (5) and (6) at (four-momentum transfer)^2, $q^2 = 0$, determine the coupling constants for the "β-decay" rate of the N*, which is impossible to determine by other means. These experiments open up a wide new field of physics, allowing us, among other properties, to determine the form factors (strong interaction properties) of the Λ, Σ, and the excited Y*, N*, etc. However, the results in a freon chamber will suffer from the same difficulties that Professor Bernardini so clearly pointed out in his lecture, namely, the serious distortion of the basic weak interaction by subsequent strong interactions of the emitted particles in the parent heavy nucleus. Obviously, these results will eventually have to be obtained in large hydrogen and deuterium bubble chambers, an achievement which is perhaps five to ten years away. The next step in the CERN chamber programme is to convert the chamber from freon to deuterated propane, to study both pure deuterium interactions as well as to use the carbon to analyse polarization of the produced nucleons. We will not turn our attention to a detailed study of polarization phenomena, in order to understand the physics that can be studied with this technique. At the conclusion of the lecture, we will outline a proposal for a new experimental programme to study nucleon form factors, using a deuterium target with carbon plate spark chambers to study polarization.

At this point, let us strictly limit our attention to an investigation of the polarization of the recoil proton from the "elastic" scattering of neutrinos or neutrons, i.e. $\nu + n \to p + \mu^-$. Our problem is to study the weak form factors for the transition $n \to p$. The most general form of the strong interaction current (we assume a current-current coupling) for this transition is

$$J_\mu = f_1\gamma_\mu + if_2\sigma_{\mu\nu}q^\nu + f_3q_\mu + if_4\gamma_\mu\gamma_5 + f_5\sigma_{\mu\nu}q^\nu\gamma_5 + if_6q_\mu\gamma_5$$

where q_μ = four-momentum transfer and all f's are functions of q^2 only. This result can be demonstrated by use of Lorentz invariance and application of the Dirac equation (students will find it an instructive exercise to verify this result). The definition of the choice of Dirac matrices and other operators, the choice of the metric, etc., are given in detail in the Appendix. In general, we adopt the notation of Schweber, Bethe and de Hoffman, Mesons and Fields. For our choice of non-hermitian γ matrices, the factors of i have been inserted so that time-reversal invariance requires that all of the f's be relatively real. Further, if we assume that G invariance is valid and that the bare nucleon coupling is $\gamma_\mu - i\gamma_\mu\gamma_5$, so that terms of opposite G parity not present in the bare coupling cannot be present in the clothed current, we normally set $f_3 = g_2 = 0$. Thus, assuming time reversal, G parity, and further, the hypothesis of a conserved vector current, we can rewrite the current as

$$J^\mu = G\left(F_V(q^2)\gamma^\mu + i\,\frac{\mu}{2M}\,F_M(q^2)\sigma^{\mu\nu}q_\nu - i\gamma\,F_A(q^2)\gamma^\mu\gamma_5 + ib\,F_P(q^2)q^\mu\gamma_5\right) ,$$

where we have chosen all F's to be unity at $q^2 = 0$. G is the universal Fermi coupling constant, $\mu = 3.71$, the difference in proton-neutron anomolous magnetic moments, and $\lambda = -G_A/G_V$ (and thus is positive, = 1.15); m is the nucleon mass.

We now ask, what is the polarization cross-section in the laboratory system for transverse polarization of the nucleon. Details of the calculation are supplied in the Appendix.

We find from (2) that no polarization perpendicular to the μ-ν plane (production plane) is possible, as long as all F's are relatively real. Further, the polarization in the production plane, transverse to the proton's direction (see Fig. 1) in the x direction, is approximately

$$\frac{(d\sigma\uparrow - d\sigma\downarrow)}{dq^2}_x = \frac{G^2}{2\pi}\sin\Theta_P\{2\lambda F_A F_V\} ,$$

while the total cross-section is approximately given by

$$\frac{d\sigma\uparrow + d\sigma\downarrow}{dq^2} = \frac{G^2}{2\pi}\left\{F_V^2 + \lambda^2 F_A^2 - \frac{q^2}{4m^2}(\mu F_M)^2\right\} .$$

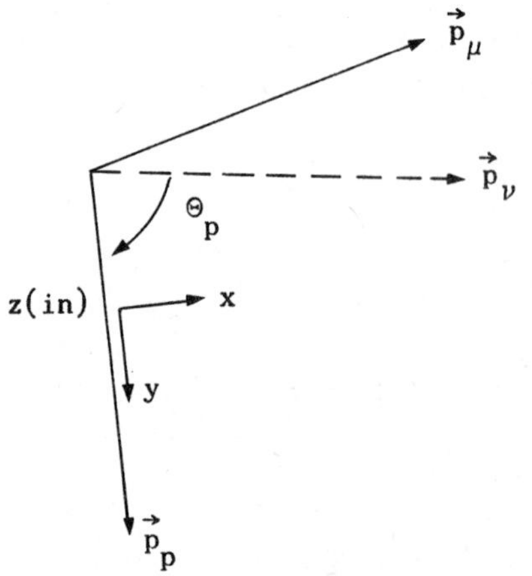

Fig. 1

We note here that our metric requires q^2 to be a negative quantity. If we take $F_V = F_A$, we see that the polarization in the x direction ~ 1 for all q^2 if no weak magnetism is present, whereas if $F_M = F_V = F_A$, the polarization depends strongly on q^2, dropping from 1 at $q^2 = 0$ to $\sim 40\%$ at $|q^2| \sim 0.5$ $(\mathrm{GeV}/c)^2$. Further, we note from (3) that a polarization cross-section measurement directly measures the product of the form factors $F_A F_V$.

Finally, we can integrate (4) directly (it is rigorously correct for $E_\nu >> m$) and obtain the total cross-section if we assume the parameterization $F_V = F_M = (1 - q^2/m_V^2)^{-2}$, $F_A = (1 - q^2/m_A^2)^{-2}$; we obtain

$$\sigma_{total}(E_\nu \to \infty) = \frac{G^2}{2\pi}\left[\frac{m_V^2}{3} + \frac{\lambda^2 m_A^2}{3} + \frac{\mu^2 m_V^2}{24}\left(\frac{m_V^2}{m}\right)\right]$$

$= 0.90 \times 10^{-38}$ cm^2 for $m_V = 0.84$ GeV (from electron-scattering experiments)

and $m_A = 1.1$ GeV (from the CERN bubble chamber neutrino experiment).

We further note that there is a substantial change in this cross-section if no weak magnetism is present, that is

$$\sigma(E_\nu \to \infty) = 0.60 \times 10^{-38}\ \mathrm{cm}^2\ , \text{ if } \mu = 0\ .$$

Thus, the polarization measurements, as well as total cross-section, depend strongly on the assumption of the conserved vector current.

Finally, we ask what will happen if time-reversal invariance (TRI) is not valid. Cabibbo, at Dubna, introduced the specific hypothesis that the currents of the second class, i.e., those terms f_3 and f_5 with opposite G parity behaviour, were relatively complex with respect to the other form factors f_1, f_2, f_4 and f_6 (all assumed to be relatively real). In a certain sense this introduces a maximal violation of TRI. This hypothesis will give us new terms which depend on q^2 and hence will not substantially contribute to the low q^2 phenomena such as neutron β-decay. Specifically, the strong current suggested by Cabibbo is written as

$$J^\mu = G\left(F_V\gamma^\mu + i\,\frac{\mu F_M}{2m}\,\sigma^{\mu\nu}\,q_\nu + i\,aF_S\,q^\mu \right.$$
$$\left. - \,i\,\gamma F_A\,\gamma^\mu\gamma_5 + \frac{icF_E}{m}\,\sigma^{\mu\nu}\,q_\nu\gamma_5 + i\,b\,F_P q^\mu\gamma_5\right)\ .$$

The term $iaF_S q^\mu$ is an induced scalar and will give contributions proportional to the lepton mass, whereas the term $i\,\frac{c}{m}\,F_E\sigma^{\mu\nu}\,q_\nu\gamma_5$ is a term corresponding to "weak electricity". Cabibbo further assumes that all coefficients F_E, F_S are comparable to the others. As shown in the Appendix, the differential cross-section at high energies is modified to be

$$\frac{d\sigma\uparrow + d\sigma\downarrow}{dq^2} = \frac{G^2}{2\pi}\left\{F_V^2 + \lambda^2\,F_A^2 - \frac{q^2}{4m^2}\left((\mu F_M)^2 + 4(cF_E)^2\right)\right\}\ ,$$

whereas

$$\left(\frac{d\sigma\uparrow - d\sigma\downarrow}{dq^2}\right)_x$$

is left unchanged. On the other hand, we have a new contribution i.e., a non-zero polarization cross-section perpendicular to the production plane. We obtain, for large E_ν,

$$\left(\frac{d\sigma\uparrow - d\sigma\downarrow}{dq^2}\right)_z \approx \frac{G^2}{2\pi} \sin \Theta_p |q| \; \{2(\lambda F_A)(cF_E)\} \; .$$

Thus, if we assume that $F_A = F_E = F_M = F_V$, and that $c \sim 1$, we get a large polarization in the z direction, $\sim 30\%$ for $0.25 \lesssim |q^2| \lesssim 1$.

A measurement of this polarization affords us a direct test of the Cabibbo hypothesis. It should perhaps be emphasized at this point that a polarization analysis of the recoil muon will also serve to test for polarization perpendicular to the production place and, hence, will also test for TRI. These polarizations perpendicular to the production plane depend only on having non-TRI interactions, as well as the assumption that weak interactions are calculated in the lowest order.

One can generalize the above results on TRI in the inelastic reaction channels; for example,

$$\nu + p \to p + \pi^+ + \mu^- \; .$$

The recoil proton also cannot be polarized perpendicular to the μ-ν plane unless TRI is invalid. If we produce a definite state, such as the reaction

$$\nu + p \to N^{*++} + \mu^- \; ,$$

the decay of the N* will analyse the polarization produced. We can prove that the N* should not be polarized in the z direction if TRI is valid. In particular, it can be shown that if Θ and φ are the polar and azimuthal decay angles of the N* decay products (in the N* cms), relative to the N* direction, and if $\varphi = 0$ corresponds to the production plane and decay plane being coincident, then the decay distribution can contain terms like $\sin \Theta \cos \Theta \sin \varphi$

if TRI is valid, but no terms in sin Θ cos Θ cos φ. However, if TRI breaks down, we will expect correlations of the form sin Θ cos Θ cos φ. Again, the reason for no polarization in the z direction for TRI is the assumption of first order weak interactions.

Finally, we now propose an experiment to measure the nucleon polarization in elastic scattering. We utilize a large deuterium target, surrounded on the sides by carbon plate spark chambers to both detect the proton and analyse its polarization from nuclear p-C scattering. Downstream, a large array of iron plates in a spark chamber assembly detect the stopping muon. Deuterium is required to avoid subsequent strong interactions of the recoil proton in the parent nucleus. We can substantially achieve with deuterium the target condition of free neutrons. The range and angle of the proton are measured, as well as the range and angle of the muon. This allows us to separate well elastic from inelastic scattering. If we construct a 5-ton deuterium target, at the current intensity rates of the CERN PS, we expect ~ 10,000 elastic scattering events in 100 days running (assumed intensity of 10^{12} per pulse). If we estimate that ~ 1 in 20 gives a usable scattering, with an average polarization analysis strength of 60%, we could detect a z polarization of 30% with an accuracy of ~ ± 8%, and thus readily establish the non-invariance under time reversal, as well as measure the form factors and check on the conserved vector current hypothesis. Experiments of this magnitude of undertaking are necessary to exploit the rich new field of physics that has been opened up with the pioneering Brookhaven and CERN neutrino runs. If the CERN accelerator is operated at lower energy, i.e. ~ 12 - 15 GeV, and the repetition rate is increased and the necessary shielding wall shortened, it may be possible to increase the neutrino flux by a factor of 5 - 10 , making the experimental apparatus more compact and, consequently, less expensive in both construction time and money.

APPENDIX

We derive here the detailed results using well-known trace techniques The more advanced student will be able to skip this section. An attempt has been made here to summarize these techniques so that the average experimental student, with a bit of practice, can perform this and similar types of calculations himself. Since weak interactions furnish us with one of the few calculations that can be done properly in theoretical physics today, no execuses are made for the tedious nature of the calculations.

We use the notation of Schweber, Bethe and de Hoffman, Mesons and Fields, throughout. The γ matrices employed are non-hermitian, and our choice of metric is such that the four vector squared $a^2 = a_0^2 - a_1^2 - a_2^2 - a_3^2$. Thus, in our notation $q \equiv (p - n)$, which stands for the four-momentum transfer, has its square modulus negative. We use covariant and contravariant four-vectors and γ matrices, related by the expression $a_\mu = g_{\mu\nu} a^\nu$, with

$$g_{\mu\nu} = \begin{pmatrix} 1 & 0 & 0 & 0 \\ 0 & -1 & 0 & 0 \\ 0 & 0 & -1 & 0 \\ 0 & 0 & 0 & -1 \end{pmatrix}, \text{ etc.}$$

We assume current-current coupling, and for the most complicated case (including violations of time reversal in the induced weak electricity and scalar terms as suggested by Cabibbo), the strongly interacting current is given by

$$J^\mu = G\left(F_V\gamma^\mu + \frac{i\mu F_M}{2m}\sigma^{\mu\nu}q_\nu + iaF_S q^\mu - i\lambda F_A\gamma^\mu\gamma_5 + \frac{ic}{m}F_E\sigma^{\mu\nu}q_\nu\gamma_5 + ibF_P q^\mu\gamma_5\right). \tag{A.1}$$

Here, we have chosen all F's and all coefficients a, b, c, μ etc., as real. We define $\sigma^{\mu\nu} = \frac{i}{2}(\gamma^\mu\gamma^\nu - \gamma^\nu\gamma^\mu)$. We can see, since $\gamma_5 = \gamma^0\gamma^1\gamma^2\gamma^3$ has the property of changing sign under time reversal, that the weak electricity terms $(icF_E/m)\sigma^{\mu\nu}q_\nu\gamma_5$ has the opposite behaviour under time reversal from the weak magnetism term $(i\mu F_M/2m)\sigma^{\mu\nu}q_\nu$, and the same is true of the induced scalar term relative to the induced pseudoscalar. Thus, these terms are chosen to have a type of maximal violation of time-reversal invariance. Since we must eventually take traces using the above expression, and since it involves $\sigma^{\mu\nu}$, a product of 2γ matrices, it turns out to be much more convenient for computation to use the Dirac equation to rewrite these terms.

We note that the matrix element of $i\sigma^{\mu\nu}q_\nu$ can be rewritten as

$$\langle \bar{p}| \left[\left(i\sigma^{\mu\nu}q_\nu\right)\right] |n\rangle = -\tfrac{1}{2} \langle \bar{p}| \left[\left(\gamma^\mu\gamma^\nu - \gamma^\nu\gamma^\mu\right)\left(p_\nu - n_\nu\right)\right] |n\rangle$$

$$= -\tfrac{1}{2} \langle \bar{p}| \left[\left(-\gamma^\nu\gamma^\mu + 2g^{\mu\nu} - \gamma^\nu\gamma^\mu\right) p^\nu - \left(\gamma^\mu\gamma^\nu + \gamma^\mu\gamma^\nu - 2g^{\mu\nu}\right) n_\nu\right] |n\rangle$$

$$= -\tfrac{1}{2} \langle \bar{p}| \left[-2\not{p}\gamma^\mu + 2p^\mu - 2\gamma^\mu\not{n} + 2n^\mu\right] |n\rangle$$

$$= \langle \bar{p}| \left[\left(m_P + m_N\right)\gamma^\mu - \left(p+n\right)^\mu\right] |n\rangle .$$

Thus,

$$i\sigma^{\mu\nu}q_\nu = \left(m_P + m_N\right)\gamma^\mu - \left(p+n\right)^\mu . \qquad \text{(A.2)}$$

In the above, we used the anticommutation relations $\gamma^\mu\gamma^\nu + \gamma^\nu\gamma^\mu = 2g^{\mu\nu}$, the metric statement that $p^\mu = g^{\mu\nu}p_\nu$, and the Feynman notation $\not{p} = \gamma_\nu p^\nu = \gamma^\nu p_\nu = \gamma^0 p^0 - \vec{\gamma} \times \vec{p}$, as well as the Dirac equation

$$\langle \bar{p}| \not{p} = m_P \langle \bar{p}| \text{ and } \not{n}|n\rangle = m_N |n\rangle .$$

In a similar fashion,

$$i\sigma^{\mu\nu}q_\nu\gamma_5 = \left(m_P - m_N\right)\gamma^\mu\gamma_5 - \left(p+n\right)^\mu\gamma_5 \ . \tag{A.3}$$

All of this algebra has been done to enable one to rewrite Eq. (1) in terms of single γ matrices, thus facilitating greatly further calculations. Therefore, if we assume $m_P = m_N = m$, we are now capable of rewriting J_μ as

$$\begin{aligned} J^\mu = G\Big\{ & \left(F_V + \mu F_M\right)\gamma^\mu - \frac{\mu F_M}{2m}\left(p+n\right)^\mu + i\,aF_S\left(p-n\right)^\mu \\ & - i\lambda F_A\gamma^\mu\gamma_5 - \frac{cF_E}{m}\left(p+n\right)^\mu\gamma_5 + i\,b\,F_P\left(p-n\right)^\mu\gamma_5\Big\} \ . \end{aligned} \tag{A.4}$$

We assume that the lepton current is given by

$$j_\mu = \frac{\gamma_\mu(1 - i\gamma_5)}{\sqrt{2}} \tag{A.5}$$

and thus, the matrix element we must compute, M, is given by

$$M = \langle\bar{p}\,|J^\mu|\,n\rangle\langle\bar{\mu}\,|\,j_\mu|\,\nu\rangle \ . \tag{A.6}$$

If we ask for the square of this matrix element, where the proton polarization is given in the "up" direction, we find, following Bethe and de Hoffman, that

$$|M(\uparrow)|^2 = \tfrac{1}{2}\left(\mathrm{Tr}\ J^\rho P_P \Lambda_P J^{\lambda\dagger} P_N\right)\times\left(\mathrm{Tr}\ j^\rho P_\mu j^{\lambda\dagger} P_\nu\right) . \tag{A.7}$$

Here, we have introduced the covariant projection operators for positive energy spin state P_P, P_N, P_μ, P_ν for proton, neutron, muon and neutrino, respectively. They are given by

$$P_a = \frac{\not{p}_a + m_a}{2m_a} \ ,$$

and they have the property that when acting on a positive energy state, they have the eigenvalue + 1 and, when acting on a negative energy state, they have the eigenvalue zero. Here, we pretend that the neutrino has a non-vanishing mass, which we can later (at the end of calculation) set equal to zero. Projection operators also have the property that $P_a^2 = P_a$, as can be explicitly demonstrated. The covariant spin "up" projection operator for the proton is $\Lambda_p = (1 - i \not{W} \gamma_5)/2$, where the direction "up" is the three-vector $\vec{W}$. For convenience of normalization we choose $W^2 = -1$. Since Λ_p must commute with P_p, we see that $(-i \not{W} \gamma_5)\not{p} = \not{p}(-i \not{W} \gamma_5)$. Thus, $\not{W}\gamma_5 p - \not{p}\not{W}\gamma_5 = 0$ or $\not{W}\not{p} + \not{p}\not{W} = 0$. This condition is satisfied if $(W \cdot p) = 0$, since, in general, $\not{a}\not{b} + \not{b}\not{a} = 2(a \cdot b)$. We can immediately verify that in the rest frame of the proton this covariant operator Λ_p reduces to the familiar $(1+ \sigma_z)/2$ non-relativistic operator. In the rest frame, since $(W \cdot p) = 0$ and $\vec{p} = 0$, we get $W_0 = 0$. Hence $W^2 = W_0^2 - |\vec{W}|^2 = -1 = -\vec{W}^2$. Let us thus pick $\vec{W} = (0,0,1)$, i.e., $\vec{W}$ is a unit vector in the z direction. Then $\not{W} = \gamma^0 W^0 - \vec{\gamma} \times \vec{W} = -\gamma_3$ and $(1 - i\not{W}\gamma_5)/2 = (1 + i\gamma_3\gamma_5)/2 = (1 + \sigma_z)/2$. Clearly, for the general case, $(1 - i\not{W}\gamma_5)/2$ is the covariant generalization of our familiar non-relativistic result. We are now in the position of being ready to evaluate (7), using (5) and (4). Let us define

$$N^{\rho\lambda} = \tfrac{1}{2} \operatorname{Tr} J^{\rho} P_p \Lambda_p J^{\lambda \dagger} P_N \tag{A.8}$$

and

$$L_{\rho\lambda} = \operatorname{Tr} j_{\rho} P_{\mu} j_{\lambda}^{\dagger} P_{\nu} \tag{A.9}$$

Written out in the long form

$$N^{\rho\lambda} = \tfrac{1}{2}\, G^2 \;\mathrm{Tr} \left\{ \left(F_V + \mu F_M\right)\gamma^\rho - \frac{\mu F_M}{2m}\left(p+n\right)^\rho + iaF_S\left(p-n\right)^\rho \right.$$

$$\left. - i\gamma F_A \gamma^\rho \gamma_5 - \frac{cF_E}{m}\left(p+n\right)^\rho \gamma_5 + ibF_P\left(p-n\right)^\rho \gamma_5 \right\} \left[\frac{(1 - i \not{W} \gamma_5)}{2} \frac{(\not{p} + m)}{2m} \right] \times$$

$$\times \left\{ \left(F_\nu + \mu F_M\right)\gamma^\lambda - \frac{\mu F_M}{2m}\left(p+n\right)^\lambda - iaF_S\left(p-n\right)^\lambda - i\lambda F_A \gamma^\lambda \gamma_5 - \frac{cF_E}{m}\left(p+n\right)^\lambda \gamma_5 \right.$$

$$\left. - ib\, F_P\left(p-n\right)^\lambda \gamma_5 \right\} \left(\frac{\not{n} + m}{2m} \right)$$

and

$$L_{\rho\lambda} = \tfrac{1}{2}\; \mathrm{Tr}\; \gamma_\rho \left(1 - i\gamma_5\right)\left(\frac{\not{\mu} + m_\mu}{2m_\mu}\right)\gamma_\lambda \left(1 - i\gamma_5\right)\left(\frac{\not{\nu}}{2m_\nu}\right)$$

where we neglect m_ν (which later goes to zero) in comparison with $\not{\nu}$.

Using the fact that γ_5 anticommutes with all γ's, and that $\gamma_5^2 = -1$

$$L_{\rho\lambda} = \tfrac{1}{8\, m_\mu m_\nu}\; \mathrm{Tr}\gamma_\rho \left(1 - i\gamma_5\right)^2 \left(\not{\mu} + m_\mu\right) \gamma_\lambda (\not{\nu})$$

$$= \tfrac{1}{4\, m_\mu m_\nu}\; \mathrm{Tr}\gamma_\rho \left(1 - i\gamma_5\right)\left(\not{\mu} + m_\mu\right)\gamma_\lambda (\not{\nu}) = \tfrac{1}{4\, m_\mu m_\nu} \left\{ \mathrm{Tr}\gamma_\rho \not{\mu} \gamma_\lambda \not{\nu} + i\, \mathrm{Tr}\, \gamma_5 \gamma_\rho \not{\mu} \gamma_\lambda \not{\nu} \right\} .$$

Here, we use the following rules about traces:

a) A trace of an <u>odd</u> number of γ matrices is zero

b) If γ_5 is present, in order to have a non-vanishing trace, it must be multiplied by <u>at least</u> four other γ matrices.

We summarize here some useful trace information

$$\mathrm{Tr}\, \gamma^\rho \gamma^\lambda = 4g^{\rho\lambda}, \quad \mathrm{Tr}\, \not{a}\not{b} = 4(a \cdot b)$$

Proof: $\mathrm{Tr}\, \not{a}\not{b} = \mathrm{Tr}\, a_\rho \gamma^\rho b_\lambda \gamma^\lambda = a_\rho b_\lambda \mathrm{Tr}\, \gamma^\rho \gamma^\lambda$

$= 4 a_\rho b_\lambda g^{\rho\lambda}$

$= 4 a_\lambda b^\lambda (= 4 a^\rho b_\rho) = 4(a \cdot b)$

$$\mathrm{Tr}\left(\gamma^\rho \gamma^\alpha \gamma^\lambda \gamma^\beta\right) = 4\left(g^{\rho\alpha}\, g^{\lambda\beta} + g^{\rho\beta}\, g^{\lambda\alpha} - g^{\alpha\beta}\, g^{\rho\lambda}\right)$$

$$\mathrm{Tr}\, \gamma^\rho \not{a} \gamma^\lambda \not{b} = 4\left(a^\rho b^\lambda + a^\lambda b^\rho - (a \cdot b)\, g^{\rho\lambda}\right)$$

$$\mathrm{Tr}\, \gamma_5 \gamma^\rho \gamma^\alpha \gamma^\lambda \gamma^\beta = -4\epsilon^{\rho\alpha\gamma\beta},$$

but

$$\mathrm{Tr}\, \gamma_5 \gamma_\rho \gamma_\alpha \gamma_\lambda \gamma_\beta = +4\epsilon_{\rho\alpha\lambda\beta}.$$

where $\epsilon_{\rho\alpha\lambda\beta} = \epsilon^{\rho\alpha\lambda\beta} = 0$ if any 2 indices are the same,

$= +1$ if they are even permutation of 0, 1, 2, 3,

$= -1$ if odd permutation of 0, 1, 2, 3

We will work out two examples

1) The lepton trace

$$L_{\rho\lambda} = \tfrac{1}{2}\ \mathrm{Tr}\ \gamma_\rho(1 - i\gamma_5)\left(\frac{\not\mu + m_\mu}{2m_\mu}\right)\gamma_\lambda(1 - i\gamma_5)\ \frac{\not\nu}{2m_\nu}$$

$$= \frac{1}{8m_\mu m_\nu}\ \mathrm{Tr}\ \gamma_\rho(1 - i\gamma_5)^2(\not\mu)\gamma_\lambda\not\nu$$

[using the fact that γ_5 anti-commutes with all other γ's, and that an <u>even</u> number of γ matrices are needed for non-vanishing terms.]

[$(1 - i\gamma_5)^2 = 1 - 2i\gamma_5 - \gamma_5^2 = 2(1 - i\gamma_5)$ since $\gamma_5^2 = -1$].

$$= \frac{1}{4m_\mu m_\nu}\ \mathrm{Tr}\ \gamma_\rho(1 - i\gamma_5)\not\mu\gamma_\lambda\not\nu$$

[since we need an <u>even</u> number of γ matrices for non-vanishing trace].

$$= \frac{1}{m_\mu m_\nu}\left[\mu_\rho\nu_\lambda + \nu_\rho\mu_\lambda - g_{\rho\lambda}(\mu\cdot\nu) + i\epsilon_{\rho\alpha\lambda\beta}\,\mu^\alpha\nu^\beta\right]$$

2) Assume $J_\mu = G\left(F_V\gamma^\mu - i\lambda F_A\gamma^\mu\gamma_5\right)$.

Then

$$N^{\rho\lambda} = \frac{G^2}{2}\ \mathrm{Tr}\left[\left(F_V\gamma^\rho - i\lambda F_A\gamma^\rho\gamma_5\right)\frac{(1 - i\not W\gamma_5)}{2}\ \frac{(\not p + m)}{2m}\right]\left[F_V\gamma^\lambda - i\lambda F_A\gamma^\lambda\gamma_5\right]\frac{\not n + m}{2m}$$

$$= \frac{G^2}{16m^2}\ \mathrm{Tr}\ (A + B + C + D)$$

$$\mathrm{Tr}\ A = \mathrm{Tr}\ F_V^2\,\gamma^\rho(1 - i\not W\gamma_5)(\not p + m)\gamma^\lambda(\not n + m)$$

$$= F_V^2\left\{\mathrm{Tr}[\gamma^\rho\not p\gamma^\lambda\not n] + m^2\,\mathrm{Tr}\gamma^\rho\gamma^\lambda + im\,\mathrm{Tr}\,\gamma_5\gamma^\rho\not W\gamma^\lambda\not p - im\,\mathrm{Tr}\,\gamma_5\gamma^\rho\not W\gamma^\lambda\not n\right]$$

$$= 4F_V^2\left\{p^\rho n^\lambda + n^\rho p^\lambda - (p\cdot n)\,g^{\rho\lambda} + m^2 g^{\rho\lambda} - im\epsilon^{\rho\alpha\lambda\beta}W_\alpha p_\beta + im\epsilon^{\rho\alpha\lambda\beta}W_\alpha n_\beta\right\}$$

$$\mathrm{Tr}\ B = \mathrm{Tr}\left(-\lambda^2 F_A^2\right)\gamma^\rho\gamma_5(1 - i\not{W}\gamma_5)(\not{p} + m)\gamma^\lambda \times \gamma_5(\not{n} + m)$$

$$= -\left(\lambda^2 F_A^2\right)\left\{\mathrm{Tr}\ \gamma^\rho\gamma_5^2(\not{p} - m)\gamma^\lambda(\not{n} + m) + \mathrm{Tr}\ \gamma^\rho\gamma_5(-i\not{W})\gamma_5^2(\not{p} - m)\gamma^\lambda(\not{n} + m)\right\}$$

$$= \lambda^2 F_A^2\left\{\mathrm{Tr}\ \gamma^\rho\not{p}\gamma^\lambda\not{n} - m^2\ \mathrm{Tr}\ \gamma^\rho\gamma^\lambda - im\,\mathrm{Tr}\,\gamma_5\gamma^\rho\not{W}\gamma^\lambda\not{p} + im\,\mathrm{Tr}\,\gamma^5\gamma^\rho\not{W}\gamma^\lambda\not{n}\right\}$$

$$= 4\lambda^2 F_A^2\left\{p^\rho n^\lambda + n^\rho p^\lambda - (p\cdot n)g^{\rho\lambda} - m^2 g^{\rho\lambda} + im\epsilon^{\rho\alpha\lambda\beta}W_\alpha p_\beta - im\epsilon^{\rho\alpha\lambda\beta}W_\alpha n_\beta\right\}.$$

$$\mathrm{Tr}\ C = \mathrm{Tr}\ F_V\gamma^\rho(1 - i\not{W}\gamma_5)(\not{p} + m)(-i\lambda F_A\gamma^\lambda\gamma_5)(\not{n} + m)$$

$$= -\,i\lambda F_V F_A\left\{\mathrm{Tr}\ \gamma^\rho\not{p}\gamma^\lambda\gamma_5\not{n} - i\,\mathrm{Tr}\,\gamma^\rho\not{W}\gamma_5^2(\not{p} - m)\gamma^\lambda(\not{n} + m)\right\}$$

$$= -\,i\lambda F_V F_A\left\{-\mathrm{Tr}\ \gamma_5\gamma^\rho\not{p}\gamma^\lambda\not{n} + im\,\mathrm{Tr}\,\gamma^\rho\not{W}\not{p}\gamma^\lambda - im\,\mathrm{Tr}\,\gamma^\rho\not{W}\gamma^\lambda\not{n}\right\}$$

$$= 4\lambda F_V F_A\left\{-i\epsilon^{\rho\alpha\lambda\beta}p_\alpha n_\beta + m\left(W^\rho p^\lambda - p^\rho W^\lambda + (W\cdot p)g^{\rho\lambda}\right)\right\}$$

$$-\ m\left[W^\rho n^\lambda + n^\rho W^\lambda - (W\cdot n)g^{\rho\lambda}\right].$$

Similarly

$$\mathrm{Tr}\ D = 4F_V F_A\left\{-i\epsilon^{\rho\alpha\lambda\beta}p_\alpha n_\beta - m\left(W^\rho p^\lambda - p^\rho W^\lambda\right) - m\left[W^\rho n^\lambda + n^\rho W^\lambda - (W\cdot n)g^{\rho\lambda}\right]\right\}.$$

Thus,

$$N^{\rho\lambda} = \frac{G^2}{4m^2}\Bigg(F_V^2\ \{p^\rho n^\lambda + n^\rho p^\lambda - (p\cdot n)g^{\rho\lambda} + m^2 g^{\rho\lambda}\}$$

$$+\ \lambda^2 F_A^2\ \{p^\rho n^\lambda + n^\rho p^\lambda - (p\cdot n)g^{\rho\lambda} - m^2 g^{\rho\lambda}\}$$

$$-\ 2\lambda F_A F_V\left\{i\epsilon^{\rho\alpha\lambda\beta}p_\alpha n_\beta\right\} + F_V^2\left\{-im\epsilon^{\rho\alpha\lambda\beta}W_\alpha p_\beta + im\epsilon^{\rho\alpha\lambda\beta}W_\alpha n_\beta\right\}$$

$$+\ \lambda^2 F_A^2\left\{+\ im\epsilon^{\rho\alpha\lambda\beta}W_\alpha p_\beta - im\epsilon^{\rho\alpha\lambda\beta}W_\alpha m_\beta\right\}$$

$$-\ 2\lambda F_A F_V\left\{W^\rho n^\lambda + n^\rho W^\lambda - (W\cdot n)g^{\rho\lambda}\right\}\Bigg)$$

We must now contract $N^{\rho\lambda}L_{\rho\lambda}$, and for this we use rules

$$p^{\rho}n^{\lambda}\mu_{\rho}\nu_{\lambda} = (p\cdot\mu)(n\cdot\nu)$$

$$g_{\rho\lambda}g^{\rho\lambda} = 4$$

$$\left(\epsilon^{\rho\alpha\lambda\beta}p_{\alpha}n_{\beta}\right)\epsilon_{\rho\alpha'\lambda\beta'}\mu^{\alpha'}\nu^{\beta'} =$$

$$2\left[(p\cdot\mu)(n\cdot\nu)-(p\cdot\nu)(n\cdot\mu)\right]$$

We obtain

$$N^{\rho\lambda}L_{\rho\lambda} = \frac{G^2}{2m^2 m_{\mu} m_{\nu}}\{F_V^2\,[(p\cdot\mu)(n\cdot\nu)+(p\cdot\nu)(n\cdot\mu)-m^2(\mu\cdot\nu)]$$

$$+\lambda^2F_A^2\,[(p\cdot\mu)(n\cdot\nu)+(p\cdot\nu)(n\cdot\mu)+m^2(\mu\cdot\nu)]$$

$$+2\lambda F_AF_{\nu}\,[(p\cdot\mu)(n\cdot\nu)-(p\cdot\nu)(n\cdot\mu)]$$

$$+F_V^2\,m[(\mu\cdot W)(\nu\cdot p)-(\mu\cdot p)(\nu\cdot W)-(\mu\cdot W)(\nu\cdot N)+(\mu\cdot N)(\nu\cdot W)]$$

$$+F_A^2\,m[-(\mu\cdot W)(\nu\cdot p)+(\mu\cdot p)(\nu\cdot W)-(\mu\cdot W)(\nu\cdot N)+(\mu\cdot N)(\nu\cdot W)]$$

$$-2\lambda F_AF_Vm[(\mu\cdot W)(\nu\cdot N)+(\nu\cdot W)(\mu\cdot N)\}]\ .$$

With our choice of normalization of $u^{\dagger}u = m/E$, we have $\bar{u}u = 1$, and our cross-section is

$$d\sigma \,\alpha\, |M|^2\, d\rho_F\ ,$$

where

$$d\rho_F = \frac{m}{(2\pi)^2}\,\frac{d\vec{p}}{E}\ .$$

Hence, when we compute a transition probability, all of the factors $1/m^2 m_\mu m_\nu$ will cancel out.

We now attempt to evaluate $M^2\uparrow$ by introducing the kinematic variables q^2, E^{*2} and t^2 defined below, and applying energy and momentum conservation, i.e. $\nu + n \rightarrow p + \mu$.

a) $q = p - n = \nu - \mu$,

b) $E^* = \nu + n = p + \mu$

c) $t = \nu - p = \mu - n$

It can be readily domonstrated that $q^2 + E^{*2} + t^2 = m_\mu^2 + m_P^2 + m_N^2$. In the following we shall ignore the muon mass and set $m_N = m_P = m$. The student can readily generalize the results for finite muon mass.

We recognize q^2 as the four-momentum transfer, and E^{*2} as the square of the energy in the c.m.s. of the collision. If the struck neutron is at rest and E_ν denotes the laboratory neutrino energy, we find that $E^{*2} = 2mE_\nu + m^2$. The necessary kinematics are found to be

$$(N \cdot \nu) = (\mu \cdot P) = mE_\nu$$

$$(p \cdot \nu) = (\mu \cdot N) = mE_\nu + q^2/2$$

$$(\nu \cdot \mu) = - q^2/2 \quad \text{and}$$

$$(p \cdot N) = m^2 - q^2/2 \ .$$

We choose to evaluate in the lab. system, where we pick $\vec{W} \perp \vec{p}$. Thus, $W_0 = 0$ and $(W \cdot n) = 0$ since $\vec{n} = 0$ and, also $(W \cdot \mu) = (W \cdot \nu) = - \sin \Theta_P E_V$.

We therefore calculate

$$\frac{|M\uparrow|^2}{G^2} = F_V^2\,(mE_\nu)^2 \left\{1 + \frac{q^2}{2mE_\nu}\left(1+\frac{m}{2E_\nu}\right) + \frac{q^4}{8m^2 E_\nu^2} + \frac{q^4}{8m^2 E_\nu^2} - \sin\Theta_p\left(\frac{q^2}{2mE_\nu}\right)\right\}$$

$$+ \lambda^2 F_A^2\,(mE_\nu)^2 \left\{1 + \frac{q^2}{2mE_\nu}\left(1-\frac{m}{2E_\nu}\right) + \frac{q^4}{8m^2 E_\nu^2}\right\}$$

$$- 2\lambda F_A F_V\,(mE_\nu)^2 \left\{\frac{q^2}{2mE_\nu} + \frac{q^2}{8m^2 E_\nu^2} - \sin\Theta_p\left(1+\frac{q^2}{4mE_\nu}\right)\right\} .$$

The general matrix element M can now be computed in a similar fashion. The differential cross-section per unit q^2 can be shown to be

$$\frac{d\sigma}{dq^2} = \frac{1}{2\pi}\,\frac{|M|^2}{2m^2 E_\nu^2} .$$

Since most of the literature uses a different metric, so that q^2_{lit} is positive, whereas our q^2 is negative, it is convenient at this point to introduce $Q^2 = -q^2$, so that formulae in Q^2 can be directly compared with the literature. We find, in this manner, that

$$\frac{d\sigma\uparrow + d\sigma\downarrow}{dQ^2} = \frac{G^2}{(2\pi)}\left\{F_V^2 + \lambda^2 F_A^2 + \frac{Q^2}{4m^2}\left[(\mu F_M)^2 + 4(cF_E)^2 + \right.\right.$$

$$+ \left(4\lambda\mu F F_A - 2(\lambda F_A - F_V)^2\right) m/E_\nu$$

$$\left. - \left(\lambda F_A (m_\mu b F_P)\frac{m_\mu}{m} - \frac{(m_\mu a F_S)^2}{4} - (\lambda^2 F_A^2 - F_V^2)\right) m^2/E_\nu^2\right]$$

$$+ \frac{Q^4}{8m^4}\left[-\left((\mu F)^2 + 4(cF_E)^2\right) m/E_\nu + \left((\lambda F_A - F_V)^2 - \right.\right.$$

$$- 2\mu F_M(\lambda F_A - F_V) + \frac{(\mu F)^2}{2} + \frac{(m_\mu b F_P)^2}{2}$$

$$\left.\left.\left. + \frac{(m_\mu a F_S)^2}{2}\right)\frac{m^2}{E_\nu^2}\right]\right\} .$$

In the high-energy limit

$$\frac{d\sigma(Q^2,\ E_\nu \to \infty)}{dq^2} = \frac{G^2}{2\pi}\left\{F_V^2 + \lambda^2 F_A^2 + \frac{Q^2}{4m^2}\left[(\mu F)^2 + 4(cF_E)^2\right]\right\} ,$$

and, as $Q^2 \to 0$, $F_V = F_A = 1$,

$$\frac{d\sigma}{dQ^2}(Q^2 = 0)_{\text{all } E_\nu} = \frac{G^2}{2\pi}(1 + \lambda^2) = 1.91 \times 10^{-38}\ \text{cm}^2/(\text{GeV}/c)^2 .$$

This last expression affords us a simple method to measure our neutrino flux, since we can compare this known cross-section with the observed number of low (zero) q^2 events as a function of the measured neutrino energy.

The expression for the polarization cross-section in the production plane can be found to be

$$\frac{(d\sigma\uparrow - d\sigma\downarrow)x}{dQ^2} = \frac{G^2}{2\pi}\sin\Theta_p\left\{2\lambda F_A F_V - \frac{Q^2}{2m^2}\left[(\lambda F_A)(\mu F_M)\right.\right.$$

$$\left. - m/E_\nu\left(F_V(F_V + \mu F_M - \lambda F_A) - (m_\mu b\ F_P)\frac{m_\mu}{2m} - \mu F_M(m_\mu b\ F_P)\frac{m_\mu}{2m}\right)\right]$$

$$\left. - \frac{Q^4}{16m^4}(m/E_\nu)\left((\mu F_M)^2 + \mu F_M(F_V - \lambda F_A)\right)\right\} .$$

The transverse polarization cross-section perpendicular to the production plane is determined as

$$\left(\frac{d\sigma\uparrow - d\sigma\downarrow}{dQ^2}\right)_z = \frac{G^2}{2\pi}\sin\Theta_p\left(\frac{\sqrt{Q^2 + Q^4/4m^2}}{m}\right)\left\{2(\lambda F_A)(cF_E) + \frac{(F_V + \mu F_M)}{2}(m_\mu a\ F_S)\left(\frac{m_\mu}{E_\nu}\right)\right.$$

$$\left. + \frac{Q^2}{2mE_\nu}(mcF_E)(F_V + \mu F_M - \lambda F_A)\right\} .$$

MEASUREMENT OF THE ANGULAR CORRELATION OF ELECTRONS RELATIVE TO Λ SPIN IN Λ^0-β DECAY

G. Conforto,

CERN, Geneva, Switzerland

I would like to report preliminary results of an experiment done at the CERN PS by J. Barlow, I. Blair, G. Conforto, P. Duke, M.I. Ferrero, A. Mann, C. Rubbia and J.C. Sens, on the β decay of the Λ^0 hyperon.

The aim of the experiment is to measure the angular correlation of the decay electron relative to the spin direction of polarized Λ^0 particles, in order to determine the form of the interaction which is responsible for the Λ-β decay.

In Fig. 1 the top view of the set-up used in the experiment is shown. Λ^0's were produced in either of the two beryllium targets according to the reaction

$$\pi^+ + n \rightarrow K^+ + \Lambda^0 \quad , \qquad (1)$$

at an incoming pion momentum of 1.0 GeV/c. The detection of the K^+ produced in reaction (1) was used as a signature of the Λ^0 production. The so-called K^+ detector consisted of:

a) Two sets of four scintillation counters (KQ_1, KQ_2, KQ_3, KQ_4 and KQ_5, KQ_6, KQ_7, KQ_8); each counter had the shape of a ¼ circle.

b) Two cylindrical water Čerenkov counters ($\check{C}_2$, $\check{C}_2'$). The water Čerenkov counter $\check{C}_1$ was in anticoincidence and was used in order to veto fast particles produced in reactions different from (1).

The K^+ detector works according to the following principle: a K^+ produced in reaction (1) crosses the first and the second set of quadrant counters (in coincidence between them) and then it stops in either of the two water Čerenkov counters. Of course, the K^+ is too slow to be detected by the two Č counters, but the K^+ decay products are, in $\sim 80\%$ of the cases, fast enough to emit Čerenkov radiation in water. Thus, the difference between the time in which a particle is detected in one of the two $\check{C}_2$'s and the time in which a particle is detected by the two sets of quadrants, fluctuates according to K^+ lifetime. This information is recorded for each event.

In order to reduce the contribution due to background prompt events, we required the $\check{C}_2$ pulse to arrive 3 nsec after the detection of a particle by the two sets of quadrants. Seventy per cent of the events fulfilling the above-mentioned criteria were, in fact, K^+'s.

The K^+ detector had a cylindrical symmetry with respect to the beam line so that the production plane (and, therefore, the Λ polarization perpendicular to it) was free to have any azimuthal angle with equal probability. The K^+ detector was also required to "see" the proton from Λ decay and this was obtained by requiring that $n \geq 2$ counters of the first set had to be crossed by a particle.

The set of spark chambers, water Čerenkov counters, and scintillation counters on the right in Fig. 1, at 90° with respect to the beam line, is the so-called "electron detector" and it is supposed to detect electrons from the decay

$$\Lambda \rightarrow p + e + \nu \quad , \tag{2}$$

and to be insensitive to pions from the normal decay mode

$$\Lambda \rightarrow p + \pi^- \quad . \tag{3}$$

The reason for having an electron detector at 90° with respect to the beam line is threefold:

a) the π momentum from the decay (3) falls rapidly at large ϑ. No π^- is able to give directly Čerenkov radiation in C_{E1} and C_{E2} if the opening angle is larger than 50°;

b) the asymmetry we want to measure is large at 90° because the Λ spin always lies in a plane perpendicular to the incoming particle in the c.m. system of production;

c) the Λ-β phase space, around 90°, is favoured over the Λ-π mode; the ratio between Λ-β decays and charged Λ-π decays at 90° is $1/400$, while the branching ratio is $1/660$.

Pictures of the spark chamber and of the displayed pulses from the four counters of the first set of quadrants, from E_1 and E_2 and from C_{E_1} and C_{E_2}, were taken whenever a final event occurred, according to the following two triggering criteria.

Λ-π events: the following conditions are required:

i) incoming beam particle;

ii) $n \geq 2$;

iii) detected K^+;

iv) no signal in E_0 or E_0' (in order to require that the particle entering the electron detector is produced in the spark chamber volume and not in the target).

Λ-β events: in addition to the Λ-π conditions, a coincidence between E_1 and E_2 was required. The main information concerning the electron detection, that is, pulses from C_{E_1} and C_{E_2}, was not included in the trigger and it was recorded on the scope picture.

A sample of pictures taken in Λ-π conditions in which the Λ decayed in the sensitive volume of the spark chambers and all the pictures taken in Λ-β conditions in which

i) the Λ decayed in the sensitive volume of the spark chamber;

ii) one track from the Λ vertex entered the electron detector arriving at least up to C_{E_1};

iii) at least one Čerenkov pulse from C_{E_1} or C_{E_2} was present on the scope display;

were measured on a digitized projector and the geometry and the kinematics were reconstructed for each of these events. From the analysis of 717 Λ-π events, mainly two results are obtained:

i) an experimental check that the production plane has really a flat distribution in the azimuthal angle within a few per cent;

ii) the best fit to the experimental $\vartheta^*_{\sigma_\Lambda p_\pi}$ distribution with a law of the type

$$1 + A \cos \vartheta^*_{\sigma_\Lambda p_\pi} ,$$

where $A = \alpha P$, gives

$$A = - 0.395$$

which, for $\alpha = - 0.62$ (see, for instance, Feynman Summary I), yields for the polarization of our sample

$$P = 64\%.$$

The measured Λ-β events have been analysed requiring that

i) the particle entering the electron detector has to emerge from C_{E_1};

ii) the opening angle has to be larger than 50°;

iii) Č pulses must have the right timing;

iv) no other track must be present in the electron detector;

v) the amplitude of pulses from E_1 and E_2 must correspond to a minimum ionizing particle;

vi) if a scattering angle larger than 10° - 15° (expected Coulomb scattering angle for 80 MeV electrons $\approx$ 4 - 5°) was present in one of the absorbers of the electron detector, this had to happen at a point incompatible with the range of the π calculated under the assumption that the event is actually a Λ-π.

This gives, at the price of losing few Λ-β which look as Λ-π, a sample of events in which the background contamination should be very small. In fact, the only background still present is due to Λ-π events in which the π is not cut by the dE/dx requirement and in which the product of the π capture (or decay) is emitted almost aligned with respect to the π track.

The result of this analysis is 39 events which show a flat coplanarity distribution (see Fig. 2) and the Λ and K^+ lifetimes obtained from them are compatible with the known values.

The $\vartheta^*_{\sigma_\Lambda p_e}$ distribution of the above-mentioned 39 events, assuming they are all Λ-β, fitted with a law of the type

$$1 + P\,\alpha_e \cos\vartheta^*_{\sigma_\Lambda p_e}$$

yields

$$\alpha_e = -(0.5 \pm 0.5)\,.$$

Comparing this to the expression for the asymmetry in terms of coupling constants as obtained by Harrington [Phys.Rev. 120, 1482 (1960)], we find the interaction to be of the form

$$A - (0.4 \pm 0.4)\,V\ .$$

In Fig. 3, the comparison between our data (dashed region) and results obtained by other authors is shown.

Hydrogen Bubble Chamber results refer to the experiment by Lind et al., to be published in Physics Review, preprint of University of Wisconsin. Heavy Liquid Bubble Chamber results refer to the experiment by Baglin et al., Physics Letters 6, 186 (1963).

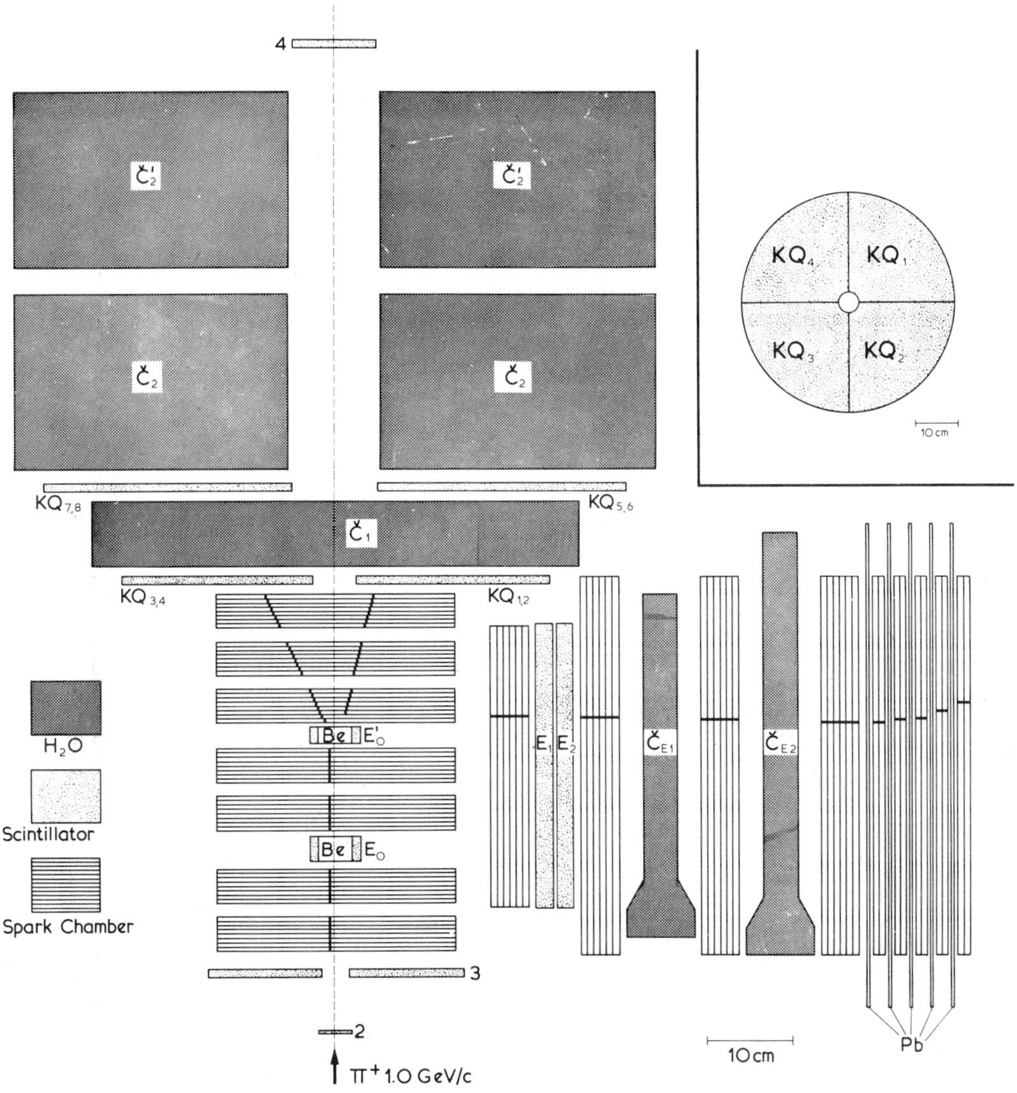
4
Č'2
Č'2
Č2
Č2
KQ4
KQ1
KQ3
KQ2
10 cm
KQ7,8
KQ5,6
Č1
KQ3,4
KQ1,2
H2O
Scintillator
Spark Chamber
Be
E'0
Be
E0
E1
E2
ČE1
ČE2
3
2
π+ 1.0 GeV/c
10cm
Pb

Fig. 1

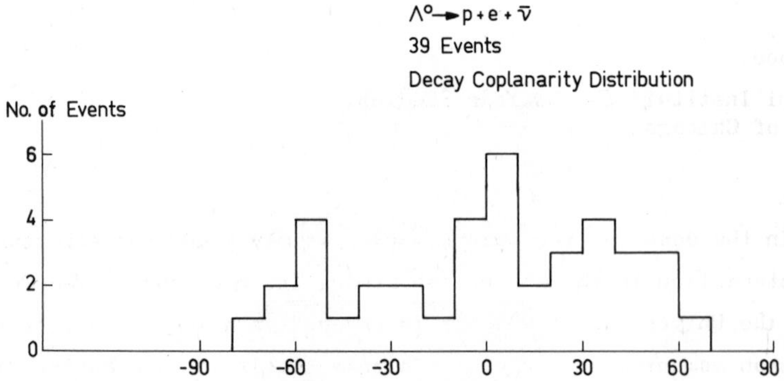
Λ°→p+e+ν̄
39 Events
Decay Coplanarity Distribution
No. of Events
6
4
2
0
-90
-60
-30
0
30
60
90

Fig. 2

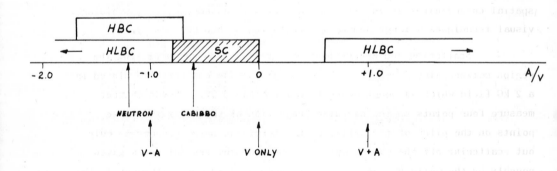

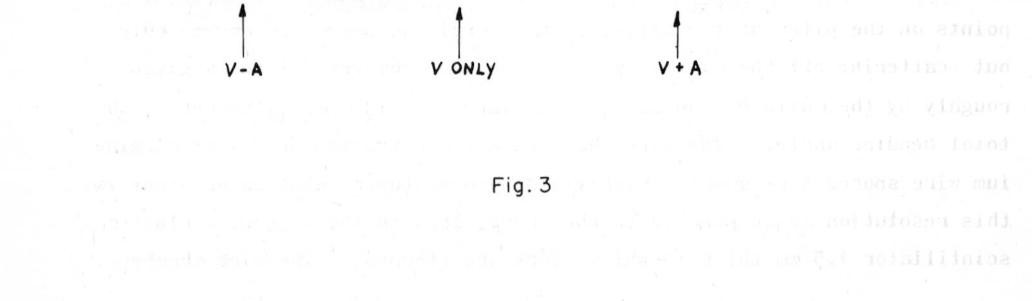
HBC
HLBC
SC
HLBC
-2.0
-1.0
0
+1.0
A/V
NEUTRON
CABIBBO
V-A
V ONLY
V+A

Fig. 3

MOMENTUM SPECTRUM OF POSITRONS FROM MUON DECAY

B.A. Sherwood,

Enrico Fermi Institute for Nuclear Studies,
University of Chicago.

In the decay of the muon $\mu \rightarrow e \nu \bar{\nu}$ we may study the structure of the weak interaction in the absence of strong interactions. The Telegdi Group[1)] at the University of Chicago is engaged in a measurement of the decay electron momentum spectrum with higher statistics and better momentum resolution than were previously available. Our aim is to measure the parameter ρ (a ratio of coupling constants predicted to be $\frac{3}{4}$ for V-A) to an accuracy of approximately 0.1%. We will also measure the electron decay asymmetry parameter as a function of momentum.

Previous momentum spectra obtained with bubble chambers were limited to approximately 10,000 events due to scanning and measuring difficulties, and to 6% momentum resolution due to multiple Coulomb scattering and energy loss. We are using digitized wire spark chambers to transmit spatial co-ordinates of the electron directly to a computer; by avoiding visual techniques a large number of events can be handled easily.

Scattering and energy loss are greatly reduced by filling the region between wire chambers with helium gas. The chambers are placed in a 2 kG field which is homogeneous to better than 0.2%. Seven chambers measure four points on the circular projection of the helix and three points on the pitch of the helix, over-determining both in order to rule out scattering off the magnet walls. The momentum resolution is given roughly by the ratio of the mean scattering angle in a wire chamber to the total bending angle. The wire chambers are constructed of 0.1 mm aluminium wire spaced 1 mm apart, which yields a momentum resolution of about 1%; this resolution is comparable to the energy loss in the source, a plastic scintillator 1.5 mm thick in which pions are stopped. The wire chambers are fired by an electron detected in the source counter and a scintillation counter following the final chamber. In addition, we require the electron to be preceded by a π-μ decay chain in the source counter. The final counter is placed perpendicular to the line connecting its centre with the centre of the small source counter, in which case the azimuthal angle subtended by the final counter in the bending plane is not a function of the bending radius, and only the pitch angle subtended varies with momentum. The result is that over a 20% momentum acceptance the solid angle, subtended by the final counter, varies only 7%.

We have tested the wire chambers outside the magnet and obtained a 0.3 mm spatial resolution. We have also obtained a few thousand events inside the magnet which have been stored, but so far not analysed. We have the cooperation of the Institute for Computer Research and the use of their computer MANIAC III. After the first exploratory run, during which all programming was done in assembly machine language, their ALGOL compiler has been modified to accept wire chamber input; this will greatly facilitate future programming.

The measurement of the asymmetry as a function of energy will be made by stopping polarized muons in the source scintillator. The muons precess at a 30 Mc rate and events are classified as forward or backward decays by the time of electron emission; this information is transmitted to the computer along with the spatial information.

It is worth mentioning that a group at Columbia, directed by A. Sachs, is at present carrying out an experiment quite similar to the one described here. This group uses sonic spark chambers in a 180° spectrometer, injecting π^+ mesons along the field.

* * *

Note added in proof: In a second run we have obtained a spectrum containing about 100,000 events. We have turned the final fiducial counter to remove the 7% solid-angle variation. Preliminary analysis has yielded $\rho = 0.746 \pm 0.01$. The Columbia Group[2] has presented their result: $\rho = 0.747 \pm 0.005$.

References

1) Bounin, Ehrlich, Fryberger, Powers, Sherwood and Telegdi.

2) A. Sachs, Bull.Am.Phys.Soc. Vol. 10, No. 1 (January, 1965).

DISCUSSION I

Question : Please elaborate upon the use of two form factors in the evaluation of matrix elements of the product of two currents.

Feynman : That question refers to the electromagnetic corrections discussed this morning. When we have two photons interacting with a proton in rapid succession, there is no reason to expect that the matrix element is essentially the square of the form factor for a single photon interacting with a proton. When a single photon interacts with a proton, the state initially is a free proton and afterwards is nothing but a proton. When two photons act in succession, the intermediate state need not be a free proton. In principle, pions could be generated in large numbers in the intermediate state. Thus, the form factor between free proton states is not appropriate. One requires, rather, a form factor linking a proton to all kinds of intermediate states.

Perhaps it is easier to see the point from a physical analogy. The same kind of idea arises when seeking information about the square of the charge density. The mean of the square of the charge density is not the same as the square of the mean.

As another example, in calculating the self-energy of a particle, we have a double photon interaction

Now, self-energy in a simplified classical sense will be the integral of the square of the electric field over the volume of the object. On the other hand, a single photon interaction is

more like the integral of the electric field over the volume of the object. This is the kind of difference that is involved. In particular, we can make several models. We might have charge distributed such that the electric field E, is smooth and nowhere very large. Then the integral of E^2 is relatively small and $\overline{E^2} \approx (\bar{E})^2$. On the other hand if we take as our model a little ball of charge which is zinging back and forth, the average field is still smooth. That would correspond to the one photon interaction. The self-energy of the system, which is the square of the electric field, would be much more the self-energy of a thing whose characteristic diameter is the diameter of the little ball, rather than the whole charge distribution. In this case $\overline{E^2} >> (\bar{E})^2$. The same kind of mathematical problem arises when one deals with hyperfine corrections or with the Compton effect at very high energy.

De Witt : Please explain in greater detail the application of this consideration in the case of beta-decay.

Feynman : In beta-decay there are electromagnetic corrections that look like this:

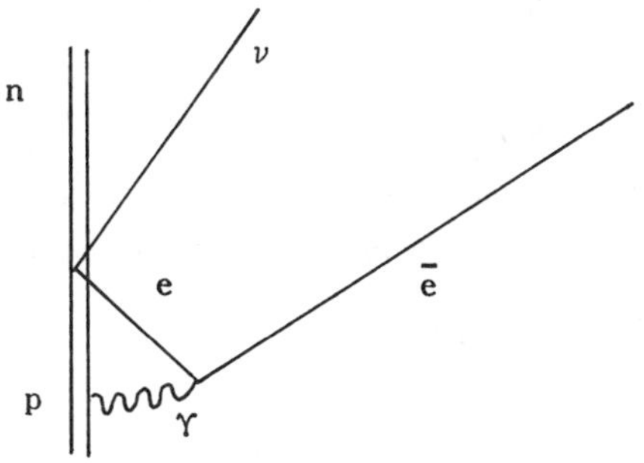

The neutrino and electron interact with the nucleus. Also, the electron interacts with a photon. The photon interaction brings in a γ_μ and there is another γ_μ from the vector part of the weak current. They would each have the same form factor as that for a photon. The weak interaction vertex does not involve a photon, but its interaction is exactly the same as that of electricity, namely a vector interaction. One might be tempted, therefore, to try to use the same form factor twice. Precisely the point of the previous comments, however, is that this is not correct.

Feynman : One remark about this discrepancy we are discussing (called to my attention by Berman who calculated this ½ per cent theoretical error) is that we also need to have knowledge of the vector and axial vector currents interacting in rapid succession. We just do not know enough at the moment about the intermediate states to be able to calculate these things properly.

Question : Why is the axial vector current renormalized, whereas the vector current is not?

Feynman : I believe the best way to look at this is: "Why is the vector current not renormalized?" I think it is clear that generally any such current would be renormalized. Actually we have no idea why the vector current is not renormalized. The point is that it is possible that the vector current is not renormalized. If the beta-decay interaction is of a certain peculiar character, namely that it interacts in a complete analogue to electricity except that a different isotopic spin component is involved, then the vector current might not be renormalized. This might follow from conservation of I-spin current, in much the same way that electric current is not renormalized.

There is no zero-momentum charge renormalization because the z component of the isospin current is conserved. Now, because of isospin symmetry of the strong interactions, the x and y components of the I-spin current are also conserved. Since the vector part of the weak interaction does couple through the conserved isospin current, it should not be renormalized.

Since it is possible for such a thing to happen and since such a thing is pretty, this guess seemed worth a try. (This idea had occurred earlier to Gerstejn and Zeldovich.) You must appreciate that when new laws are found it does not happen by deductive reasoning, but by plain guessing.

In the next lecture I will mention some of the experimental indications that the conserved vector current idea might be correct.

Berman : The fact that the Fermi coupling constants, determined from various nuclei, agree seems to indicate that the conserved current coupling must hold. It is known that inside a nucleus there are exchange currents carried by pions and other virtual particles. These currents give important corrections to electromagnetic form factors. It would seem that if these exchange currents were not included for the weak-interaction matrix elements, then one could not expect close agreement between Al^{26} and O^{14}.

Feynman : I would be hard pressed to estimate the degree to which exchange currents are present. Nevertheless, I do not think the currents are necessarily large so I would not say that this, by itself, indicates that other pion terms must be utilized. However, the rate of disintegration of $\pi^+ \to \pi^0 + e^+ + \nu$ has been measured. The rate implies, according to the conserved current hypothesis, that the pion term is there to eight per cent. When a number is predicted to be one and is found to be one within eight per cent, then that number is very likely one.

Other less direct tests have been made. The weak vector current is analogous to electric current, so when we go to higher momentum interactions, the weak current should have the same form factor and same character as electrical current. We know from the magnetic moment interaction, which is one order higher in momentum, how the next term behaves for the z-component current of I spin. Thus, we know there should be an analogue of the magnetic moment interaction for beta-decay and how large the effect should be. Gell-Mann pointed out that although the term is proportional to q and therefore very small in ordinary beta-decay, it was possible to detect it from the shapes of the positron and electron spectra from $N^{12} \rightarrow C^{12}$ and $B^{12} \rightarrow C^{12}$. The shapes of the spectra do agree with the predictions of this "weak magnetism" theory. This suggests again that the theory has an element of truth.

In passing, I remark that there is no renormalization only if the momentum is exactly zero. In these decays the electron and neutrino have little energy so the momenta involved are very small. That is why this theory may be all right. Also, with O^{14} the energy change is very small and we are again close to the zero-momentum limit.

Question : How sensitive is the form factor ratio to changes in the momentum.

Block : I find from the data, with all form factors normalized to one at the origin, that the ratio of the axial vector form factor to the vector form factor goes up to about two at a momentum transfer of about 3 GeV. This is 2 ± 1.5.

Question : Some decays are only possible because of splitting of I-spin symmetry. How does this relate to the two per cent.

<u>Feynman</u> : The mass splittings are presumed to be electromagnetic in origin. The z component of isospin current is unchanged and it seems reasonable that there might be a 0.1% or 1% or so effect from the splitting. However, we are calculating the amplitude for such an interaction, even if the energy is supplied from somewhere else -- that is, even if there were no mass splitting. The mass splitting only gives a phase-space factor (which may be essentially zero), but we are interested in the matrix element now and not the phase-space factor.

This kind of effect might be expected to influence the matrix element significantly in the $O^{14} \rightarrow N^{14}$ case, due to the different Coulomb forces in O^{14} and N^{14}. I have attempted to figure out how large this effect might be in this case. I can tell you that the effect is amazingly small. Instead of the overlap integral being one, it looks like it is over 99½ per cent.

<u>Block</u> : For electron-proton scattering there are some proton polarizations which cannot be produced by a single photon exchange. These polarizations must be produced by diagrams like

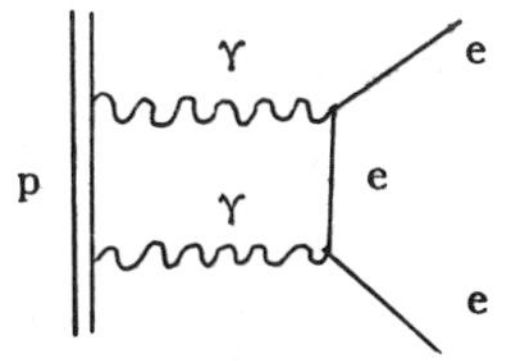

Thus, if you measure the rate at which those particular polarizations are produced, you have a measure of the higher order effects.

<u>Feynman</u> : A similar programme, suggested to me by Sands, involves measuring the proton-positron interaction. Due to a

difference of sign in the single photon diagrams

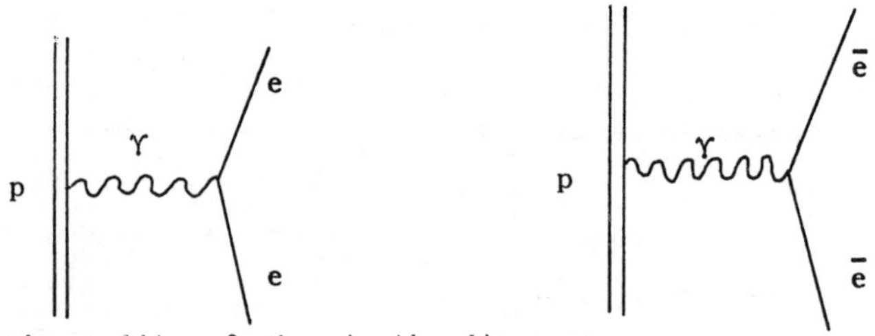

and equality of sign in the diagrams

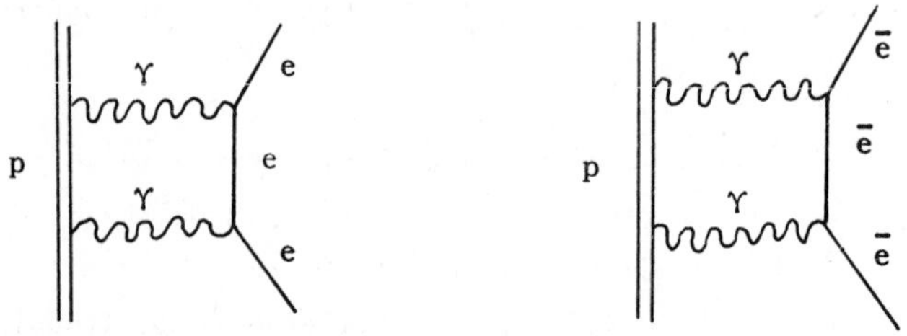

one finds that the difference in rates for the two processes is due to the effects of the second photon. We can hardly expect the difference to be more than about a percentage.

Biedenharn : Is it possible that the uncertainty in the nuclear radius for the Coulomb wave function could account for the discrepancy in the rates.

Berman : The Coulomb wave function is relatively insensitive to changes in the nuclear radius by factors of two, i.e. the change in the f value is less than 1% in O^{14}. Calculations with charge distributions which are not point like (e.g. by M.E. Rose) indicates that effects of finite size become non-negligible only at high Z values.

Feynman : In conclusion, I believe that there really is a discrepancy of 1 or 2% between the nucleon and muon-decay couplings. It would be nice to know exactly how much the discrepancy really is, instead of this $2\% \pm \frac{1}{2}\%$. The possible physical significance of the existence of this discrepancy will be discussed in the lectures.

DISCUSSION II

Block : What do you mean by a particle.

Feynman : I distinguish particles from antiparticles in beta-decay by associating the particles with those decay products which have, preferentially, a left-handed polarization.

Question : Is it possible to construct an axial vector current which is not renormalized.

Feynman : I do not think so. In my work I have only been able to make the divergence of the axial vector current vanish if the pion mass is zero.

Question : Can you prove that it is impossible to construct such a current.

Feynman : Nobody can prove it is impossible. Mathematicians can prove it is impossible only under the assumption that the current is constructed in a certain way.

Question : In your more sophisticated approach to the Goldberger-Treiman relation you had two terms: a direct term and a pion term. The coefficient of the direct term was G_A, the experimental axial vector coupling constant. Should not G_A have included all the contributions from the pion term?

Feynman : No, my pion term vanishes as $q \to 0$, so that the beta-decay coupling is measured by G_A. However, for non-zero q the matrix element of the axial vector current can contain a term of the form $q_\alpha \gamma_5$, which is commonly called the induced pseudoscalar coupling. It is this latter type of term that I obtain with my pion term. This induced pseudoscalar coupling is important in the analysis of data on μ capture. The sign and magnitude of the coupling, as given by the pion term, are in reasonable agreement with the data.

Question : What do you mean by intrinsic parity.

Feynman : Let me approach the topic of intrinsic parity now, using familiar concepts from non-relativistic quantum mechanics. I assume the concept of parity is understood. Suppose we have two apparatuses which are constructed so that one imitates the mirror image of the other. Then, the two wave functions are related by an operator P, the parity operator, which Wick, Wightman and Wigner showed can be chosen so that $P^2 = 1$, without any loss of generality. The eigenvalues of this operator are thus ± 1.

Consider now a simple example of a system with intrinsic parity -1. Suppose you have two spin ½ particles in a triplet P state, $^3P_0$. The spin wave function is unchanged upon inversion of coordinates, so that the parity of the wave function of the system is -1. Now think of this system being a single "particle". Since the total spin of this "particle" is zero, we might expect the parity of the system to be $+1$. We can describe this situation by saying that the "particle" has an intrinsic parity -1.

Now in elementary particle physics we become more sophisticated by abstracting the result that an object with angular momentum J can have either parity. We do not insist upon thinking that a particle with intrinsic parity -1 must be made of two or more other objects, in the same way as we do not insist that the spin angular momentum be interpreted as the orbital angular momentum of some yet-to-be-discovered constituents of an object with a spin.

The intrinsic parity concept has a useful meaning only when we discuss interactions among particles. Furthermore, the idea is useful only if many of nature's interactions do conserve parity. We define and determine the intrinsic parity of a particle by means of some interaction. Unless there are other interactions in which that particle participates with the same "intrinsic parity", then the intrinsic parity assignment is useless.

It turns out that a set of intrinsic parity assignments can be made for the particles such that in the strong and electromagnetic interactions, all the determinations of intrinsic parity that have been made are consistent. In other words, any given particle is always found to have the same intrinsic parity when participating in a strong or electromagnetic interaction.

The fact that all of our assignments are consistent implies that if a new particle is discovered coupled into the strong interactions, then all of the determinations of its intrinsic parity will also be consistent.

If the interactions are such that all the particles involved are not the same, then there can be some ambiguity in the definition of intrinsic parity. This ambiguity can always be resolved by adopting a suitable convention. For example, the charged pion can couple to the proton and neutron through a matrix element of the form $\bar{p}\gamma_5 n$. If we stipulate that p and n have the same intrinsic parity, that is, that the wave functions acquire the same phase factor upon inversion of coordinates, then we would say that the pion has negative intrinsic parity. However, if we stipulate that the proton acquires a relative minus sign, compared to the neutron upon inversion, then we would say that the charged pion has positive intrinsic parity.

Such a modification is always possible when there are other conserved quantities. If I define a parity operator P, somebody else is certainly free to define his parity operator $P' = (-)^Q P$, where Q is any conserved quantity, that is, charge, baryon number, lepton number. For example, the customary definition of P results in the following eigenvalues p : +, n : +, $\pi^{\pm}$: -, π^{0} : -. Consider three alternate definitions of the parity operator. Call them: $P' = (-)^{Q}P$, $P'' = (-)^{B}P$, $P''' = (-)^{Q+B}P$, where Q is the electric charge and B is the baryon number. Using these operators we get the following table of parity eigenvalues:

	p	n	$\pi^{\pm}$	π^{0}
P	+	+	-	-
P′	-	+	+	-
P″	-	-	-	-
P‴	+	-	+	-

Any one of these operators would be a satisfactory choice, but some may be more convenient than others.

Question : It was stated that gauge transformations depending on a single parameter generate local conservation laws. Would you distinguish local conservation laws from global conservation laws.

Feynman : If a cat were to disappear in Pasadena and at the same time appear in Erice, that would be an example of global conservation of cats. This is not the way cats are conserved. Cats or charge or baryons are conserved in a much more continuous way. If any of these quantities begin to disappear in a region, then they begin to appear in a neighbouring region. Consequently, we can identify a flow of charge out of a region with the disappearance of charge inside the region. This identification of the divergence of a flux with the time rate of change of a charge density is called a local conservation law. A local conservation law implies that the total charge is conserved globally, but the reverse does not hold. However, relativistically it is clear that non-local global conservation laws cannot exist, since to a moving observer the cat will appear in Erice before it disappears in Pasadena.

DISCUSSION III

Reichert : Gell-Mann's latest method for deriving the Goldberger-Treiman relation uses dispersion theory. Perhaps Wagner would like to explain this approach.

Wagner : Gell-Mann, over the course of several years, has developed more and more abstract ways of looking at the Goldberger-Treiman relation. One of his earlier abstractions consisted of the hypothesis that the divergence of the axial vector current was proportional to the pion field. Today, because there is much question about the existence of a pion field from a fundamental view, he likes to talk about the relation in terms of dispersion theory. The divergence of the axial vector current is certainly dominated by the pion pole term near $q^2 = m_\pi^2$. The Goldberger-Treiman relation is obtained under the assumption that the divergence of the axial vector current continues to be dominated by the pion term, in the sense of dispersion theory, near $q^2 = 0$. To demonstrate this let us write down the most general possible expression for the matrix element of the axial vector current between two nucleons. It is

$$\left\{ \bar{P}[-G_A\gamma_\mu i\gamma_5\alpha(q^2) + i\gamma_5 q_\mu \beta(q^2)]N \right\}, \quad \alpha(0) = 1 \, .$$

Its divergence is obtained by multiplying by q_μ. Using the Dirac equation we find the divergence to be

$$[-G_A 2M\alpha(q^2) + q^2\beta(q^2)] \; \{\bar{P}i\gamma_5 N\} \, .$$

The contribution to this matrix element from the pion pole term

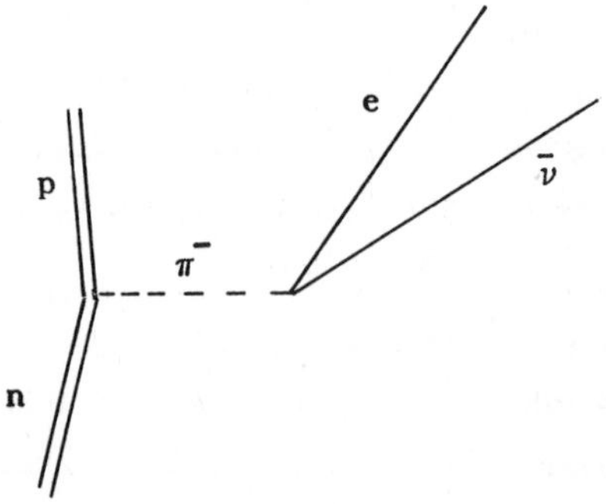

is

$$g \frac{1}{q^2 - m_\pi^2} \sqrt{8\pi} \, (\bar{P} i \gamma_5 N) \; .$$

Equating the two expressions near $q^2 = 0$ we get

$$- G_A = \sqrt{8\pi} \; F_\pi \frac{g}{2M} \; .$$

The essence of the validity of the Goldberger-Treiman relation thus lies in the degree to which the pion pole term dominates the dispersion relation for the axial vector current, not near $q^2 = m_\pi^2$ where it automatically must dominate because it is singular, but near $q^2 = 0$.

Question : Please explain why the SU_3 mass formulae are sometimes written in terms of the squares of the masses and sometimes in terms of the masses themselves.

Feynman : This is a purely empirical matter. However, one can almost glimpse the reason that the squares of the masses should appear in the meson mass formulae. For mesons the propagator is of the form $(q^2 - m^2)^{-1}$. Now when mass renormalization diagrams are included, as in the lectures, one obtains the corrected propagator: $[q^2 - m_0^2 + F(q^2)]^{-1}$ This propagator has a pole for some value of q^2. This pole determines the experimentally observed mass. Now, if $F(q^2)$ is small, then the propagator is approximately $[q^2 - m_0^2 + F(m_0^2)]^{-1}$. The pole of this propagator is at $q^2_{pole} \equiv m_e^2 \approx m_0^2 + F(m_0^2)$. Seeing the correction appear in this form involving the squares of the masses, might lead one to expect SU_3 mass relations to be in terms of the mass squared.

Now for fermions we know that the mass formulae work best when the masses themselves are used. Some people are tempted to say that this is clear from the fact that the Dirac fermion propagator is $[\not{p} - m_0]^{-1}$. However, this expression is not so linear as it looks because $\not{p}$ is a matrix! Thus, it is not at all clear that the mass relations for fermions should be linear.

There have been other attempts to explain this empirical procedure. Lee and Gürsey have an interesting approach. Consider a zero mass particle moving with very large momentum. Then $E = \sqrt{p^2 + m^2} \approx p + m^2/2p$, and the correction to the energy involves the mass squared. This suggests again that one might use the squares of the masses in the SU_3 relations. One troublesome point with this approach, however, is that there is no reason to believe the fermion formulae should be linear in the masses.

One should be aware that as long as the argument is based on the fact that the correction is small, then it is most difficult to tell what power of the mass should be used. For example,

linear:	$M + a$	(where a is a small correction)
quadratic:	$(M + a)^2 \approx M^2 + 2aM$	
cubic:	$(M + a)^3 \approx M^3 + 3aM^2$.	

See that there is a "small correction" to any power of the mass.

<u>Zweig</u> What about particles with spin $3/2$. Supposedly we should use a linear relation for the masses.

Feynman : The rule is that for any fermion one should use the first power of the masses. But again I state: this is an empirical rule!

Question : How good may we expect mass relations to be? Can we hope that they can be improved to eliminate discrepancies of several MeV.

Zweig : This question is concerned with higher order mass formulae. For the octuplet the second order gives no mass formula. For the decuplet the first order gives the famous "equal spacing", but there is also a second order mass formula.

Feynman : Let me mention an interesting problem associated with the equal spacing law of the decuplet. Under the strong interactions Ω^- is stable, but Σ^+ is not. Now, when a particle can disintegrate, then its mass has an imaginary part,

$$M = M_R + iM_I$$

where iM_I is often written as $i\,\Gamma/2$. Γ is then the decay width. Now suppose the masses change slowly until suddenly the Σ^+ cannot disintegrate. This gives rise to a discontinuity in the imaginary part of the mass. Now Yang and Oakes realized that a discontinuity in the imaginary part would imply, through a dispersion integral, a discontinuity in the real part of the mass. Such a discontinuity is called the Wigner-Thomas-Ehrman shift in nuclear physics.

Yang and Oakes argued that one should get rid of such mass shifts before putting particles into the mass formulae. In other words, the mass relations as they are customarily written should be very bad. Frautschi addressed himself to this problem and found that, indeed, this is a problem in the relativistic case, but that an accident happens that makes the equal spacing law work.

There are many channels, open and closed, that are available to the Σ^+. Frautschi found that the sums of all of the shifts induced by these channels are all equally spaced. Hence, the equal spacing law should work.

Now if one is interested in discrepancies of several MeV, he must be aware of such complications and take them into careful consideration.

Kabir : How much was the contribution of these linear shifts to the spacing.

Feynman : I must refer you to Frautschi's paper for details, but I remember that the contribution was very large; perhaps 70 MeV or so.

Question : If time reversal invariance is not valid can one still remove a particle from one side of an equation and put its antiparticle on the other side.

Feynman : Yes, because this rule comes from the TCP theorem.

De Witt : It is possible that failure of time reversal invariance may not destroy the concept and properties of entropy. It might be that in both universes, ours and the time reversed one, entropy increases, but at different rates.

DISCUSSION IV

Websdale : This morning Cabibbo discussed a force which could give different potentials to K^0 and $\overline{K^0}$, and hence a vacuum regeneration. He said that if gravitation were responsible the effect would be much too large. Is this, then, indirect experimental evidence for the same behaviour of matter and antimatter in the gravitational field.

Feynman : Gravitation can be shown numerically to produce an effect far too strong if K^0 and $\overline{K^0}$ were at different potentials under its influence. A long range field producing a potential difference consistent with the small $K_2^0 \rightarrow 2\pi$ rate observed would consist of contributions from the earth, from the galaxy and of extra-galactic origin.

The fact is that the very large effect which should be produced from a gravitational potential difference is not observed. This is evidence that the effect is the same on particles and antiparticles. There is other indirect experimental data giving the same conclusion and nothing to the contrary.

Question : Isn't this theory (about an external field affecting K^0 and $\overline{K^0}$ differently) contradictory to relativity.

Feynman : Yes, in a certain sense it is. It is usually said that if you transform the whole coordinate system you get the same phenomenon. That is trivial. If you transformed everything and got the same phenomenon then there would be no physical content to that. The proposition of relativity is this: if you move in a space ship in a straight line at a uniform velocity past the stars, there is no observable effect.

It might be that there is an effect if you move past the stars, but, if we move the nebulae along, then there is no detectable effect. Now, the whole history of relativity is that experiments made on the earth, which is moving, without moving the nebulae, show no effect. So the prediction is that there is no effect of absolute motion relative to the stars.

This new theory (about an external field affecting K^0 and $\overline{K^0}$ differently) means something a little different, in that it changes the traditional spirit of relativity. It means that we could tell how fast we are moving relative to a kind of centre of gravity of the galaxy by a direct experiment, provided that the law of this field is such that the mass difference depends on the speed of the particles. This is against the principle of relativity as stated by Einstein or Poincaré.

The marvellous thing about relativity is that if you take a new piece of apparatus, rotated with respect to the old, to prepare a state and measure it with the old apparatus, there is a relationship between your new results and those obtained previously. It does not say that if you rotate both the preparing apparatus and the observing apparatus that you get the same answer, that is rather a dull remark. The fact is that we can prepare the system and that all the past history of preparation can be summarized by a few numbers, called the amplitudes for the various states, and then for predictions we need only those numbers.

<u>Parkinson</u> : Why would the existence of such a background field (for the K_2^0 decay) contradict special relativity? After all there may be sources for this field (just as for E.M., for example).

<u>Feynman</u> : This may be the case. Even so, we would have something new which could be measured to give us a velocity with respect to the galaxies, without looking at them. This contradicts the old idea of special relativity, which did not include such things.

De Witt : You suggest that the effect of the earth on the K_2^0 decay, through a hypothetical vector potential, may be regarded as negligible compared to the effect of galactic matter. Why.

Feynman : Because the ratio (number of nucleons/distance) is vastly larger for the galaxies than it is for the earth.

Telegdi : In as much as we are speaking of things that are pretty far out, consider antimatter. If you charge conjugate the source, this is the same as going from $K \rightarrow \bar{K}$ and leaving the source alone. Now, the number of galaxies of matter and antimatter in the universe might be about equal. Would the effect of distant matter not cancel in that case.

Feynman : It could well be (under certain prejudiced ideas about what galaxies are) that our galaxy is made out of pro-"goo" and that Andromeda, perhaps, is made out of anti-"goo" and that galaxy NGC 167 is made out of pro-"goo" again, and that they average out. Then it would be true that the effect would average very small, unless there is a statistical ... I'd have to think, but I think it averages to zero. I am not sure because it might be a plus or minus the square root of something.

[But if the average were small it would then be legitimate to discuss the contribution from our galaxy alone.]

Yes, you are right. Thank you. I had not thought about that, I was thinking they were all made out of matter. That is a bad prejudice.

Gotsman : Do you believe that the Fermi-Yang model of the pion is just a mathematical technique for calculating, or that it has some physical content.

Feynman : It is a useful tool for calculating. Considering the pion as a bound state of a $N \bar{N}$ pair gives the right answer for the beta-decay coupling constant. I believe models are useful whenever they give the correct answer.

Fuchs : You spoke in the preceding discussion of a discontinuity which would occur in the real part of the mass of a particle if a new channel of disintegration was opened. Could you give details on this fact.

Feynman : Suppose a stable particle which has only a real mass M becomes unstable. That means that an imaginary part of the mass will appear. This imaginary part, which was equal to zero before instability appears, suddenly is different from zero and varying. Therefore, here is a discontinuity in this imaginary part. Now the whole mass is an analytic function so it sounds reasonable that if there is a discontinuity in the imaginary part there is also a discontinuity in the real part.

For instance, take a decay in the S state at low energy. The amplitude of disintegration is a constant. The density of final states is proportional to $\sqrt{Q^2}$ so $\Gamma = \alpha \sqrt{Q^2}$. To say that the particle cannot decay means that $Q^2 < 0$. Thus, the $i\Gamma$ part of the mass becomes real, creating the discontinuity. By the way, it has been remarked that when the mass formula in the octet case is corrected for this Wigner-Thomas-Ehrman shift, it no longer gives as good results as we have at present.

Kirz : Are there not an infinite number of closed channels? How does one handle these.

Feynman : Yes, there are, but the farther they are, the less their effect, and the shift comes from the channels open to some members of the multiplet, closed to others.

Faissner : Why did Block violate CP in the matrix element for $\nu_\mu + n \rightarrow \mu^- + p$ by means of the currents of the second kind? In principle, we could have taken any of the form factors and given it an imaginary part. If he had taken, in particular, just the induced pseudoscalar term, the violation would not have shown up in beta-decay.

Berman : Cabibbo has introduced CP violation in this particular way because he wants to have each current and its Hermitian conjugate in the same isospin multiplet.

DISCUSSION V

Bergia : Is the fact that the coupling of vector mesons to the baryon current is assumed to be F type, a consequence of SU_3 or of some independent hypothesis.

Feynman : I believe it is an assumption from somewhere external to SU_3. The original idea was that there should be such currents and that they should have the right transformation law. The hope was that the conservation of this current would result from the potential coupling directly to the current just like the electrical potential couples to the current. Thus, the conservation of the current, which would be approximately right if the masses were almost equal, would be a part of group theory. It was natural to do that in analogy with electricity. As far as I can see it is just a good guess, and it would be equally possible to have, in addition, a D type coupling.

De Witt : Suppose you have a charged plasma contained in an irregularly shaped container and placed in an external magnetic field. This system is not invariant under time reversal, and yet we do not question the fact that the entropy of this system increases with time regardless of the direction of the magnetic field. What, if anything, is wrong with using this system as an example to argue that lack of time reversal invariance in elementary particle interactions should give us no worries about the entropy problem.

Feynman : The fact is that this system does not really violate time reversal. It is a part of a larger system in which the electromagnetic field has dynamical properties. Time reversal of the whole system requires a change in the direction of the magnetic field, and the whole system then becomes time reversal invariant.

In a similar manner, the main reason for the attempts which have been made to introduce an external long-range field to account for the K_2 decay is to restore time reversal invariance to the whole combined system.

De Witt : Well, that is not quite what I had in mind when I suggested the plasma system. Suppose you were given simply the Hamiltonian of the plasma system and were asked to analyse it purely as a mathematical problem. You would then not recognize the magnetic field as part of a larger dynamical system, and the mathematical problem would be similar to what we are now faced with in particle decays. The purely mathematical analysis, combined with the standard assumptions of statistical mechanics, would still lead to the consequence that entropy increases with time. Is it not likely that the same is true of the K_2 system.

Feynman : Yes, I see what you mean. Yes, I think you are probably right; but one would have to look at it.

De Witt : It is also worth adding that although time reversal invariance is violated in the K_2 decays, the Hamiltonian is nevertheless still Hermitian, and since the pertinent interaction is very weak the principle of detailed balance over distinct quantum states continues to hold.

Faissner : Could you explain why your concept of an antiparticle, namely, that it is an object moving backwards in time, does not violate causality.

Feynman : The best proof I know is that this theory is mathematically equivalent to the usual Dirac hole theory. The Dirac theory may violate many of your feelings, but certainly it does not violate causality. Furthermore, if you accept the seemingly paradoxical situation of a particle moving backwards in time, you are just not able to construct a concrete physical situation where you can send information back into the past.

<u>De Witt</u> : Suppose you have a system with a conserved <u>bare</u> current and that this current becomes (infinitely) renormalized when certain interactions are switched on. Am I correct in understanding that what you mean by a <u>non-renormalized current</u> is one which suffers no additional renormalizations when other interactions are switched on.

<u>Feynman</u> : Not exactly. Consider the e, γ, p, n, π system with the pion-nucleon interaction switched off. Then the bare charges of e, p, $\pi^{\pm}$ are all renormalized by coupling to the electromagnetic field, and the renormalization is in each case by the same amount. Now switch on the pion-nucleon interaction. There will then be a further renormalization of charge due to diagrams, for example, of the form

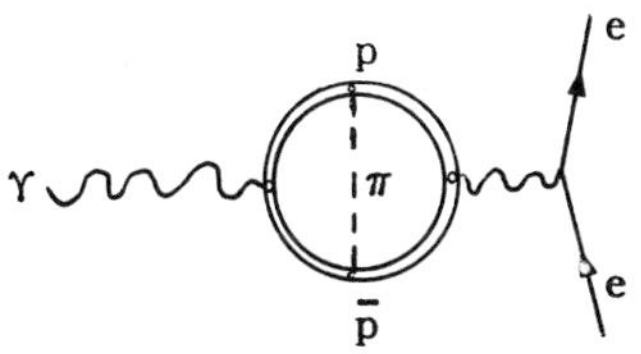

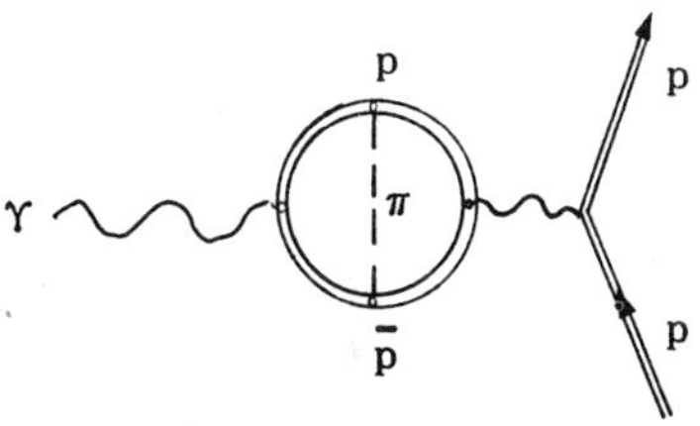

However, this additional renormalization is also the same for all charged particles, <u>regardless of whether they are directly involved in the pion-nucleon coupling or not</u>. This is because diagrams of the form

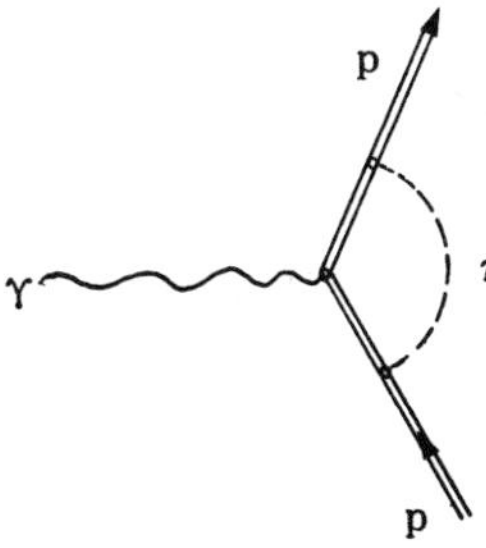

do not contribute to the charge renormalization, on account of identities like the Ward identity. Hence the electron, for example, continues to serve as a standard for electric charge, even though it is not directly coupled to pions. That is what is meant by a non-renormalized charge or current.

Carmi From looking at the vacuum K_1 regeneration term in the K decay Hamiltonian (in which a "cosmic" potential V acts with opposite signs on K_0 and $\bar{K}_0$), and remembering that V is quite well approximated by a constant function of position (because the sources are so far away), and hence V is forceless, it seems that we have here an effect similar to the Ahavanov-Bohm quantum effect of potentials in a forceless region.

Feynman : Yes, but even more so. The Aharonov-Bohm experiment depends on the line integrals of the potential, whereas here the effect depends on the value of the potential itself.

Zienau : With what confidence can one assert that the n-p mass difference is of electromagnetic origin? That is, can one calculate it.

Feynman : Cut-off dependent old fashioned calculations suffice to show that m_n could be larger than m_p, which seems mysterious at first sight. This can be understood from the energy of the magnetic moment of the neutron. Dispersion theoretical calculations in recent years relate the n-p mass difference to the Hofstadter form factors. I do not believe these calculations since they involve the interaction of two vector currents as mentioned before. An unpublished thesis of R. Dashen (California Institute of Technology, 1964) goes beyond this and provides a dispersion theoretical calculation with a carefully studied approximation.

Bergia : How does the fact that gauge invariance of the second kind requires the existence of a massless vector field reconcile with the assumption currently made that massive vector boson fields are generated by the same principle.

Feynman : The fact is that first it was assumed that the vector meson coupling was analogous to the electromagnetic coupling. Then in order to make the theory gauge invariant, the meson had to be massless. But the vector mesons are not massless. However, people preferred not to change the coupling and instead gave up gauge invariance. Really, the most reasonable thing would be a combination of F and D couplings.

Lipman : Should SU_3 predictions of strong interaction rates be expected to hold to, say, 10% (equals the mass splitting) or to a factor 2 or 10.

Feynman : Isospin works very accurately in nature (mass splitting being $< 1\%$). SU_3 involves much larger mass splitting. If SU_3 cannot predict strong interaction rates then it loses its usefulness. There are, in fact, large discrepancies $\sim$ factor 10. One might expect rates to be not very much disturbed by the mass splitting. If the theory does not predict the rates correctly and we put in large perturbation corrections, the theory steadily loses its simplicity and its usefulness.

DISCUSSION VI

Isabelle : To explain in the SU_3 model the formation of the octet, decuplet, etc., in which the observable particles are contained, we may introduce objects called "quarks" and corresponding anti-objects. Do we have to expect to see these objects.

Feynman : No. In the case of isotopic spin we know that we can explain the rotation properties of an I-spin I object by saying that they are obtained by taking the product of two I-spin ½ quantities. In the same way we can explain the transformation properties of the members of an octet or decuplet by deriving from the product of "3" by a "$\bar{3}$". But that does not mean that the I-spin ½ quantities really exist.

Rahm : Is there anything in the theory that will give a scale of mass of those quarks.

Feynman : No, as this is not a dynamical model.

Telegdi : Some time ago, the g_P/g_A ratio in muon capture (predicted by the Goldberger-Treiman relation as +8) was found to be high (say, +12) from capture and radiative experiments in complex nuclei. A recent evaluation of the $p\mu p$ molecular wave functions gives, from the H_2 experimental capture rate, good agreement with theory.

Is it really reasonable that the theory actually worked out for isolated protons should apply inside nuclear matter? What does your intuition say about the corrections (say, due to exchange currents) that could raise the G_P/G_A ratio.

Feynman : This is a very good question, but I will have to think about it.

Yeh : Why does CP correspond to the matrix σ_x? What is the matrix corresponding to charge conjugation C.

Cabibbo : By definition $CP|K^0\rangle = |\bar{K}^0\rangle$. P operation only changes sign, i.e. $P|K^0\rangle = -|\bar{K}^0\rangle$. Hence C corresponds to $-\sigma_x$.

Bergia : It has been stressed by Berman that the knowledge of the interactions that break SU_3 symmetry is about as important as the existence of the symmetry itself. Is there a way of learning something about these interactions by means of processes which are forbidden by the exact symmetry and which might occur via such interactions.

Sherwood : In response to Bergia's question, Lipkin in a seminar at Argonne pointed out that in the presently assigned multiplets (8, 10) there are no reactions forbidden explicitly by SU_3 that are not already forbidden by previously known conservation laws (S, B, I etc.). However, in larger multiplet representations such as "35" such selection rules do arise.

Feynman : This seems to be the case, essentially because it is difficult to produce states such as $\Lambda^0 + \sqrt{3}\,\Sigma^0$!

Moneti : Does this not mean that SU_3 is contained in the other known symmetry principles.

Feynman : No, the fact that there are no processes forbidden by SU_3 only is purely technical, so to speak. But SU_3 predicts ratios between reaction rates which are not contained in the other symmetry principles.

Lipman : SU_3 is dominating our thinking in strong interactions and weak interactions, yet it is based on relatively weak evidence. At what stage do you feel one should reject SU_3? Would SU_3 be in trouble if more than one octet or decuplet existed with the same quantum numbers (J^P).

Feynman : It is true that there is an enthusiasm for SU_3 based on very little data. SU_3 will allow any number of groups with the same quantum numbers and so this will not be a difficulty. A most worrying situation will arise if we find J^P of $\Omega^- \neq 3/2^+$, or if for example Ξ is found to have $J^P \neq 1/2^+$; we must look for a new theory. With regard to interaction rates, SU_3 is an inexact theory and we can always make the symmetry breaking fit the facts. The rates for weak interactions are in reasonable agreement with the predictions; but the data are not accurate enough to precisely test SU_3. My current prejudice is in favour of SU_3, but the situation is not completely tidy at the moment.

Parkinson : What about $\varphi \to 2K/\varphi \to 3\pi$.

Cabibbo : A possible naive interpretation of the fact that $(\varphi \to 3\pi) \ll (\omega \to 3\pi)$ is the following. Suppose the 3π state is the main contribution to $\varphi - \omega$ mixing. Call $\bar{\varphi}$ and $\bar{\omega}$ the unmixed (octet and singlet states) and suppose they have the same unperturbed mass (this seems true if one determines the masses from the experimental ω and φ masses, and the Gell-Mann Okubo mass formula). Call then

$$a(\bar{\varphi} \to 3\pi) = a \qquad (1)$$
$$a(\bar{\omega} \to 3\pi) = b \; .$$

We then define two new orthogonal states

$$\varphi^0 = b\varphi - a\bar{\omega} \qquad (2)$$
$$\omega^0 = a\bar{\varphi} + b\omega \; .$$

It is easy to see that φ^0 cannot go into 3π while ω^0 can. Now, if the ratio a/b is nearly constant also off the mass shell, the 3π state will contribute to the ω^0 self energy, not to the φ^0 self energy. If the 3π state is the main intermediate state, the physical ω and φ particles will be near the ω^0 and φ^0 combinations, and the φ will decay into 3π with a smaller rate than ω. This experimental fact could therefore find a dynamical basis.

This thought is interesting in view of the fact that K_2^0 decays weakly into $\pi^+ + \pi^-$; some sort of dynamical effect could be the basis of this nearly perfect imitation of CP invariance.

Buccella : From the rate of φ and ω going into 3π's, may we find the ω-φ mixing angle by making a theory similar to that of K^0 and $\bar{K}^0$ going into 2π's.

Feynman : We cannot, unless we measure the pure rate of decay into 3π's.

Astbury : Is there any a priori reason to expect the existence of a scalar meson octet.

Feynman : According to SU_3 it is possible, but there are no particular reasons to expect it, except on the basis of special models.

PRESENT STATUS OF STRONG ELECTROMAGNETIC AND WEAK INTERACTIONS

R.P. Feynman,
California Institute of Technology.

Rather than summarizing the present situation in the theory of aces, or the latest version of Cabibbo's theory, I shall review our knowledge of symmetries in general. Therefore, I shall not merely give a summary of this course, but rather a summary covering the entire field of physics.

I. BASIC PHYSICS

The first thing to do in physics is to distinguish the fundamental problems from the less fundamental ones. There are certain fields, say superconductivity, solid state physics, or chemical physics, which can be understood, in principle, as soon as the fundamental laws are known. Let me put it this way: we do not believe that a thorough study of superconductivity would require a modification of a fundamental law of physics.

What are the areas of fundamental physics, as of today? First of all there is gravitation, although many of you might have forgotten about it. Other areas are electromagnetism, weak interactions, and the strong interactions -- and that is all. Maybe some day there will be another branch of physics which has to do with the development of the universe as a whole: cosmology, but today this is nothing but astronomical history.

The first remarkable thing about the four basic interactions is that the numbers characterizing their strengths are rather odd. I list them in the table below. In order to be able to compare them to each other I made them dimensionless, with the help of a fundamental length, which I chose to be the radius of the proton $\approx 10^{-13}$ cm. Here they are:

	Interaction	Strength	Particle
1	Gravitation	10^{-40}	graviton
2	Electromagnetism	10^{-2}	photon
3	Weak interactions	10^{-5}	W meson (?)
4	Strong interactions	1 - 10	mesons

What is our present knowledge about these interactions? I believe that we understand gravitation, at least in the classical limit. It is quite possible that we even understand it in the quantum limit. I therefore add in the table, the particle corresponding to the gravity waves predicted by general relativity: the graviton, a particle with spin 2 and zero mass.

The theory of gravitation, namely general relativity, devised by Albert Einstein, is a beautiful theory. It is just gorgeous! The trouble is, it has not yet been adequately tested. It correctly predicts a few phenomena. However, the gravitational waves it predicts have not yet been seen even in the classical limit.

Let us summarize what we know about electrodynamics. I think the laws are completely known, at least if the energies are not too high, say $\lesssim$ 1 GeV. Unlike gravitation, electrodynamics is very well tested by a large number of highly accurate and delicate experiments. As a matter of fact, most things which we write down for other interactions are guessed in a sort of analogy with electrodynamics. There are still some difficulties with divergencies arising from virtual states of high momenta. From time to time somebody claims that these difficulties are now completely overcome. I do not think that this is the case. But, apart from these divergencies, the situation is very satisfactory indeed.

This cannot be said about the weak interactions. Here, the laws are only partially known. It is not quite clear which particles are coupled to which. At high energies (> 1 GeV) the laws are not known. It is quite possible that there we have structure, not only from the strong interactions, but also from the weak interaction itself -- for instance from an intermediate boson W. There have also been strange things invented, such as neutral currents which are not coupled to the leptons. Surely, there are still quite a few mysteries left in the field!

Finally, for the strong interactions the dynamical laws are not known at all. You may say that they are not known for energies above 1 GeV, but since the rest masses are of the order 1 GeV, everything strong occurs at energies above that.

Thus, an interesting way of summarizing our present knowledge of fundamental physics may well be to say: everything below 1 GeV is known and everything above that is unknown. That is to say: we know physics down to distances of the order of 10^{-14} cm, and all our troubles come from what is inside that length.

II. CONSERVATION LAWS

In analysing physical phenomena we assume the validity of two principles:

1) Special relativity,
2) the superposition of quantum mechanical amplitudes.

As far as we know these principles are exact. They have not been invalidated by any experiment, including the recent beautiful one on the $K_2^0 \to 2\pi$ decay.

The stage upon which all is played is the flat Minkowski space. (Let us except here gravitation. It could be treated also in flat space, but this would be a dirty way of doing it, similar to the mapping of the earth's surface on a plane.)

The principle of superposition of quantum amplitudes is fundamental for our understanding of elementary processes. It implies a deep connection between symmetry principles and conservation laws.

Now, as of today, what are those conservation laws? First of all we have several quantities which are exactly conserved.

a) Momentum-energy. This conservation law corresponds to symmetry under translations in space-time.

b) Angular momentum. This corresponds to rotational invariance.

Then there are conservation laws of a somewhat different type, related to quantities which you can count. They are:

c) The charge.

d) The baryon number. (The number of units of nuclear goo.)

These conservation laws seem to be exact too. The corresponding transformations have to do with shifts in phase, as has been discussed in the lectures. Incidentally, I am passing over the fact that the charges of all particles are multiples of the same basic unit. This still paralyses the mind -- I mean nobody knows the reason.

There are other conservation laws which are similar.

e) The number of electrons plus electron-neutrinos, the electronic lepton number. The laws of β-decay, as we write them today, couple the electron only to its neutrino, and therefore the conservation law follows. How deep it is, I do not know, but it is probably pretty deep.

f) The number of muons plus μ-neutrinos.

Thus we have altogether four numbers of this kind and all of them seem to be exactly conserved. In addition, we have all these funny symmetries, about which a great deal has been said in these courses.

g) CPT. This, as far as we know, could be exact. If it is not, then we do not know how to write things, but this does not prove it must hold.

h) CP, charge-conjugation times parity. This is almost an exact symmetry. If I had given this lecture a few months' ago I would have called it an exact symmetry too. However, as you have heard, there is now definite evidence that this law is not true. Let me put it this way: almost all the interactions do conserve CP. The weak interactions now appear not to satisfy it, but actually we are not sure, since it might be that the violation is caused by something else, such as electricity in a high approximation. Perhaps the particular technique for discovering the violation using the weak interactions was only a method of finding that. So, whether the violation is strictly speaking in the weak interactions or lies somewhere else, cannot be decided until we have a theory of it. Actually, if you just forget about that one annoying experiment, then CP is satisfied.

i) Time reversal. As far as T is concerned you take the two preceding statements and combine them. It really depends on what you believe There are several ways to keep it an exact symmetry.

k) Parity. P is violated in weak interactions, but electromagnetic and strong interactions seem to preserve it.

l) Isotopic spin. Heisenberg's invention, I, is violated both by weak interactions and by electricity. It is still good in strong interactions, however.

m) Unitary symmetry or SU_3. This is another possible symmetry among elementary particles. To be definite, we really mean here, the eight-fold way of Gell-Mann and Ne'eman. This is violated by the weak interactions, by electromagnetism and by the strong interactions. There is nothing left which does not violate it. So we wonder: what it is doing here. Of course, the secret is that SU_3 is violated by strong interactions in some smooth, gentle way, and that some of the underlying symmetry is still preserved.

And then I wonder if we should include, amongst the conservation laws, this questionable rule of $\Delta I = \frac{1}{2}$ in non-leptonic decays. The moment you write it down together with these other laws, you see it is dirty, good for nothing, and probably not right -- just somebody's concoction.

In talking about symmetry it is worth noting something rather interesting. If there were no masses the symmetry would be greatly enhanced. This is maybe absolutely insane -- but it is worth contemplating as an idea! It is a cock-eyed idea since there exists absolutely no way to define it precisely -- no way to turn off the masses. It would be completely definable if all theories could be written in Lagrangian form, like electricity. Whether the mass terms could be identified in other types of theories is not known.

What would be the consequences of the absence of mass terms?

1) There would be no scale of lengths. So, for instance, the size of the hydrogen atom would be indeterminate. This has many consequences in different places.
2) In the case of spinors there is a special transformation. If you change Ψ into $\gamma_5\Psi$, the system is invariant. In the case of neutrinos, which in fact have no mass, this does indeed permit the existence of neutrinos of only one helicity.
3) Electromagnetism is conformal: you can expand or contract the coordinate system without changing the laws. But this is just part of a wider group, under which electromagnetism is invariant. Many people have noticed that in accelerated coordinate systems with a constant acceleration (not just a constant velocity!) the laws of electromagnetism are unchanged, provided one transforms the current and charge densities appropriately. If the objects producing the currents were massive, you could not shift to an accelerated frame without putting forces on them to give them that acceleration. If, however, you had charges without mass then you could do it just as for the case of uniform velocity.

The possibility is very suggestive: the true meaning of SU_3 may lie in this idea. When we finally find the correct laws, and when we are able to define and kick out the mass terms, then SU_3 would be perfect!

4) Also, there is the rather poor idea mentioned previously in my lectures, that possibly you can change the amplitude of a meson-wave function by a constant: $\varphi \to \varphi + \lambda$. But this is really not as deep as the other things.

III. EXISTENTIAL QUESTIONS

Let us discuss the theories in more detail and mention some of the problems which exist in physics today. In the first place, we should mention the laws of electrodynamics. We believe that they can be summarized in the following three statements.

1) There is an amplitude for an electron to go from one place to another, which is $1/(\not{p} - m_e)$.
2) There is an amplitude for a photon to go from one place to another, which is $1/q^2$.
3) There is an amplitude for an electron to be coupled to a photon by the operator γ_μ with a coupling constant of 0.3.

That is all of electrodynamics (provided there are only electrons). What is the 0.3? Well, it is the square root of $4\pi e^2$ which is the square root of $4\pi/137$. (I write it in this way in order to shock people who feel that 1/137 is mystic, because it is so small.)

It is rather remarkable that so few words can describe the whole theory. Of course, the reason is that you know what the γ-matrices mean, what relativity is, and the rules for putting everything together. It is this language with which we describe all the other theories. But let me remind you of the simplicity of electrodynamics, particularly since we have been working so hard on that dirty corner, the strong interactions. There is still beauty left in physics; there are things that work.

However, there is another particle, the muon. The propagator is just the same as for the electron, except that we insert the μ mass. Electrodynamics is used not only for electrons and muons, but also for strongly interacting particles. Since they carry electrical charge, they emit gamma rays, and we are now struggling to discover how to write that.

There is an important point that has been made by Gell-Mann in particular: knowledge of one field, namely electrodynamics, requires us to be able to define in another field, namely strong interactions, something which corresponds to the matrix element of the current between one strongly interacting state and another.

Gell-Mann has, in recent times, concentrated on formulating strong interactions in terms of something which is physically definable. The original Lagrangian seems not to be physically definable. We do not know which particles to insert into a Lagrangian. In strong interactions one gets less and less inclined to call certain particles, say the baryons, fundamental and to derive the others from them. We really do not know where to start. Therefore, Gell-Mann would like to have a different method that does not depend on the particular way of writing. The usual S-matrix approach stays within the realm of strong interactions and talks about the scattering of one particle by another. It says, if you understood this matrix, everything is understood -- never mind the machinery underneath it. But it may be that the relations among the S-matrix elements are very complicated. Let me therefore point out that there is another way of describing things, which is also experimentally real. It has to do with the current densities, which can be defined because electrodynamics are relatively weak. You can probe the strong interactions with electromagnetic interactions. Gell-Mann suggests that matrix elements of the current operator and generalizations thereof, over the SU_3 group as a matter of fact, are the fundamental objects to be studied. To this he adds the corresponding axial currents, since they are involved in weak interactions.

Now let us look at the fundamental problems we have in physics. What do we not yet know? You can roughly divide these questions into two types, namely existential problems and dynamical problems. The separation is not clear-cut; the problems move from one class to another, as you will see in a moment. An existential problem appears in the form: "Why is such-and-such a thing there?" Clearly this is not the kind of question which is answered experimentally in physics. Nevertheless, their first appearance is in this vague philosophical form.

1) Why is the gravitational constant so small? What I should really ask is: is this constant related to any other numbers in nature? Is this small number, for example, the ratio of the size of a proton to the size of the universe? Is there some understanding of gravitation which comes from other fields of physics? That is what I really mean by an existential problem. Can it be explained in terms of something else; can we reduce the number of independent dimensionless constants?
2) The next question of the same kind, which has been with us a long time, was advertised by Eddington. What determines $e^2/\hbar c$ to be $^1/_{137}$? What we mean is this: is it possible that when Schmaltz discovers his correct formulation of electricity and magnetism, known for all momenta, he gets a complicated self-interacting Glupwogg. Then when he solves the equations, and works things out, he finds that to an excellent approximation, for energies below 10 GeV, the mathematics of his marvellous non-linear Wogg can be approximated very simply by saying that there is a vector particle coupled to a spinor particle with a coupling γ_μ multiplied by the square root of 4π times a <u>number</u>, which comes out as the root of a transcendental equation involving Bessel functions. That is what I mean by understanding 137!
3) Why are there two neutrinos and two charged leptons? What the question really means is: are you sure there are not three neutrinos and six charged leptons? In the old days there was speculation that the electron had an internal structure and could be excited. It is easy to cook up $m_\mu/m_e = 210$, for instance $\pi/2 \times 137$, and there you are.

There are two things which show that the muon is <u>not</u> an excited electron. One is that the magnetic moment of the muon is that of an elementary particle without an internal structure -- which is nerve racking. But the coup de grâce is that there are two neutrinos. If the muon were an excited state of the electron, then when it went through the beta decay it would come out with the electron's neutrino; but instead it comes out clutching a different particle. So it is qualitatively different! Therefore, the μ is not the excited state of the electron unless the μ neutrino is the corresponding excited state of the neutrino. Then that excitation cannot be electromagnetic, as the neutrinos are not coupled to electricity. It does look as if we have a sheer duplication, everything repeated at a different mass level, without clue. This is the worst possible situation.

4) What is the source of weak interactions? Historically, explanation in physics has related one field to another: heat is derived from mechanics, chemistry from quantum mechanics. Can we explain weak interactions in terms of the others? -- No! Weak interactions are so peculiar! They violate parity. Besides there are neutrinos which are only weakly coupled. It might be rather the other way around: electromagnetic and strong interactions might be derivable from the weak ones. If we have a parity-violating interaction acting twice, parity can be conserved. It is extremely unlikely that nature really works this way.

Next comes questions which may not be so deep. Which particles are coupled by left-hand threads? The answer is probably not hard. What determines the Cabibbo angle? Some theories say it is 45°, but the strong interactions tilt it.

It is easy to see where these queries come from: every number leads to a question.

5) Why are there strongly interacting particles, and what are they? Let us start with the proton. Then why is there a neutron? We are used to it, of course. But what is the origin of the neutral counterpart of the proton in the isospin doublet? And why are they equal when looked at via strong interactions, and as different as night and day for electromagnetism?

6) Finally, in looking at the numbers consider the relationships among the masses. We already talked about the electron-muon mass ratio What determines the ratio between baryon and lepton masses?

7) There are some more numbers but let me rather ask a general question, one that has to do with the symmetry proposals. It is related to the question of parity violation, and to the violation of all the other symmetries.

Parity is violated only by the weak interactions so it is only slightly violated in the world. We allow a considerable violation in SU_3 and still call it an approximate symmetry. Therefore, we do have some examples of slightly ruined symmetries. There is then the general question of understanding the existence of partly satisfied symmetries. I find this is a very difficult question. We like symmetries. If something is perfectly symmetric, nobody asks why. The world was thought to satisfy parity invariance. Why should it do so? If there is no such conservation, there is no problem. So, we should perhaps have asked in the past the question, why are such symmetries there and why are they so good?

It is worth recalling the argument of the Greeks about the orbits of the planets. They are circles because circles are so perfect. Physicists laugh at this stupid reasoning, but if translated into modern language it would sound something like this.

The orbits of the planets must be circles proceeding at uniform velocity around the sun, because there is a fundamental symmetry. As viewed from the sun the position and velocity of the planet always appears the same! So, from that grand law, the orbit is a perfect circle. Only it is not! It is an ellipse. Now state the law! The symmetry is nearly there, only it is slightly broken. But, the true understanding is not that the thing is first a circle and then slightly off, but that it is just plain nothing and it gets more and more like a circle due to tidal friction, which is a complicated dynamical business.

Perhaps the true explanation of the symmetry problem, the problem of partially satisfied symmetries, will ultimately be answered in a similar way: the world is unsymmetrical. Due to some large, strong interactions, electrodynamics appear perfectly symmetrical with respect to the parity operation.

Only the weak interactions are not affected in a way which destroys the asymmetry; they remain asymmetric. Is this possible? Yes! It is not such a dumb idea. If you can explain why there should be a zero mass particle coupled in a gauge invariant manner to charges, then you practically also explain why parity is conserved. It is extremely difficult to write any reasonable interactions between photon and electron which violate parity and remain gauge invariant. The same argument holds for isotopic spin and the character of the strong π meson interaction. The argument about the K meson coupling with the strongly interacting particles does not go in the same way. If SU_3 were more perfect, then a simple type of interaction, without complicated momentum dependence between mesons and baryons, would be parity conserving. So it is possible some day that the partially satisfied symmetries will be understood as resulting from "tidal friction".

IV. THE QUESTION OF DYNAMICS

We now turn to dynamics. The type of questions are as follows: What is the law of electricity and magnetism at very high momenta? Answer: unknown. What is the general law of weak interaction? What is its momentum dependence? Is there a W meson -- and so on? Far more important however, is the <u>absolute lack</u> of any dynamical theory for strong interactions. We have been in this frustrating situation since 1934 when Yukawa proposed his meson theory.

We cannot calculate anything in the strong interactions and so we cannot answer many other questions. For instance, the charge distribution in the proton cannot be calculated and so we cannot compare it with experiment. If we could perform this calculation we might be able to say something about the validity of electrodynamics at high momentum transfers. If we could calculate in the strong interactions we could then compute the corrections due to the weak interactions as predicted by some model. Thus, we could test such proposals very quickly.

When we have a symmetry in the strong interactions such as I spin or SU_3, we obtain ratios of numbers for instance, of reaction amplitudes. But we need more than these ratios. So, the real thing which holds up everything like a log jam, and against which more and more problems pile up, is this complete lack of calculational methods for strong interaction dynamics.

A dynamical theory must be able to calculate more than these ratios and cannot rely solely on the symmetries. So the reason why we perpetually concentrate on the symmetries and are glad to find a symmetry as imperfect as the SU_3 symmetry (and I think it is a correctly discovered symmetry just visible through a cloud of distortions), is that it provides us with the only means to deduce some numbers. Any other symmetry that is more widely broken than SU_3 will probably not be seen at all. We are near an end with symmetry.

In my opinion the central problem of physics today is the dynamical theory for the strong interactions. Probably this has nothing to do with CP violation. It has nothing to do with weak interactions, and it has no connection with electricity and magnetism.

I give you some of the history of the problem. At the beginning, Yukawa used perturbation theory in direct analogy with electrodynamics. Later, it was found that the coupling was too big to allow the perturbation theory to work. The higher order terms turn out as big or bigger than those retained. Therefore, strong coupling theories were developed, but for these the coupling is not strong enough. These theories have long since died. Perturbation theory never died completely. One always deferred the higher order terms to the next generation. The next generation worked them out and found them too large.

Then we had the Tamm-Dancoff approximation which adds up all the so-called single meson diagrams. This was the beginning of schemes for adding up all diagrams of a certain type in the perturbation theory, and then neglecting those of another type as small. I need not tell you what happened to that scheme. It takes a lot of work to figure out the terms which can be summed and to compare them to experiments, but one cannot justify the neglect of the rest which are not summed.

Then we had the analysis of Chew and Low of the low-energy scattering of pions from nucleons. This was the first and last good theory of strong interactions. It worked and gave us a good understanding of low-energy pion-nucleon scattering. The model is not very good for s waves but quite successful for the p waves, and it clarified the connection between photoproduction and scattering. This led to a continuous restudy of exactly what Chew and Low did, and one tried to put the theory into a more sophisticated form. For example, one took the recoil of the proton into account, etc. Eventually one began to see that one had an analogue to the dispersion theorem for light, which is a relation between the real and imaginary part of the amplitude for forward scattering of light.

This is the beginning of dispersion theory. The discovery of the connection between the real part of the amplitude and an integral involving the total cross-section was extended to finite angles and different masses. For the 3,3 resonance one obtained a successful model. Never again has this success been repeated. In the decuplet where the 3,3 resonance is found, none of the other resonances were placed correctly by calculation. Dispersion theory is again the same game of keeping some pieces in a calculation and throwing others away. In the π-N system the new bumps should have been predictions of theory. Instead a long comet tail of energetic theorists moves into each experimental bump as soon as it is discovered,to satisfy themselves that the parameters of some model can be adjusted accordingly. Explanations after the event do not impress me.

Dispersion theory was extended by Mandelstam into a general analytic representation for two variables. But with this we cannot discuss any production reaction, and cannot accommodate virtual states with more than two particles. This cannot be the whole of physics, as some enthusiasts have asserted. To do any calculations in dispersion theory using the Mandelstam representation, one must throw away terms without being able to assess their importance.

Next there came back a version of perturbation theory with a more respectable dispersion theoretic cloak to it. This is called polology and is no more than a scheme which picks out a certain particle exchange as a leading term at a specified energy and momentum transfer. In contrast to simple perturbation theory, modified or renormalized coupling constants appear. Here and there this has been partially successful, but such methods need separate justification in each new case, and cannot be transferred from one physical situation to another by mere analogy.

Then came the Regge pole idea, which is a transformation from the energy plane to the complex angular momentum plane. In the energy plane the situation is complicated; there are cuts and branch points and other singularities. One hoped for a dominant pole in the angular momentum plane, but if you take a complicated situation with poles, branch points and so on, and look at it through a curved lens, you will still have branch cuts and poles -- and this is what was found in the angular momentum plane. There is just as much complexity in the new plane as in the old one. So here again there is a game, where one takes the nearest pole, neglects everything else, and hopes for the best. This theory is also rather difficult for more than two particles. The world is not at all simple in this theory.

Recently there have been some new ideas called bootstrap methods. This consists of writing down some equations from one of these games and attempting to make them internally consistent. One believes that one can discover the mass splittings and more, but these equations are non-linear and the general system of equations to which the bootstrap equations are special approximations, has never been written down. I find it impossible to judge the accuracy of this scheme.

The most serious fault of all recent attempts is the refusal to take processes with more than two particles seriously, as part of the formulation of the fundamental equations.

An idea, which merits mentioning, has been stressed by Heisenberg and also by Schwinger. This is the idea that the breaking of the symmetry may come from the dynamics. It is often supposed that if one starts with a symmetrical theory and calculates to a very high order, then the result must also be symmetrical. This is not so! An example by Heisenberg illustrates this: the Hamiltonian of a piece of iron is invariant under rotation but has eigenstates completely polarized in some arbitrary direction. It is then no longer useful to insist on the rotational invariance of the original Hamiltonian in discussing excitation from a particular ground state. The axis of polarization of the magnet is the important one, relative to which, one calculates in the next higher approximation. The preferred direction in this basically symmetrical situation is perhaps due to accident, nevertheless it is there. Thus, unsymmetrical physics can result from a symmetry-preserving Hamiltonian.

Where do we go from here? What about the validity of SU_3? The reactions of $\pi^- + p \rightarrow Y^* + \binom{\pi^-}{K^-}$ in the decuplet give reduced matrix elements which differ by factors of twenty from the prediction of the SU_3 theory, but there are many uncertainties in this connection. The K mass differs so much from the π mass and any momentum dependence of the matrix elements makes it hard to decide at which energies to compare the reactions. We are in a very weak position since the masses are split by such a large amount. A difference by a factor of twenty is not the end of SU_3, for a poorly satisfied symmetry is only expected to give approximate agreement with its laws. It seems reasonable to assume that SU_3 is valid. So what then? What should we measure experimentally in order to perceive the correct dynamical theory of strongly interacting particles? I think that nothing new is required. One day when the dynamical theory of these strong interactions is discovered, we will ask ourselves: "Why did somebody notthink of it way back in 1964?" We have all the evidence and enough data on strong interactions for an Einstein to find their law. I do not believe that there is a fundamental clue missing.

V. ADVICE FOR THE FUTURE

Since we are at school here and you are supposed to be students, I will take the liberty to act like an old professor and offer some advice. What should you do as a student? First, learn to calculate! Everybody should be capable of computing F_π/m_π from the observed rate of decay of the pion, using the interaction $F_\pi P^\mu_\pi(\bar{\mu}\, \gamma_\mu\, a\, \nu)$. This does not require more than one page. Certainly every theoretician must be able to connect these numbers. If you cannot and still call yourself a theoretician, then you are a mathematician and may never be able to contribute to the development of physics. There is also no excuse for any experimentalist not to be able to perform such simple calculations. You will learn by experience and will see how simple it really is. There is only one number in my set of lectures which is more difficult to obtain and that is the $(4 \pm 1\%)$ deviation between the μ and the N decay rates after the electromagnetic corrections are inserted. These electromagnetic corrections are rather elaborate.

If you are theorists I would urge you to connect yourselves to nature by calculating such numbers. You should develop a feeling for the subtle interplay between the general and the specific. You should cultivate both. By general and specific I mean this: if you work out a number of examples you may be able to generalize to a general principle. The general and the specific work together. This holds in both directions. We cannot work without making mistakes. Many of the theorems have been proved by mistake. How can one find out if a proof is wrong? One way is to do it over and over again. That is a dumb way. A better way is to take some specific example of the theorem and try to figure it out numerically to see whether it works. You can reverse this: find your general proposition by noticing properties of special examples. By working out a number of special examples you may discover a general result and then later a proof. I emphasize, it is important to go in both directions. I have found that there are many people who work either entirely too generally, or entirely too specially. And there are also people who do not calculate at all. Then there are a few people in the opposite party; all they do is figure out things without any soul, they just keep calculating and never think about any principle. I have hope that the theorists will improve the stuff that they put out, and have some pride in their work. When you publish a paper you should have at least the confidence that what you say is right and will last one year. Maybe later, experiment finds something that is wrong, but please let us not have any of those papers with "Oh well I was wrong, you know, I put it out too fast, etc." This is just a waste of everybody's time. You can cook up theories every five minutes, but you should also calculate results which enable you to find out whether the theory is right or wrong, and not let somebody else do that. It is of no use to you to publish a very general theory which everybody can disprove by calculating a special example on one piece of paper. How can you feel proud after that? Second, you should have more come out than goes in. It is not very useful to say $\Delta I = \frac{1}{2}$; I do not know why it is, the explanation is that there is an enhancement of $I = \frac{1}{2}$ in the matrix element.

Now the same kind of suggestion applies for experimenters. Experimenters should finish the experiment; they should also have pride in their work, their result should last more than one year. If the result is given as 1.5 ± 0.2, it should not later turn out that it is 0.8 ± 0.1. It sounds ridiculous, but it is true that data disagree with each other by numbers greater than the errors. The reason is that the stated errors are usually statistical errors only, which is a very lazy way to write down the result of an experiment! Who cares what the statistical error is? You want to know what the number is! The sources of systematic errors must be investigated to a point where you are sure what the real number is. When in ten years from now the exact number is found, it has to be close to what you said it was, within one or two standard deviations you quoted.

It is again the same idea of having pride in your work. To take a good example, let me mention the experiment about the K_2^0 decay into two π's. It is unassailable, and valuable for that reason, and only for that reason. If there was a little flaw in it nobody would care about it at all. It is the old story: "I got six possible candidates for the W meson". The answer is: "I do not care for a possible one, I care for one that <u>must</u> be a W particle". So it is with all experiments. We do not want a whole lot of experiments which confirm the possibility that CP is violated. We want others of the same degree of precision as the one already made, which demonstrate that CP <u>is</u> violated.

So in both theory and experiment, to improve the physics of the future, I would like to see a little more pride in the work.

LIST OF PARTICIPANTS

Lecturers

ASHKIN, J.	Carnegie Institute of Technology, Department of Physics, Schenley Park, Pittsburgh, Pennsylvania, U.S.A.
BERMAN, S.M.	Stanford Linear Accelerator Center, P.O. Box 4349, Stanford, California, U.S.A.
BERNARDINI, G.	Istituto di Fisica "Guglielmo Marconi", Università di Roma, Piazzale delle Scienze 5, Rome, Italy.
BIEDENHARN, L.C.	Duke University, Department of Physics, Durham, North Carolina, U.S.A.
BLOCK, M.	Northwestern Universities, Evanston, Illinois, U.S.A.
CABIBBO, N.	CERN, Geneva 23, Switzerland.
FEYNMAN, R.P.	Norman Bridge Laboratory of Physics, California Institute of Technology, Pasadena, California, U.S.A.
GATTO, R.	Istituto di Fisica, Università di Firenze, Florence, Italy
KABIR, P.	CERN, Geneva 23. Switzerland.
TARJANNE, P.	University of Helsinki, Department of Theoretical Physics, Helsinki, Finland.
ZWEIG, G.	Norman Bridge Laboratory of Physics, California Institute of Technology, Pasadena, California, U.S.A.

ADAMSON, A.M.
Institut du Radium, Laboratoire Curie,
11 rue Pierre Curie, Paris V, France.

ALTERELLI, G.
Istituto di Fisica Teorica
dell'Università di Firenze,
via S. Leonardo 71, (Arcetri),
Florence, Italy.

ANTOINE, J.P.
Université de Louvain, Centre de
Physique Nucléaire, Parc d'Arenberg,
Avenue Cardinal Mercier, Héverlé,
Louvain, Belgium.

ASTBURY, P.
Imperial College of Science and Technology,
University of London, Department of Physics,
Prince Consort Road, South Kensington,
London S.W.7, England.

BADIER, J.
Laboratoire Leprince-Ringuet,
Ecole Polytechnique, 17 rue Descartes,
Paris V, France.

BADIER, S.
Laboratoire de Physique Théorique et
Hautes Energies, Bâtiment 211,
Facultés des Sciences d'Orsay,
Orsay, (S. and O.), France.

BAIER, R.
Institut für Theoretische Physik der
Universität Graz,
Universitätsplatz 5,
Graz, Austria.

BAKER, S.L.
Imperial College of Science and Technology,
University of London, Department of Physics,
Prince Consort Road, South Kensington,
London S.W.7, England.

BAREYRE,
Centre d'Etudes Nucléaires,
B.P.2. Gif-sur-Yvette, (S. and O.), France.

BERGIA, S.
Istituto di Fisica "A. Righi",
dell'Università degli Studi di Bologna,
via Irnerio 46, Bologna, Italy.

BONGAARTS, P.J.M.	Instuut Lorentz voor Theoretische Natuurkunde, Steenschuur, Leiden, Netherlands.
BUCCELLA, F.	Istituto di Fisica dell'Università di Firenze, via S. Leonardo 71, (Arcetri), Florence, Italy.
BYER, T.A.	University of Cambridge, Department of Physics, Cavendish Laboratory, Free School Lane, Cambridge, England.
CAHILL, K.	Harvard University, Department of Physics, Lyman Laboratory of Physics, Cambridge 38, Massachusetts, U.S.A.
CARMI, G.	Yeshiva University, Physics Department, New York, U.S.A.
CONFORTO, B.	CERN, Geneva 23, Switzerland.
CONFORTO, G.	CERN, Geneva 23, Switzerland.
CONVERSI, M.	Istituto di Fisica dell'Università di Roma, Piazzale delle Scienze 8, Rome, Italy.
COSENZA, G	Istituto di Fisica "A. Righi", dell'Università degli Studi di Bologna, via Irnerio 46, Bologna, Italy.
CVIJANOVICH, G.B.	Physikalisches Institut, Universität Bern, Sidlestrasse 5, Bern, Switzerland.
DE KERF, E.A.	Instituut voor Theoretische Fysica, Universiteit van Amsterdam, Valckenierstraat 65, Amsterdam-C, Netherlands.
DE WITT, B.S.	The University of North Carolina, Department of Physics, Chapel Hill, North Carolina, U.S.A.
DE WITT, C.	The University of North Carolina, Department of Physics, Chapel Hill, North Carolina, U.S.A.

DIVAKARAN, P.	University of Oxford, Department of Theoretical Physics, Clarendon Laboratory, Parks Road, Oxford, England.
ENFLO, B	Stockholm Universitet, Institutionen för Teoretisk Fysik, Vanadisvägen 9, Stockholm VA, Sweden.
FAISSNER, H.	CERN, Geneva 23, Switzerland.
FORMANEK, J.	Faculty of Technical and Nuclear Physics, Prague 1, Myslikova 7, Czechoslovakia.
FOTIADI, D.	Ecole Polytechnique, Centre de Physique Théorique, 17 rue Descartes, Paris V, France.
FROYLAND, J.	Universitetet I Oslo, Institute of Physics, Blindern, Norway.
FUCHS, G.	Ecole Polytechnique, Centre de Physique Théorique, 17 rue Descartes, Paris V, France.
GARFAGNINI, R.	Istituto di Fisica dell'Università di Torino, via P. Giuria 1, Turin, Italy.
GOTSMAN, E.	Ministry of Defence, Atomic Energy Commission, Soreq Research Establishment, Yavne, Israel.
HALBWACHS, F.	Laboratoire de Relativité, Faculté des Sciences, Place Victor Hugo, Marseille 3, France
HEIKO, L.	Brandeis University, Department of Physics, Waltham 54, Massachusetts, U.S.A.
HELDER, J.C.	Instituut voor Theoretische Fysica, Universiteit van Nijmegen, Driehuizerweg 200, Nijmegen, Netherlands.

HEYN, M.P. — Instituut voor Theoretische Fysica, Universiteit van Amsterdam, Valckeniertstraat 65, Amsterdam-C, Netherlands.

HUGENTOBLER, E. — Physikalisches Institut der Universität Fribourg, Fribourg, Switzerland.

HUGHES-JONES, R. — The University of Sussex, School of Physical Sciences, Physics Building, Falmer, Sussex, England.

HUSMANN, D. — Physikalisches Institut der Universität Bonn, Nussallee 12, Bonn, Germany.

ISABELLE, D. — Laboratoire de l'Accélérateur Linéaire, B.P. No. 5, Orsay, (S. and O.), France.

JAKSIC, B. — Institut "Ruder Bošković", Bijenička cesta 54, Zagreb, Yugoslavia.

JASSELETTE, P. — Service de Physique Mathématique, Université de Liège, 15 Avenue des Tilleuls, Liège, Belgium.

KARSHON, U. — The Weizmann Institute of Science, Department of Nuclear Physics, P.O.B. 26, Rehovoth, Israel.

KASCHLUHN, F. — Institut für Theoretische Physik der Humbolt Universität zu Berlin, Berlin W 8, Unter den Linden 6, German Democratic Republic.

KEREN, J. — University of Canberra, Canberra, Australia.

KIRZ, J. — Lawrence Radiation Laboratory, Berkeley 4, California, U.S.A.

KORTHALS ALTES, C.	Instituut voor Theoretische Fysica, Universiteit van Amsterdam, Valckeniertstraat 65, Amsterdam-C, Netherlands.
KRISTENSEN, L.K.	Institute of Physics, University of Aarhus, Aarhus C, Denmark.
LAURENT, B.	Stockholms Universitet, Institutionen för Theoretisk Fysik Vanadisvägen 9, Stockholm VA, Sweden.
LEVINE, M.J.	CERN, Geneva 23, Switzerland.
LIPMAN, N.H.	National Institute for Research in Nuclear Science, Rutherford High-Energy Laboratory, Chilton, Didcot, Berkshire, England.
MALOS, J.	University of Bristol, H.H. Wills Physics Laboratory, Royal Fort, Bristol 8, England.
MANNING, G.	National Institute for Research in Nuclear Science, Rutherford High-Energy Laboratory, Chilton, Didcot, Berkshire, England.
MASSAM, T.	CERN, Geneva 23, Switzerland.
McKERRELL, A.	The University of Glasgow, Department of Natural Philosophy, Glasgow W.2, Scotland.
MINNAERT, P.	Ecole Polytechnique, Centre de Physique Théorique, 17 rue Descartes, Paris V, France.
MITTNER, P.	Ecole Polytechnique, Laboratoire de Physique Leprince-Ringuet, 17 rue Descartes, Paris V, France.
MONETI, G.C.	Istituto di Fisica "Guglielmo Marconi", Università degli Studi Roma, Piazzale delle Scienze 5, Rome, Italy.

MULLER, Th. — University of Strasbourg,
Strasbourg, France.

MULLER, W. — Institut für Theoretische Physik
der Universität Marburg,
355 Marburg/Lahn, Renthof 7, Germany.

NATH, L.M. — Tait Institute for Mathematical Physics,
Edinburgh University,
1 Roxburgh Street,
Edinburgh 8, Scotland.

NIEDERLE, J. — Institute of Physics,
Czechoslovak Academy of Science,
Rudé armády 305,
Prague 8, Czechoslovakia.

OADES, G.C. — University College of London,
Department of Physics,
Gower Street, London W.C.1, England.

ORKIN-LECOURTOIS, A. — Laboratoire de Physique Nucléaire
du Collège de France,
Paris, France.

PAPINI, G. — Laboratorio di Fisica,
Istituto Superiore di Sanità,
Viale Regina Elena 299, Rome, Italy.

PARKINSON, M. — The University of Chicago,
The Enrico Fermi Institute for
Nuclear Studies,
Chicago 37, Illinois, U.S.A.

PELLEGRINI, C. — Laboratori Nazionali di Frascati,
Frascati, Rome, Italy.

PENENGO, P. — Istituto di Fisica dell'Università
di Torino,
via P. Giuria 1, Turin, Italy.

PHILLIPS, A.C. — Imperial College of Science and Technology,
Department of Physics,
Prince Consort Road,
South Kensington, London S.W.7, England.

PICCIARELLI, V. — Istituto di Fisica,
Università degli Studi di Bari,
via G. Amendola 173,
Bari, Italy.

POWERS, R. — The University of Chicago,
The Enrico Fermi Institute for
Nuclear Studies,
Chicago 37, Illinois, U.S.A.

PRADAL, J. — Institut du Radium,
Laboratoire Joliot-Curie,
B.P. 1, Orsay, (S. and O.), France.

PRORIOL, J. — Institut de Physique Nucléaire,
Faculté des Sciences,
1 rue Raulin, Lyon, France.

RAHM, D.C. — Brookhaven National Laboratory,
Department of Physics,
Upton, Long Island,
New York, U.S.A.

REICHERT, J.D. — Norman Bridge Laboratory of Physics,
California Institute of Technology,
Pasadena, California, U.S.A.

RICHTER, A. — Max-Planck Institut,
Postfach 1248,
69 Heidelberg, Germany.

ROCCO, E. — Università di Trieste,
Trieste, Italy.

SANDS, M. — Stanford Linear Accelerator Center,
P.O. Box 4349,
Stanford, California, U.S.A.

SCHNEEGANS, M. — Centre de Recherches Nucléaires,
Strasbourg, France.

SCRIMAGLIO, R. — Laboratori Nazionali di Frascati,
Frascati, Rome, Italy.

SEN, R.N. — Istituto di Fisica Teorica,
Università di Napoli,
Mostra d'Oltremare,
Pad 19, Naples, Italy.

SERAPHIMIDOU, A.	Nuclear Research Centre "Democritus", Physics Division, Athens, Greece.
SERIO, S.	Università di Palermo, Palermo, Sicily, Italy.
SHERWOOD, B.A.	The University of Chicago, The Enrico Fermi Institute for Nuclear Studies, Chicago 37, Illinois, U.S.A.
SIAUD, J.	Ecole Polytechnique, Laboratoire Leprince-Ringuet, 17 rue Descartes, Paris V, France.
SIMAK, V.	Institute of Physics, Czechoslovak Academy of Science, Lumumbova 1, Prague 8, Czechoslovakia.
SIMOPOULOU, E.	Nuclear Research Centre "Democritus", Physics Division, Athens, Greece.
SIX, J.	Ecole Polytechnique, Laboratoire Leprince-Ringuet, 17 rue Descartes, Paris V, France.
SMITH, L.T.	University of California, Department of Physics, Los Angeles, California 90024, U.S.A.
SPETH, R.	Physikalisches Institut der Technischen Hochschule Aachen, Abteilung Kernphysik, Aachen, Charlottenstrasse 14, Germany.
STEIN, J.	The Hebrew University of Jerusalem, Jerusalem, Israel.
TELEGDI, V.	The University of Chicago, The Enrico Fermi Institute for Nuclear Studies, Chicago 37, Illinois, U.S.A.

TJON, J.A.	Instituut voor Theoretische Fysica, Universiteit van Nijmegen, Driehuizerweg 200, Nijmegen, Netherlands.
TURLAY, R.	Palmer Physical Laboratory, Princeton University, Princeton, New Jersey, U.S.A.
UNAL, B.C.	University of Ankara, Ankara, Turkey.
VAN KLINKEN, J.	Natuurkundig Laboratorium der Rijksuniversiteit Gröningen, Gröningen, Netherlands.
VON DER LINDEN, F.J.M.	Instituut voor Theoretische Fysica, Universiteit van Nijmegen, Driehuizerweg 200, Nijmegen, Netherlands.
WAGNER, W.G.	Norman Bridge Laboratory of Physics, California Institute of Technology, Pasadena, California, U.S.A.
WALKER, T.G.	National Institute for Research in Nuclear Science, Rutherford High-Energy Laboratory, Chilton, Didcot, Berkshire, England.
WEBSDALE, D.M.	Imperial College of Science and Technology, Department of Physics, Prince Consort Road, South Kensington, London S.W.7, England.
WILLIS, W.J.	Brookhaven National Laboratory, Department of Physics, Upton, Long Island, New York, U.S.A.
YEH, H.Y.	Dublin Institute for Advanced Studies, School of Theoretical Physics, 64-65 Merrion Square, Dublin 2, Ireland.
ZAMBOTTI, G.	Istituto di Fisica Nucleare, Università di Pavia, Pavia, Italy.